Acclaim for
Smoke and Mirrors

Dr. Ruby fearlessly rips the mask off mental health industry guilds. Combining evidence with powerful stories – including about himself – in straightforward and clear prose, he reveals what's in it for the guilds and Big Pharma and describes humane ways that really do help those who long for surcease from anguish.

> **Paula J. Caplan, Ph.D.** – Psychologist – Author of *They Say You're Crazy: How the World's Most Powerful Psychiatrists Decide Who's Normal* and *The Myth of Women's Masochism*

In *Smoke and Mirrors*, Dr. Ruby takes readers on a lucid, entertaining journey, artfully deconstructing the "mental illness" story that has been told to us for the past decades, and, at the same time, reminding us that to suffer and to struggle is to be human. By the book's end, readers will have one thought: please let an understanding of our common humanity be the philosophical foundation for a new psychiatry that will replace the old.

> **Robert Whitaker** –Author of *Mad in America: Bad Science, Bad Medicine, and the Enduring Mistreatment of the Mentally Ill* and *Anatomy of an Epidemic: Magic Bullets, Psychiatric Drugs, and the Astonishing Rise of Mental Illness in America*

Dr. Ruby exposes the muddled language that leads emotionally distressed people to seek drugs from physicians when they might seek counselors who teach from wisdom, example, and tested evidence. Against the seductive but dangerous trends of medicalized labels and fake disease constructs, *Smoke and Mirrors* helps persons to emancipate themselves from oppressive conditions by perfecting their speech, and therefore their thinking, about the human predicament.

> **David Cohen, Ph.D.** – Professor of Social Welfare, UCLA – Coauthor of *Mad Science: Psychiatric Coercion, Diagnosis, and Drugs*

Smoke and Mirrors is the best book on mental "health" and mental "illness" that I have read in the 45 years that I have been a clinical psychologist. It is also engagingly written. Although written for a lay audience, it should be required reading for all professionals in the field. I recommend it highly.

> **Irving Kirsch, Ph.D.** – Psychologist – Harvard Medical School, University of Connecticut, and University of Hull – Author of *The Emperor's New Drugs: Exploding the Antidepressant Myth*

Be warned… Dr. Ruby's *Smoke and Mirrors* exposes the orthodox mental health industry's deceptive claim that everyday distress and difficulties must be eradicated with medical treatment. The result is an explosion of chemical prescriptions causing diseases such as diabetes, gynecomastia, and tardive dyskinesia, which justify legal remedies. A must read!

Stephen Sheller, Esq. – Attorney – Plaintiff's co-counsel in Murray vs. Janssen Pharmaceuticals – Author of *Big Pharma, Big Greed: The Inside Story of One Lawyer's Battle to Stem the Flood of Dangerous Medicines and Protect Public Health*

Today, psychiatry's highest authorities admit that their "chemical imbalance theory of mental illness" is invalid. *Smoke and Mirrors* details how the mental health industry lacks any scientific underpinnings but is instead a religion – a morality crusade that makes arrogant assumptions about what aspects of our humanity are illnesses.

Bruce E. Levine, Ph.D. – Clinical Psychologist – Author of *Resisting Illegitimate Authority: A Thinking Person's Guide to Being an Anti-Authoritarian – Strategies, Tools, and Models*

Dr. Ruby is the Mr. Spock of psychology. With unassailable logic, he tackles such topics as diagnoses, psychiatric drugs, psychotherapy, and even the nature of reality. *Smoke and Mirrors* deconstructs the unscientific and harmful mental illness industry and replaces it with a humane model of knowing and helping others. Fabulous!

Jim Gottstein, Esq. – Attorney – Author of *The Zyprexa Papers*

Smoke and Mirrors provides a superb overview of the deceitful, dangerous practices at the heart of psychiatry and the mental health industry. Dr. Ruby carefully exposes the industry's myth-making and general chicanery, painting a vivid picture of what reimagined, more effective and more humane help might look like. Highly recommended!

Eric Maisel, Ph.D. – Creativity Coach – Author of *The Future of Mental Health: Deconstructing the Mental Disorder Paradigm*

SMOKE AND MIRRORS

How You Are Being Fooled About Mental Illness

. . .

An Insider's Warning to Consumers

Chuck Ruby, Ph.D.

Clear Publishing
Welcome, Maryland

Printed in the United States of America

First Printing, 2020

Clear Publishing
5884 Joshua Place
Welcome, MD 20693
docruby@me.com

ISBN 978-0-578-63926-0 (paperback)
ISBN 978-0-578-63928-4 (e-book)

Library of Congress Control Number: 2020905209

Cover art by Evan Leszczynski
evanleszczynski@icloud.com

Desktop publishing by Pam Midboe
Purple Loon Publications, LLC
pmidboe@comcast.net

To the millions of consumers who have been deceived and harmed by the Industry, and to the millions more who have yet to know this fate. May you have the faith and courage to stand up for your humanity.

Acknowledgments

I want to thank the people who have honored me over the years by inviting me to join them on their journeys of angst and uncertainty. While they know me as their therapist, I know them as my teachers. Without their lessons, the revelations in this book would not be possible.

I also want to thank three of my colleagues who helped with the production of this book. Paula Caplan, Ph.D., Grace Jackson, M.D., and Jay Joseph, Psy.D. were gracious enough to review portions falling within their areas of expertise. It is comforting for those of us who rebel against the conventional wisdom to have such caring and supportive companions in our efforts to rehumanize our professions.

I also have a few personal acknowledgements among the many in my family who deserve recognition. The first is to my parents, Chuck and Jo Ruby. Despite their many hardships, they stoically and tirelessly sacrificed to offer sturdy support throughout my life, far into my adulthood. This instilled in me a sense of grounding necessary to follow through with such a project like this and to be willing to speak up about my views, regardless of how radical and irreverent they may seem to the status quo.

Next, I want to thank my wife Debbie for supporting and tolerating me during this process. She not only served as a reviewer and sounding board, she also helped me stay focused and not drift away too far with excessive psychobabble. She patiently allowed me the countless hours, days, and months to devote my full attention to it, which took me away from the time I could have been spending with her.

And finally, I am forever grateful to my son Donnie, who was my inspiration for wading into this formidable undertaking in the first place, despite the recognition that it would certainly bring professional criticism. Watching him stand tall in the face of the difficulties he endured as an adopted child of color into a white family showed me how faith, courage, and persistence can overcome the most demanding and oppressive of life's challenges.

Contents

Introduction

> For the great enemy of truth is very often not the lie – deliberate, contrived, and dishonest – but the myth – persistent, persuasive, and unrealistic. Too often we hold fast to the clichés of our forebears. We subject all facts to a prefabricated set of interpretations. We enjoy the comfort of opinion without the discomfort of thought.
>
> - John F. Kennedy, 1962[1]

In his 1962 Yale University commencement address, President John Kennedy warned about the dangers of political myths. Even though they are without substance, they are repeated over and over again, widely accepted without question, and resistant to critical thinking. This danger is still with us in today's world of politics where salacious rumors and conspiracy theories seem to trump the demonstrable facts. As a result, much of the public confidently believes information that is false, yet it is the basis of their reality and it forms the rationale for their actions. Most importantly, these political myths dictate who holds the reins of power.

In this book I address a similar danger within the "mental health" industry (hereinafter called "the Industry").[2] As with politics, there are myths about the problems we call "mental illness" that are "persistent, persuasive, and unrealistic," based on a "prefabricated set of interpretations," and they provide the "comfort of opinion" maintained by the Industry's "forebears." Even though they are without merit, they too determine who wields power in our society. However, this kind of power is exercised without regard to personal liberty, due process of law, or intellectual honesty. It is inhumane.

Nearly 60 years ago, the very concept of "mental illness" was exposed as a myth in a groundbreaking book entitled, *The Myth of Mental Illness: Foundations of a Theory of Personal Conduct.*[3] In it, psychiatrist Thomas Szasz, M.D., professor at the Upstate Medical University in Syracuse, New York, challenged the orthodox *belief system.*[4] Undaunted by attempts to silence and retaliate against him, he defiantly announced that psychiatry was abusing the power and prestige of the medical profession to perpetuate a falsehood that was being used to stigmatize and control people who were not actually suffering from illnesses.

Szasz accurately pointed out that no medical evidence existed to support the notion of "mental illness" as true illness. He asserted the term was a misapplication of medical language to describe emotional distress and wayward conduct and doing so led to unethical and harmful consequences. However, despite Szasz's persuasive arguments and those made by many others since then, the "myth of mental illness" (hereinafter called "the Myth") continues to the present day. Why is this?

It is because psychiatry and the allied professions have succeeded in perpetuating an illusion through subtle twists of language, logical fallacies, pseudoscience, and repeated false claims that fool you about its true nature. This illusion gives the impression that "mental illness" is about *disease or defect* in people that is best understood as a medical problem to be corrected through medical means and by medically oriented professionals.

But the sad truth is the Industry is merely a system of dispensing moral judgments about the appropriateness of human experiences and conduct, and then enforcing compliance with proper ways of being. It is neither based in science nor focused on the diagnosis and treatment of literal illnesses. This truth is hiding in plain sight, but it is difficult to see because the story has been peddled for decades in such a way as to give the impression of disease and medicine.

However, if you look past the smoke and mirrors, you will see no evidence that supports this story. Unfortunately, despite our many attempts to spread the word about the Myth (see Appendix A), our voices have been like whispers in a shouting match. The Myth continues to be widely accepted without question by consumers as well as by most of the Industry's professionals.

Those who perpetuate and guard the Myth do what people typically do when trying to defend an indefensible position. They either resort to personal attacks against those who challenge the Myth, or they just shout louder and louder and repeat the same failed arguments with the hope of drowning out our voices and creating enough confusion that people will just accept the conventional story. In President Kennedy's words, they do not welcome the "discomfort of thought."

My main purpose in writing this book is to do more than just "preach to the choir," as many of us who are critical of the Industry do on a daily basis with our like-minded colleagues. I want to present an insider's view of this serious problem and expose the smoke and mirrors to you, the consumer. This will ensure a more accurate and informed understanding of the very real problems you face and the assistance you seek, to include the potential dangers of that assistance.

This book may also be of interest to my fellow professionals who are conventionally minded and who uncritically accept the Myth. I suspect some understand its mythical nature, but they are afraid to rock the boat and jeopardize their livelihoods, because challenging the very foundation of the powerful Industry of which they are a part can result in severe criticism from their peers as well as from leaders of their professions. However, I know many of them accept the Myth just because that's what they've been taught, and they haven't yet heard about the serious weaknesses of the Industry as will be exposed in this book.

At the heart of things, whether the problems labeled "mental illness" are considered real or mythical depends on how we define *illness.* One common definition often used within the Industry distinguishes between illness and disease. This definition identifies illness is *any* state of unease or unwell, regardless of whether there is an associated malfunction or disease process in the body.[5] In other words, it proposes that illness is what the person feels while disease is what infects the body.

With this definition, it is claimed both can exist without the other. While it is true that disease can be asymptomatic and so the person wouldn't have a sense of unease, it strains reason to include in the definition of illness any state of unease, even those that are not produced by some type of defect in the person.

It must be remembered that definitions are not absolute or "God-given." They all reflect the values of those doing the defining. So if we, as a society, value the idea that any feelings of unease brought on by life struggles are illnesses to be subjected to medical forms of oversight and care, even without evidence or theory of disease processes underlying those feelings of unease, then "mental illness" would rightly fit the definition of illness and I would stop writing this book.

But, with such a definition, a teenager's intense aversion to homework and my great distaste for shopping could also be considered illnesses, as could just about any painfully tinged personal matter. As another example, a multitude of people are currently experiencing a great deal of unease about the ongoing political mischief in our country. Are these people to be considered ill, defective, and in need of medical care?

A broad definition like this would be so all-encompassing that it would nearly lose meaning and place the Industry in the position of ministering to an overwhelming amount of human problems far detached from medical science and for which those professionals have no expertise. It would be the same as putting your auto mechanic in the position, not just of repairing your car's engine, but also of dictating which car to buy and where to go on vacation.

Contrary to this broad and loose definition, most people understand illness as having something to do with disease; in other words, some type of internal malfunction. Something *in the person* is not working right. While the malfunction might be associated with mental problems, such as how nutritional deficiencies and brain tumors can be reflected in feelings of unease and strange behaviors, it would be illogical to call those malfunctions "*mental* illnesses." Instead, they are straightforward illnesses that have mental and behavioral symptoms. The key to treating them is to tackle the problems in the body, not just to alleviate the feelings of unease or to prevent the strange behaviors.

On the other hand, the problems that get called "mental illnesses" are not caused by something malfunctioning in the person. They are meaningful but problematic personal reactions to difficult life situations. They are not illnesses, because the brain and body are working just fine. Instead, something *in the person's life* is not working right. Who would want Industry professionals labeling us ill for being upset about difficult life challenges or dictating the best way to react to those challenges? I don't think many of us would want them determining what is healthy living, except when that kind of living interferes with the mechanical and chemical ways our bodies function to sustain life. And we certainly wouldn't want them to have the authority to force us into living in prescribed ways or believing prescribed things.

Each of us has the right to choose how much stress and pain we endure. We have the right to choose if and to what extent we connect with others. We have the right to choose what to believe. We have the right to choose how to act. Of course, we will also reap the consequences of those choices, especially when we violate the law or disturb social customs. When we get to the point of feeling overwhelmed or otherwise dissatisfied with our lives, we also have the right to seek out various forms of help, both lay and professional. But *we get to decide* whether we want help, not them. Industry professionals have no expertise in the matter. It is entirely about personal preferences and choices.

If we gave them the power to choose for us, these professionals would regulate most of life. They would have a say in whether we should be minimalists or hoarders, drug users or abstainers, socially active or complacent, assertive or passive, engaged or disengaged, reformists or conformists, cautious or carefree, eccentric or conventional, liberal or conservative, sympathetic or callous, emotional or intellectual, excitable or stoic, intuitive or logical, or any of the other personally meaningful preferences and choices we make each day.

Can you imagine the absurdity of this? Where would it stop if we defined illness as any significant feeling of unease? Shockingly though, this very thing appears to be happening. During the last few decades, we have witnessed an ever-increasing medicalization of human distress and diversity.[6] And, in many cases, the person isn't the one complaining of unease. Instead, the Industry paternalistically makes that decision for him.

The only way to curb this kind of paternalistic and medical regulation of people's lives is to define illness strictly in terms of disease defects in the physiological functioning of the body. To do otherwise ultimately leads to Orwellian control of everyday human life such as we've seen in totalitarian countries where "mental illness" diagnoses are used as political tools to control people who refuse to conform to the government's notions of appropriate conduct.[7]

So, just like a magician uses sleight of hand to make you believe something that isn't true, the Industry uses smoke and mirrors to create the illusion that one thing is something else. Those who depend on this illusion – drug companies, professionals and their member organizations, health insurance companies, professional schools and universities, professional journals, grassroots advocacy organizations, and even sometimes the unwitting consumers of the Industry's services – make "mental illness" appear to be about real health and illness and, as such, a matter to be viewed through medical lenses.

But nothing could be further from the truth. These human problems are fundamentally about personal, relational, spiritual, existential, financial, and political human dilemmas. Therefore, they are not about literal health and illness, and so they would neither be the jurisdiction of the Industry nor subjected to medical forms of assessment and treatment.

This misapplication of a medical model to human struggles is reflected in the surprising fact that the bulk of Industry professionals aren't medical specialists. Psychiatrists are the only ones who have medical training and medical degrees. On the other hand, clinical psychologists, psychotherapists, clinical social workers, marriage and family therapists, and clinical counselors do not. With some exceptions, their education and training does not include medical subjects such as neurology, anatomy, immunology, or any other topics regarding human physiological functioning or disease processes. At best, they are professionals of the social and human sciences, not medical science. Yet, despite this fact, these non-medical professionals represent 94% of all Industry practitioners in the United States.[8] Doesn't this seem odd to you, given that the Industry claims to be dealing with *health* and *illness*? Still, most people continue to mistake them for medical specialists.

Many think the same thing about themselves. One extreme example was a social worker at a hospital where I once worked who routinely wore a white lab coat. I wondered why he did this. After all, he never did anything that would require it, like being in contact with blood, wounds, or infections. He just talked to people. I guess it made him feel like a real doctor. He had a doctoral degree in social work and so people did, in fact, address him as "Doctor." I half expected to see him walk in one day with a stethoscope around his neck and surgical booties covering his shoes! But all humor aside, unless we redefine what it means to be medical, just like the question about how we define illness, the professionals who make up this 94% are not medical specialists. It is a mistake for people to think they are. It is an even greater mistake, dishonest, and unethical for them to present themselves as such.

These oxymoronic *non-medical healthcare* professionals straddle a metaphorical-literal fence, taking advantage of both sides and waffling between the two depending on how it suits them. They take advantage of the metaphorical side to explain the fact that they are not medically trained as physicians and there is no scientific evidence that emotional distress and problematic behaviors are illnesses. But they also take advantage of the literal side to explain why they call themselves *healthcare* practitioners and why they refer to the problems they work with as *illnesses*. The very existence of the Industry is founded upon this split personality.

Using different terms when talking about human suffering would make things clearer and more honest. We would be better served with terms that don't give the impression of illness, disease, and medicine but more accurately describe the very real and distressing problems people endure. It would be especially helpful if we could find good substitutes for the very terms "mental illness" and "mental health," as they falsely imply medical problems and defective people.

This medical language is probably the single most deceptive, yet subtle, influence in perpetuating the Myth. You are being fooled about it by the very language used in talking and thinking about it. For this reason, I am going to take on the difficult task of using non-medical terms in writing this book. It is difficult because the whole culture is immersed in medical terminology and many forms of human distress are described with it.

So, instead of saying "mental illness," I'll use phrases such as "significant problems in living" and "problematic emotions and behaviors." The latter are accurate portrayals and do not mislead the reader into believing those problems are illnesses. I'll also use such terms as "label" for "diagnosis," and "complaint" for "symptom." The crucial difference between these kinds of terms is the first in each pair is in non-medical language and the second is in medical language. They may refer to the same actual problems, such as sadness and confusion, but the medical language misleadingly, and often harmfully, implies they are signs of illness.

Several years ago, during my residency (notice the medical term?), I decided it would be more straightforward and honest to abandon this medical language and all its trappings. Despite being instructed to do so, I resisted using the term "patient." Instead, I tried to use the person's name or the pronouns "he" and "she" when writing my notes and discussing my work with supervisors. I also avoided terms such as "treatment" and instead referred to what I was doing as "talking to," "helping," or "working with" people.

I ignored diagnostic labels as much as I could and tried instead to focus on the actual problems people were having in their lives. I rejected the common practice of equating people with their diagnoses, such as "he's a borderline" or "she's a schizophrenic," as if it were some kind of despised religious or political affiliation.

I didn't use the lengthy list of officially approved Latin-based medical terminology that seemed like a secret code shared only among members of an equally secret society. I never understood the harm in writing "John came to his appointment complaining of dissatisfaction with life." instead of "Pt presented for tx c̄ dysphoria sxs." (Pt = patient; presented = came to his appointment; tx = treatment; c̄ = with; dysphoria = dissatisfaction with life; sxs = symptoms).

Many Industry professionals who want to be seen on par with physicians happily adopt this arcane language just like the social worker I knew who was fond of wearing medical garb. But for my refusal to fall in line with this medical model I was scolded for being "polemical," too informal, and getting too close to the "patients." I thought I was just being humane. But that humanity is seen as a threat to what has been called the Industry's "accoutrements designed to inspire awe and maximize a placebo effect: white coats, walls studded with prestigious diplomas, and prescriptions written in Latin."[9]

So, throughout this book, the only instances where I will use terms like "mental illness," "diagnosis," "depression," "symptom," and "treatment," will be when quoting others who use the Industry's language or in trying to juxtapose more accurate and humane language with the medical terms used by the Industry. In those cases, I'll use "air quotes" in an attempt to lessen the misleading nature of those terms and to indicate they are, at best, metaphorical uses of language. But remember: these terms don't refer to anything medical, and they have very little to do with real health or illness, even though they can refer to very serious problems.

Using medical terms in a metaphorical sense is similar to how one might refer to an IT technician "diagnosing" a computer's problems, or how John Dean, the White House counsel during the Watergate years, told President Nixon there was a "cancer" growing on the presidency. In those situations, we understand clearly what such figurative language means. We wouldn't believe a computer can be infected with a coronavirus or melanoma was spreading throughout the halls of the White House in 1973. But more importantly, we wouldn't use a vaccine to prevent a computer's problems or use chemotherapy to eliminate presidential corruption.

Despite my solid criticism of the Industry, I still see much value in helping people who desire to explore better ways of understanding themselves and enhancing their lives. In the time I've spent within the clinical psychology profession, I have come to know very caring colleagues who are intellectually honest about the limitations of their expertise, have a genuine sense of respect for the people they try to help, and demonstrate a devotion to the principles of self-determination and autonomy. We can still help people who struggle with meaningful life problems without buying into the Myth or using medical language.

It is certainly true that people experience real difficulties in living and they can be intensely distressed, deeply confused, and seem wildly out of control. Even more so today, with the ever-increasing pace, complexity, and demands of our social world, there is greater and greater potential for us to become overwhelmed, and it seems this state of affairs is not getting any better. To make matters worse, individual differences have become a problem in a world that appears to place increasing value on conformity.

I would like to conclude this Introduction with a few comments about *informed consent*, which is really what this book is all about. In other words, I hope to provide consumers with accurate information so they can make more informed decisions about their lives. Informed consent is perhaps the most cherished principle of our professions, second only possibly to the common maxim "do no harm." It means we are ethically bound to fully and honestly inform you about the nature of your problems and how we might be able to help you so you can freely consent to our help, knowing completely what you are getting yourself into. This ensures human dignity is maintained.

Sadly, though, this principle is routinely tossed aside within the Industry. Informed consent is usually given only a token nod with the legalistic forms completed at the outset of any visit to a psychiatrist or psychotherapist, and they are mostly intended to protect the professional, not necessarily the consumer. Besides, people rarely read these lengthy forms before they sign them, and the forms typically don't contain accurate information about the true nature of the problems they are experiencing.

Instead, *misinformed consent* is sought by many mainstream professionals who routinely tell people the falsehood that they have an illness "just like diabetes," caused by a malfunctioning brain or an elusive psychological defect of the mind and psychiatric drugs are needed, possibly for life, just to manage the so-called "symptoms." In the few cases when they do not receive a prescription, they are still frequently cajoled into some form of psychotherapy or counseling focused on correcting the supposed defect.

More alarmingly, any disagreement with the professional's opinion is all too often seen as part of the problem. This is called *anosognosia*, which allegedly impairs the person's ability to recognize she has a problem. Doesn't this sound like a Catch-22? If you agree with the professional, you are "mentally ill." If you disagree with the professional, you are "mentally ill." Anosognosia is frequently used as evidence that the person needs "treatment," even involuntarily, without her consent.

In addition to the prescription of toxic chemicals, this can include electric shock, forced confinement and drugging in prisons called "hospitals," and sometimes the euphemistic "assisted outpatient treatment," which translates to compulsory drugging and psychotherapy but without confinement to a hospital. This latter form is not much different than wearing an ankle bracelet or having to check in with a probation officer.

The Industry does not give you accurate or truthful information so you can give your informed consent to proceed. Instead, the Industry's smoke and mirrors are fooling you. This book is my attempt to speak up about this charade and to correct it.

Part I

The Disguise

> The relations between rhetoric and ethics are disturbing: the ease with which language can be twisted is worrisome, and the fact that our minds accept these perverse games so docilely is no less cause for concern.
>
> - Octavio Paz, 1991[1]

In the first part of this book I want to be clear about my complaint. It is that the Industry in its current form is a moral system of identifying and controlling troublesome and inconvenient people who are not suffering from real illnesses. Instead, they are suffering from emotional angst and problematic behaviors.

One of Thomas Szasz's protégés, Ron Leifer, M.D., pointed out the Industry nonetheless hides this reality behind a medical disguise.[2] In short, it portrays quite natural human struggles as illnesses and the attempts to help with those problems as treatment. Moreover, this kind of help is often forced upon people against their will, and as their problems become more serious or annoying to others, there is an increasing chance that the system will be imposed upon them without concern for their desires or their right to self-determination.

This is probably the most misunderstood element in our critique of the Industry and its Myth. In classic straw man form, the guardians of the Myth frequently accuse us of claiming "mental illness" doesn't exist or we don't believe in it. That accusation is a distraction, as it makes it appear we are claiming there is no such thing as distressing emotions and behaviors. But that isn't our claim.

Human suffering is quite real, and it can have devastating effects. Our claim is that these various forms of human suffering are not illnesses, such as in pulmonary, gastric, brain, or other human malfunctioning. Instead, the phrase "mental illness" is a figure of speech whose figurative meaning is hidden behind a medical disguise that makes it appear to be about literal health and illness. There are far-reaching and harmful consequences of this masquerade.

In Part I, I'll expand on this idea that the Industry operates in disguise. In particular, I'll explain how language has been used to create the illusion that common human problems are illnesses. I'll show how "mental illness" was invented rather than discovered and how the very idea of abnormality as it applies to human behavior and experiences is meaningless and irrelevant to understanding and assisting people in distress.

Then, I'll address how financial and guild interests have helped this invented and illegitimate system survive over the years behind the disguise. The Industry operates more like a religion than a medical specialty, taking wide-ranging and common human problems and making judgments about whether or not they are appropriate. Yet it claims they are medical or scientific judgments about illnesses to be treated by Industry professionals, even though there is no scientific evidence to support that claim of illness.

I'll close out Part I by explaining how Industry interventions are attempts to get people to stop complaining about their problems through various methods that many times cross over a line and become coercive paternalism. When successful, it is fraudulently called "symptom reduction" and "effective treatment." Further, many of the standard of care types of interventions, as procedures that can be prescribed for and applied to people, have little scientific basis.

Chapter 1
Illusions of Language

Things Aren't Always What They Seem

In the epigraph for Part I, Nobel Prize winner Octavio Paz talked about how corrupt totalitarian leaders twist language in order to create illusions that keep their constituents content enough to remain obedient, yet misinformed. I will apply this language problem to the totalitarianism of the Industry in its attempts to control people in the same way. But before we get into the details of how this happens, let's start out by seeing how we can be fooled by simple illusions.

We are all familiar with the tricks of optical illusions. For example, most people have seen the Necker cube on the next page. Even though it is a two-dimensional figure, it seems to be three-dimensional, rising out of the page, and it appears to shift its orientation the longer we stare at it. Which square is the front of the cube and which is the back? Is the front of the cube pointing to the top right or to the bottom left? Is the left or right side angled toward you?

The apparent depth and shifting of the cube happen because we are three-dimensional beings and we interpret depth in what we see. It is nearly impossible to see this for what it is: a two-dimensional drawing of 12 intersecting lines with no depth. There are limitless other examples of optical illusions like this, as well as other sensory illusions, and they can be far more misleading than the Necker cube. Some illusions can fool you into confidently believing something that demonstrably isn't true.

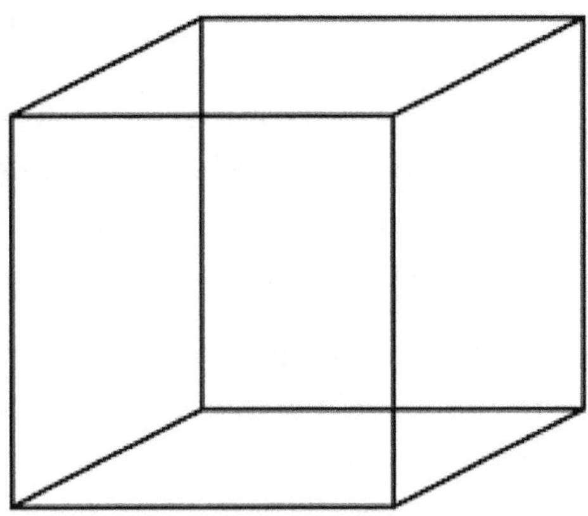

This same sort of thing can happen, but more deceptively, with language illusions. The 20th century philosopher of language Ludwig Wittgenstein (1889-1951) emphasized the terms we use in language are not exact representations of things in nature.[1] Instead, they are context specific and used in "language-games" to imply particular ideas and concepts. But sometimes the true meaning of a term is not clear, whether through intentional deception or unintentional mistake.

We see this frequently in commercial advertisements and political campaigns where certain phrases are used to imply something that isn't true. When terms are used differently from how the reader thinks they are being used, they can create language illusions that imply false meanings. With this in mind, statements can be presented in such a way that they appear to be saying something they really aren't. For example, consider the following riddle that has been making its rounds on social media:

> There are 30 cows in a field and 28 chickens. How many didn't?

Most people get quite confused with this riddle and don't know how to answer it. It seems nonsensical. But that is only because it is presented with language-games. The language used in presenting this riddle, as well as all other riddles, misleads you into believing one thing when it is actually saying something else. That's how riddles work. The riddle's mystery dissolves when it is worded differently:

> There are 30 cows in a field and *20 ate* chickens. How many didn't?

Now things are much clearer. The answer is 10. Just changing one number (28) into a number and a word (20 ate) has a considerable impact on its meaning, notwithstanding the fact that cows don't eat chickens. That is because the riddle is presented in speech, not in writing. Setting up the riddle by first referring to 30 cows, leads one to assume "28" refers to the number 28 and not the phonetically identical number and word "20 ate."

This kind of misleading use of language is fun when it comes to riddles. But it also unfortunately applies to the Industry where medical language is frequently used to describe things that aren't illnesses, yet it gives the false impression they are. Within the Industry, terms such as "treatment," "symptoms," "patient," "diagnosis," "mental illness," and all diagnostic labels imply illness, and because of how they are used repeatedly in medical contexts by apparent medical professionals, they have taken on the meaning of literal health and illness.[2] However, they are actually referring to non-medical, non-disease, and non-illness matters.

Consider this statement, which is something one would hear uttered by those who have embraced the Industry's medical model of human suffering:

> The treatment was effective in reducing the patient's symptoms of depression.

This statement sounds medical and having to do with illness. But, as with the cows and chickens riddle, it can be made clearer by removing the disguise of medical language-games, showing us what it really means. In doing so, we see it has nothing to do with illness.

> Having several conversations with her helped to lessen her emotional pain, thus reducing her complaints about and detachment from life.

Or alternately,

> The prescribed chemicals interfered with normal brain functioning, sedating her to the point that she wasn't able to fully notice her emotional pain, thus reducing her complaints about and detachment from life.

The first statement is worded in the language-games of medicine and it gives the impression the person was a patient who had an illness called "depression" and a doctor cured her through a medical form of treatment. The second two statements, on the other hand, make it clear there was nothing diseased or defective with her. There was no illness. Instead, she was suffering from a natural, but difficult, set of life circumstances from which she was trying to disengage through the intense passivity that the Industry calls "depression."

The circumstances and the attempt to help her were disguised in medical terms. This is a very common feature of language used in the Industry. By using terms such as "treatment," "patient," "symptoms," and "depression," it implies a matter of illness when no such illness exists. The language obscures a more humane and non-illness matter.

Human Struggles as Illnesses

This is just a simple example of how the Industry's smoke and mirrors can easily fool you into believing something that isn't true. This linguistic tactic is used over and over again by those who want to perpetuate the Myth that difficult human dilemmas are illnesses instead of understandable, meaningful, and natural struggles of human living.

Many practitioners and academics knowingly use this trick to defend self and professional interests. But I think most just get caught up in the Industry's language and culture and parrot what they are told along the way. This is exactly what happened to me when I started out in a clinical psychology graduate program in the early 1990s. I merely adopted the language used by professors, fellow students, and the Industry.

Because the language implied illness, it had a subtle but powerful effect on what I assumed about emotional distress and problematic behaviors. It affected what I *believed* and so it affected how I portrayed these problems to others and what I thought were the best ways to help people with these alleged illnesses. It wasn't until I had the rare opportunity of a mentor relationship with an unorthodox psychologist[3] who practiced a humane and compassionate form of helping others that I started to become disillusioned with this conventional medical model wisdom.

These medical language-games also show up in our popular culture. For example, the late, great comedian and critic of society, George Carlin, humorously described an example of how language-games are used to perpetuate the Myth. During a 1990 standup comedy routine called *Euphemisms*,[4] he criticized how the understanding of war trauma evolved over time using the tricks of language to misdirect and eventually give the impression of illness.

He traced what it was called from the early 20th century through the Vietnam War. Carlin explained that in World War I its name was *shell shock*, a straightforward description of the actual trauma that represented the very explosive horrors of war. Later, in World War II, it became *battle fatigue*, a more abstract and softened description, yet it still retained the element of combat (battle); the very thing that was traumatic. Then, during the Korean War, which my father had the unfortunate opportunity to experience, it morphed into *operational exhaustion*, which seems to have a corporate or business-like sound to it that went along with the expanding U.S. economy in the 1950s. Also, with this term, the focus clearly turned toward the person (exhaustion) and away from war. Finally, during the Vietnam War, it changed to *post-traumatic stress disorder (PTSD)*, an "illness."

Carlin's message was that a very natural and expected human reaction to the volatile terrors of war slowly transformed over the years with language games into an illness to be treated as something wrong with the person, rather than as something wrong with war. Unfortunately, nearly 50 years after Vietnam and a few wars later, its name hasn't changed. As a result, thousands of military members and veterans have been subjected to the inhumane onslaught of harmful psychiatric interventions for being human, instead of being understood and helped to integrate back into the strangeness of a non-war situation.

The Myth is kept alive by using misleading medical language when talking about it. Therefore, it seems appropriate at the outset that I give you a glossary to help understand what those medical terms really mean behind the disguise. See Appendix B. Keep in mind none of these terms refer to disease, illness, medicine, or health. Now, with an understanding of how language can create illusions and fool you, let's take a look at the origins of the Myth.

Chapter 2

The Invention of a Myth

The Discovery?

The best way to understand the problems the Industry calls "mental illness" is to look at how they were discovered. If they were truly about illness "just like diabetes and cancer," as is often claimed, then one would expect it to be a fairly straightforward matter. They would have been discovered because people complained about symptoms, which were studied in order to determine the disease causing those symptoms. This is how medical science works. Symptoms[1] are clues to underlying bodily disease.

For instance, in the case of diabetes it was discovered that a defect in the body's production and use of insulin causes symptoms such as persistent thirst, frequent urination, and blurred vision. These symptoms are clues to the bodily defect causing them. Further, the defect can be detected through laboratory tests. A blood test showing elevated levels of glucose is evidence of the defect responsible for diabetes. When the test confirms the defect, diabetes is diagnosed. Without medical treatment, the person can eventually die. The protocol for medical diagnosis and treatment goes: (1) symptoms; (2) hypothesized disease; (3) laboratory tests; (4) diagnosis, and (5) treatment.

There are some diseases reasonably assumed to be present even though laboratory tests might not be able to detect them. For example, we can safely assume the symptom of head pain is caused by some kind of defective process with the muscles, nerves, blood vessels, or other structures in the head, even if a brain scan fails to show any of these things. Physical pain signifies danger and something in the body not working right. Similarly, when an aging person starts to progressively loose motor control, we would assume that a defect such as Parkinson's disease causes the symptoms, even though we cannot use a test to confirm the defect while the person is alive.[2]

But "mental illness" was not discovered by investigating symptoms and identifying the diseases responsible for the symptoms. Instead, it was *invented* as a medical-sounding name for distressing experiences and behaviors people exhibit or complain about. This is consistent with what I pointed out in the Introduction that the Industry commonly defines any sense of unease or unwell as an illness, even when there is no bodily disease present.[3] The important point is that it is not based on any scientific evidence or reasonable theory of bodily disease or malfunctioning. It is solely based on a person's complaints or actions, and it is only an administrative or bureaucratic designation of the problems it describes.

There are some real illnesses that frequently get mislabeled "mental illness." One example is neurosyphilis.[4] This is a bacterial brain infection that occurs after a person has been living with untreated syphilis for several years. Some symptoms of neurosyphilis are paranoia, mood swings, and personality changes. On the surface, this can be mistaken and labeled "schizophrenia." There are many other examples of real illnesses that manifest in mental symptoms. Examples are such claims as Lyme's disease causes "bipolar disorder,"[5] thyroid deficiencies cause "depression,"[6] caffeine intoxication causes "anxiety,"[7] and lead poisoning causes "attention-deficit/hyperactivity disorder."[8] But the paranoia from neurosyphilis, mood changes from Lyme's disease, lethargy from hypothyroidism, agitation from too much caffeine, and inattention and impulsivity from lead poisoning are symptoms of *real* illnesses, not mental ones.

When there is an identifiable or reasonably theorized biological malfunction in the body, the symptoms of that malfunction are not symptoms of "mental illness" even though they manifest themselves in mental or behavioral form. Illnesses are illnesses, regardless of how they reveal themselves, whether in symptoms considered mental or symptoms that are considered physical. If bodily pathology is discovered or reasonably theorized as responsible for symptoms, it is a real illness. If a person suffers from neurosyphilis or hypothyroidism, they wouldn't go to a psychiatrist or seek out psychotherapy, and they wouldn't be called "mentally ill." If medical science discovers a currently labeled "mental illness" is caused by bodily pathology, it would no longer be considered "mental illness" and "mental health" professionals would not deal with it. It would be a real illness to be handled by real health professionals.

Despite this fact, the Industry continues this tactic of conflating real medical conditions with so-called "mental illnesses." It even comingles the two in its official guidebook, the *Diagnostic and Statistical Manual of Mental Disorders* (*DSM*).[9] Consider the following diagnoses found in the *DSM*:

- Major and mild neurocognitive disorder due to Alzheimer's disease[10]
- Major and mild neurocognitive disorder due to Parkinson's disease[11]
- Major and mild neurocognitive disorder due to HIV infection[12]
- [Substance] withdrawal[13]
- Breathing-related sleep disorders[14]
- Substance/Medication induced [depressive/anxiety/bipolar] disorder[15]
- [Anxiety/Depressive/Bipolar] disorder due to another medical condition[16]

These diagnoses, and others like them, do not belong in the *DSM*. Just like neurosyphilis, Lyme's disease, hypothyroidism, caffeine intoxication, and lead poisoning, they are real diseases affecting mental functioning and reveal themselves in mental and behavioral symptoms. Placing them in the *DSM* would be like including dehydration, urinary tract infections, and brain tumors in the *DSM* because their symptoms include cognitive confusion and odd behaviors. That would be ridiculous.

Yet including these illnesses in the *DSM* gives the impression the other diagnostic names appearing in the manual are also illnesses. It also greatly expands the jurisdiction of the Industry. These illnesses are the domain of medical professionals such as physicians, surgeons, physician assistants, and nurses, not psychiatrists, psychologists, social workers, and counselors. Is the Industry claiming authority over diseases that happen to have mental or behavioral symptoms in order to increase its market of potential consumers?

This is why it is a good idea to get a full medical examination prior to seeing an Industry professional, in order to rule out any real diseases that might be affecting mental functioning and behaviors. This includes matters related to nutrition, exercise, and sleep. Using the services of a psychiatrist or psychotherapist for real diseases like the mood changes associated with Lyme's disease or the inattention from lead poisoning is a waste of time. In those cases, the person would benefit from genuine medical treatment.

Of course, if these diseases present people with a sense of fear, despair, or frustration, those are meaningful reactions to the realization of having the disease. They are not symptoms of the disease. Such a person might seek out Industry services for help in coping with the consequences of having the disease. But those services would not be treating the disease. And in keeping with the principle theme of this book regarding the misleading nature of medical language, they are neither mental "health" services nor "treatment."

If we used this medical protocol of diagnosing so-called "mental illnesses," the process would go from symptoms and then straight to diagnosis and treatment. There are no second or third steps of hypothesizing what disease might be causing the symptoms, and then testing to confirm the nature of the disease. This is because there is no disease for which to test. And in this process, the medical terms "symptoms," "diagnosis," and "treatment" are part of the smoke and mirrors, making it seem medical when it is not.

With real illness, disease causes the symptoms. With "mental illness," the "symptoms" cause the "disease." The tail is wagging the dog. In essence, the problem is first declared an illness and then the specifics of the problem are called "symptoms" and the name of the problem is called a "diagnosis." But the initial declaration of illness is not based on scientific evidence or reasonable theory of disease.

These problems called "mental illnesses" by the Industry are not caused by malfunctioning bodily systems. They are not like viruses, broken bones, inflamed colons, or aneurysms. Those things are, in fact, defects of bodily functioning and they produce real symptoms for which the correct diagnosis is essential. It is critical for a physician to know whether the symptom of excessive thirst is due to diabetes, dehydration, or kidney failure. Knowing the disease dictates the treatment. It would be dangerous for your doctor to just treat the symptoms without looking for the underlying disease. It would be even more dangerous to assume the symptoms were due to diabetes, without doing a blood test, and then to prescribe insulin. If the true cause of the symptoms was dehydration or kidney failure, such treatment could be lethal.

In contrast to this, getting the correct "diagnosis" for significant problems in human living is not important. Regardless of what we call the problems, it has no substantive effect on what we do in an attempt to help the person. The important issue is to understand the real-life difficulties and then to tailor assistance to target those difficulties. In medicine, the physician ideally treats the disease causing the symptoms. With "mental illness," practitioners only treat the so-called "symptoms" because there is no disease to treat.

The problem identified as "bipolar disorder," for example, is not a pathological condition causing people to become very excited, spend excessive amounts of money, go without sleep, and eventually crash in despair. Instead, "bipolar disorder" is the label we use to designate ("diagnose") people who do those things. We could just as well call it "very excited disorder," "intermittent despair disorder," or "XYZ disorder." It wouldn't matter what we call it. What matters is whether we understand the problems the person is encountering and how that person is responding to those problems.

To see it otherwise would be the same as describing a person walking down the street as having "walking disorder" or "walking disorder is causing him to take steps." Equivalent comments about "bipolar disorder" would be, "he has bipolar disorder" and "his bipolar disorder is causing mania." Such comments are widely accepted but speaking the same way about walking, or any other common human action, reveals just how absurd a "mental illness" diagnosis is. A better way to describe it would be, "that person is *bipolaring*" since the label refers to a set of human actions and experiences, just like walking is such a label. It would actually be best just to discard the label altogether because it does not refer to a disease or illness. See more about this action-oriented view in Part II.

The Chemical Imbalance Theory

Despite their decades-long, but failed, attempts to find any kind of disease basis for the problems they call "mental illness," the Industry still searches in vain. In matters of science, when the data are inconsistent with the theory, the theory is adjusted to fit the data, and if enough time passes without any supportive data, the theory is discarded. But within the Industry, when the data is inconsistent with their theory of disease, the Industry rejects the data, guards the theory, and keeps looking in the hopes of finding support.

One theory that has been heavily marketed is that of neurochemical imbalances in the brain, which is widely accepted by the lay public. One survey found about 80% of people believed "depression" was caused by an imbalance of brain chemistry. About 85% believed the same thing for "schizophrenia."[17] Notwithstanding this popular belief, there are serious problems with the chemical imbalance theory.

First and foremost, the theory is difficult to test (scientific theories must be testable). The difficulty lies in the fact that we have no accurate ways to measure neurochemicals, especially while the person is alive. Only indirect estimates are possible. For instance, blood, urine, and saliva tests can be used to estimate the levels of neurochemicals. Second, we have no way to establish what a healthy balance would be and, therefore, what constitutes an unhealthy imbalance. But even if these tests accurately identified levels of brain chemicals and found they were elevated or depleted in people who have been labeled "mentally ill," it still would not support the chemical imbalance theory because of a far more substantial problem.

This is because the theory fails to address the core issue of *pathological vs. non-pathological* brain functioning. All of our behaviors and experiences are accompanied by signature chemical fluctuations in our brains. For instance, when we are sad, our neurochemicals change in a particular way. When we are excited, they change in a different way. But we would not conclude those changes constitute an imbalance or represent defective brain chemistry. Neither would we conclude the sadness and excitement are illnesses or symptoms of disease.

If we assumed a non-sad or non-excited brain state constituted a balance, then of course the chemical changes occurring when we become sad or excited would be considered, by definition, a chemical imbalance. But that would be ridiculous. It would mean any neurochemical state other than a balanced and resting state would be considered an imbalance, and therefore, an illness. Further, how would we ever determine that resting state since our brains are constantly active?

In 2011, Ronald Pies, M.D., the Editor-in-Chief Emeritus of *Psychiatric Times*, a trade publication for the psychiatric profession, described the chemical imbalance theory this way. He said in his 30 years as a psychiatrist:

> I don't believe I have ever heard a knowledgeable, well-trained psychiatrist make such a preposterous claim, except perhaps to mock it.... In truth, the 'chemical imbalance' notion was always a kind of urban legend – never a theory seriously propounded by well-informed psychiatrists.[18]

Keep in mind this was from one of the staunchest defenders of the Myth. Still, his comment is an accurate admission that no scientific evidence supports the notion that human distress and troublesome behaviors are illnesses caused by chemical imbalances in the brain or that signature chemical changes in the brain associated with those problems equate to pathology. Alarmingly, though, his proclamation shocked us who challenge the Myth. We know firsthand, as do those of you who have seen the psychiatric drug[19] ads on television and who have sought out the help of the Industry, that the scientifically empty chemical imbalance theory is liberally promoted to this very day. Pies just recently reiterated his claim that mainstream psychiatry has never promoted the chemical imbalance theory[20] despite clear evidence to the contrary.[21]

In the same year Pies made his original claim, the Director of the National Institute of Mental Health (NIMH), Thomas Insel, M.D., asserted brain malfunctioning as the cause of "mental illness" when he said it was "due to disorders of brain circuits."[22] One would wonder why he put it this way and differentiated chemical imbalances from brain circuit failings, as flaws in brain circuits necessarily involve the chemicals that regulate those circuits. Even the Harvard Medical School contradicts Pies's claim as they promote the notion that brain chemicals are responsible, but in a more complex way:

> To be sure, chemicals are involved in this process, but it is not a simple matter of one chemical being too low and another too high. Rather, many chemicals are involved, working both inside and outside nerve cells. There are millions, even billions, of chemical reactions that make up the dynamic system that is responsible for your mood, perceptions, and how you experience life.[23]

In further contradiction to Pies's assertion that he has never known a "knowledgeable, well-trained psychiatrist make such a preposterous claim," as recently as January 2020, the American Psychiatric Association (APA) website said, "Differences in certain chemicals in the brain may contribute to symptoms of depression."[24] This seems to be a watered-down version of the chemical imbalance theory as it claims those chemicals are only one causative factor. However, they are still considered a factor. The APA is the premier professional organization representing more than 38,000 psychiatrists in the United States. I assume its leaders are "knowledgeable, well-trained psychiatrist[s]."

Other comments by Industry leaders appear to have the intent of trying to apologize for the lack of evidence for the chemical imbalance theory, while still justifying why the theory continues to be peddled. Specifically, in 2014 it was claimed the chemical imbalance theory, although incorrect, served as a rationale for getting people to come out of the closet about their problems. For instance, in an interview with National Public Radio (NPR), Alan Frazer, Ph.D., Professor and Chair of the Department of Pharmacology at the University of Texas (UT) Health Sciences Center at San Antonio, said it was a good thing if people (falsely) believed in the chemical imbalance theory. If they did, it would give them a reason to seek out prescriptions for psychiatric drugs.[25]

This excuse for perpetuating the unscientific chemical imbalance theory was also made by Pedro Delgado, M.D., Chair of the Psychiatry Department at the same university. Despite having conducted research into the theory and demonstrating that depleted levels of neurochemicals are not associated with "mental illness," he nonetheless said the theory has benefit. Specifically, he said it provides a sense of certainty (again, falsely) about the cause of those problems, and this has a positive impact on people. He said, "When you feel that you [falsely] understand it, a lot of the stress levels dramatically are reduced....So stress, hormones and a lot of biological factors change."[26] I have heard similar statements by Industry professionals who support the chemical imbalance theory, not because it has scientific merit, but because it can pacify potential consumers. These comments are examples of the paternalistic interest of the Industry and they demonstrate that science takes a back seat to that interest. Furthermore, this is blatantly in opposition to the ethical principle of informed consent.

The popular critic of psychiatry, Peter Breggin, M.D., said the chemical imbalance theory was the brainchild of Eli Lilly, the drug company that brought Prozac onto the market in the late 1980s. According to Breggin, the notion was proposed, not as a serious scientific theory hatched from the toils of medical research, but as a corporate marketing strategy to brand Eli Lilly's new product as a medication that corrects those unproven chemical imbalances.[27] Many other drug companies have followed suit in claiming their products correct brain chemistry without providing any evidence of the correction or the chemical imbalances.

It must be remembered that in science, the burden of proof is on those who make a claim (theory). They must provide evidence to support the claim. It is not up to skeptics to prove the claim wrong. So, it is not up to us, as critics of the Industry, to prove "mental illness" is *not* caused by chemical imbalances or other bodily defects. What we can say with certainty is no evidence supports such an assertion, and so it is without scientific merit, and therefore, there is no justification in calling it illness.

Accepting a theory because there is no evidence it is wrong is an example of the *argument from ignorance* or *negative proof* logical fallacy. In other words, it runs against logic to accept a claim, such as "mental illness" is caused by chemical imbalances in the brain, or "mental illness" is truly an illness, just because there is no evidence to the contrary. It is illogical to assume something is true because it has not yet been proven false. We could also say no one has proven unicorns *don't* exist. But the burden of proof rests with those who claim they do. If those who make the claim offer no reasonable evidence to support it, then the claim would be discarded as scientifically illegitimate.

Yet, after two centuries since the medical specialty of psychiatry came into being, no evidence has ever been presented that supports the Industry's claim of neurochemical imbalances, or any other brain malfunctioning, as the disease underpinnings that cause troublesome behaviors and emotional distress. So, there is no rationale for calling those problems illnesses, as it is a scientifically illegitimate claim. Still, the Industry continues in vain to look for evidence of bodily defects by using two other areas of research: brain scans and genetics. But as will be shown, both of these are also scientifically illegitimate.

Brain Scan Research

You've probably seen the side-by-side comparisons of colorful brain scans that show the brains of people identified as "mentally ill" look different than people who haven't been identified. A type of scan commonly used is called the magnetic resonance imaging (MRI) scan, which measures changes in blood flow and oxygen levels in the brain. This shows what areas are "working" the most, as active brain areas require more oxygen and, thus, more blood flow. Other scans are also used, such as the positron emission tomography (PET) scan, which detects metabolic processes showing what brain areas are active. These brain differences are presented as biological evidence of the disease basis of distressing human emotions and actions. If this were true, it would support the claim that those problems are real brain illnesses. However, it is not true.

Brain scan research does, in fact, demonstrate a biological difference between the brains of people who are labeled "mentally ill" and those who aren't. This has been reported with "depression,"[28] "post-traumatic stress disorder,"[29] "obsessive-compulsive disorder,"[30] and "attention-deficit/hyperactivity disorder."[31] We must be careful, though, when interpreting the meaning of these brain scans.

First, are the unique brain patterns evidence of disease causing the problems, or are the problems causing changes in brain patterns? We know biological changes accompany psychological distress. For instance, besides unique brain activity, a person who lives a life of chronic tension and hypervigilance also has alterations in the gastric system, which cause problems such as ulcers and acid reflux. But it would be silly to conclude from this that the ulcers and acid reflux are the disease processes causing "anxiety."

Second, there are a multitude of other environmental factors that can affect brain patterns but are usually not accounted for in these brain scan studies. Are people who are labeled with "mental illnesses" also more prone to be suffering from environmental insults that can negatively affect brain activity, such as poverty, nutritional deficiencies, trauma, pollutants, and illicit drug use? Also, these people are very likely taking psychiatric drugs known to have negative effects on brain activity. Are these environmental and chemical factors negatively affecting brain patterns seen in the brain scans?

Above and beyond these problems, the principal weakness of brain scan research is that brain *differences* are not the same as brain *disease*. When evaluating these brain scans, we must remember what I said earlier about chemical changes in the brain. That is, various brain areas become active when a person is doing, thinking, or feeling anything. For instance, when looking at something, the occipital lobe in the back of the brain becomes active and this would show up on a brain scan. When hearing something or when moving a certain body part, this would also be reflected in signature activity in the auditory and motor areas of the brain, respectively.

But this happens with any experience or behavior. Areas of the brain involved "light up" when those experiences and behaviors occur. People who are doing, thinking, and feeling different things will have unique brains scans and they will differ from others who aren't affected by those things. A person who is watching a movie and a person who is listening to a song will have different brain scan patterns. Similarly, a person who is living a life of chronic hypervigilance and who has been labeled with "generalized anxiety disorder" can be expected to have a different brain scan than a person who isn't living that kind of life. It would also be different from a person who is living a life of chronic passivity and who has been labeled with "depression." But these unique brain scans have nothing necessarily to do with brain disease. As was noted in a critique of brain scan research:

> The brain research conducted thus far actually appears to indicate that most of the conditions referred to as "mental illnesses" are likely otherwise healthy adaptive processes in response to extreme environmental experiences. So although it appears that such adaptive processes often do correlate with changes within the brain and that they may lead to certain long-term problems for the individual, these changes do not necessarily signify biological disease.[32]

Another thing to remember is the brain is "plastic," meaning those parts used the most can change structurally and functionally over time.[33] This is somewhat like how our muscles change when we use them. Muscles used the most will get bigger and more toned. Although the brain is not a muscle, it still shares this same feature of change based on how it is used. For instance, someone who has been identified by the Industry as "depressed" is living a life characterized by a consistent and unique set of behaviors and experiences reflected in brain activity. This person is chronically passive, avoidant, and disinterested in life. So it is reasonable to conclude the areas of the brain involved in those behaviors and experiences will undergo unique histories of activation which, because of plasticity, would likely result in organizational, structural, and functional differences when compared to someone who is not living that kind of life or from a person who is experiencing a different kind of chronic problem.

It is important to reiterate that neural activation patterns and plastic changes will happen with *any* human activity. Playing the piano,[34] composing music,[35] reading Braille,[36] meditating,[37] thinking of different kinds of words,[38] and even embracing different political ideologies[39] have their own distinct brain scan activity patterns and, therefore, brain plasticity would suggest those brains would change over time in unique ways. But, given this alone, we wouldn't conclude those common human activities were illnesses or signs of malfunctioning or diseased brains, even though their brain scans would clearly be unique in appearance.

In short, these brain scans do not confirm illness because they are not revealing brain *pathology* or *disease.* Instead, they are revealing natural brain *differences.* It is ridiculous to consider mere brain differences as biomarkers of illnesses. Imagine concluding a politically conservative person and a piano virtuoso are suffering from illnesses because their brain scans differ from other people who do not hold conservative views or play the piano! Thus, brain scans of these differences in activation and plasticity cannot be legitimately used as evidence of brain pathology or to claim common human problems in living are illnesses.

In addition to understanding how brain activation and plasticity are mistaken for brain disease, it is also important to recognize the limitations of brain scan technology. These limitations prevent brain scans from obtaining precise pictures of what is going on in the brain. Whereas there are unique brain scan images corresponding to different patterns of experiences and behaviors, as described earlier, they are not precise enough for the purposes of making an accurate identification of the particular form of suffering endured by any one person. The same limitation would apply in using a brain scan to guess if a person is a piano or guitar player. Brain scan technology just isn't advanced enough to have sufficient confidence in the results for identification purposes like this. For one thing, the brain scans you typically see reported in the news or in scientific journals are not pictures of one person's brain. Instead, they are composites, or averages, of the scans of several individuals.[40] The individual scans in the composite can differ substantially.

Another problem with this technology is how it can produce false positives and false negatives. The sensitivity must be adjusted but when it is made more sensitive, there is a greater chance of detecting brain activity not really there. When it is adjusted to be less sensitive, there is a greater chance of failing to detect activity. This problem can lead to absurd test results. For instance, a 2010 study humorously demonstrated how a brain scan revealed activity in a *dead* fish while it was "shown the same social perspective-taking task that was later administered to a group of human subjects."[41]

These problems make one seriously question the usefulness of brain scans as precise and accurate reflections of ongoing brain activity and plasticity, not to mention the far more important point that those things are not the same as disease. Still, despite these weaknesses, brain scan research is commonly presented to make it appear that human emotional and behavioral problems are brain illnesses.

For instance, a study entitled, "Hippocampal GABA enables inhibitory control over unwanted thoughts," focuses on brain activity as the key to understanding the intrusive thoughts common to the problems that get diagnosed as "post-traumatic stress disorder," "schizophrenia," "depression," and "anxiety."[42] But the study is peppered with misleading medical language that not only implies illness, it also equates meaningful intrusive thinking with biological changes, when the two are vastly different. It further insinuates those biological changes are evidence of disease. Here are several examples of obscure medical language from the article, along with a more honest, humane, and non-disease translation in italics that remove the linguistic smoke and mirrors:

> These debilitating symptoms are widely believed to reflect, in part, the diminished engagement of the lateral prefrontal cortex to stop unwanted mental processes, a process known as inhibitory control. (*Translation: When people are experiencing intrusive thoughts, we notice a part of their brain becomes less active.*)
>
> In individuals with schizophrenia, the severity of positive symptoms, such as hallucinations, increases with hippocampal hyperactivity, as indexed from abnormally elevated resting blood oxygen-level-dependent (BOLD) activity, or increased regional cerebral blood flow, blood volume, or blood glucose metabolic rate. (*Translation: When the severity of intrusive thoughts increases, we notice another part of their brain becomes more active.*)
>
> Consistent with this view, animal models of schizophrenia show that disrupting GABAergic inhibition in the hippocampus by transgenic or pharmacological manipulations reliably reproduces hippocampal hyperactivity and volume loss, along with behavioral phenomena paralleling symptoms present in this disorder. (*Translation: When we disrupt the natural workings of the brain it causes problems for the owner of the brain.*)
>
> We hypothesized that GABAergic inhibition in the hippocampus forms a critical link in a fronto-hippocampal inhibitory control pathway that suppresses unwanted thoughts. (*Translation: We think two areas of the brain change in activity level when people experience intrusive thoughts.*)

I could go on with this study, in addition to a multitude of other daily reports about brain scans and show how language is used like this to create the illusion of disease and illness. These italicized translations of otherwise cryptic and medical-sounding statements make it clear the human problems in this study have nothing to do with disease of the brain.

Instead, the researchers are merely pointing out that brain activity naturally varies with different human experiences. When people think intrusively, their brains are going to reflect that activity, just like how unique brain changes occur with piano playing and meditating. It is not evidence of malfunctioning brain circuits. But in order to make it sound like disease and illness, the researchers present their findings with phrases like "diminished engagement," "inhibition in the hippocampus," and "inhibitory control pathway that suppresses unwanted thoughts," alluding to the idea that those areas of the brain are defective. This language also anthropomorphizes brains, making it seem brains can "engage," be "inhibited," and "suppress" things. Brains don't do that; people do. Brains merely react to input consistent with how they are structured.

Scientific journals and popular news accounts of these brain scan studies are replete with this kind of misleading language, which fools you into believing something that isn't true. Despite all the medical-sounding terms used, no evidence is ever presented in this study, or any other, that the human experiences and behaviors labeled "mental illness" have anything to do with malfunctioning brains. The only thing this study shows is when people are thinking in an intrusive fashion their brains are working in a unique way. But we already knew this.

Perhaps an analogy would help understand just how misleading this language can be. What if we noticed when people are playing baseball their brains react in a unique way? Would we then conclude playing baseball is a "mental illness"? Of course, we wouldn't. Further, we wouldn't say things like:

> In individuals with baseball playing disorder, the severity of positive symptoms, such as throwing and catching a baseball, increases with motor and sensory cortex hyperactivity, as indexed from abnormally elevated resting blood oxygen-level-dependent (BOLD) activity, or increased regional cerebral blood flow, blood volume, or blood glucose metabolic rate.

That would be preposterous. The defenders of the Myth might criticize this analogy by claiming baseball players are not experiencing the emotional pain typical of so-called "mental illness." In other words, playing baseball is not emotionally or behaviorally problematic. In response to their criticism, though, I would wonder if any of them have ever played baseball, or if they have considered how the players and fans of the losing team of the World Series felt.

The brain changes that occur while playing baseball is not evidence of illness. It is simply how our brains work when we are playing baseball, regardless of how difficult or easy the behavior is. More importantly, those changes are not the same as the meaningful human experiences of the game, both for the players and the fans. Likewise, hippocampal and prefrontal cortex activation in the brain during intrusive thinking is not evidence of illness. Those brain activation patterns are how our brains work when we are thinking intrusively. Further, they are not the same thing as the meaningful human experience of intrusive thoughts. Thinking intrusively and the underlying brain activity are two completely different matters. The former is experiential, and the latter is biological, yet neither is illness. See more in Part II about this difference between the experiential and biological, or the mind and the brain.

Genetic Research

In addition to brain scans, the defenders of the Myth also use genetic research in an attempt to claim distressing human problems are illnesses. Because those problems appear to run in families, it is a common belief they are caused by genetic anomalies. For instance, children of parents who suffer from those problems seem to be at higher risk of developing similar problems.[43] The same thing appears to be the case with children who are sexually abused being at higher risk of becoming perpetrators themselves,[44] and why the offspring of adults with substance abuse problems seem to be at higher risk of developing related problems.[45] However, a closer examination reveals no evidence that faulty or diseased genes are the culprit. A lot of things run in families, including religious views, political views, the language one speaks, and even loyalties to particular sports teams. But we would never conclude those things are genetically determined, and we definitely wouldn't call them illnesses.

These observations are merely indications that children can be affected by their parents' emotional distress and behavioral problems. It also means family members tend to share general beliefs about the world and the implicit rules for behaving in that world. These include broad beliefs such as whether the world is a safe or dangerous place, whether people are trustworthy or not, whether one has the power to change things, whether one is worthy, and what is the best way to respond to distressing situations. The fact that people in the same genetic family might have a higher chance of being similar to each other regarding these issues doesn't mean they are genetically inherited, and it certainly doesn't mean they are illnesses or symptoms of disease.

Each of us is born into a family that shares a common familial culture. Unwittingly, we think, believe, and do what is expected in that family culture. This influence widens into community, ethnic, and national cultures as we grow up and expand our connections outside the family. The fact that people who share cultural influences also tend to think, act, and feel similarly to each other only points out the powerful effects of one's environmental expectations, assumptions, and cultural norms. These influences have their effects on us subtly. Just like the air we breathe they envelop and sustain us outside our awareness of them and they form the meaningful foundations of our lives.

Still, just as with neurochemical imbalances and brain scans, the Industry continues in vain to look for genetic evidence to support their claims. The standard research protocol used in this search is the *twin study* method, which examines the *concordance rates* of twins in a family. The concordance rate is the extent to which twins are labeled with the same "mental illness." The results of these studies demonstrate the more genetically similar twins are, the more likely they will share the same label, suggesting the problems identified with that label are caused by inherited genetic abnormalities. For instance, the pooled concordance rate for 16 twin studies of the problems labeled "schizophrenia" is 40% for identical twins and 8% for fraternal twins.[46] If these problems were genetically determined, this relative difference in concordance rates is what we would expect to see, given the fact that identical twins are more genetically similar than fraternal twins. The obvious question, though, about the results of this analysis is why isn't the concordance rate for identical twins 100% and for fraternal twins 50%? These would be the absolute concordance rates we would expect to see for an illness that is caused by an inherited genetic glitch.

These twin studies suffer from an even more serious flaw. It is the false assumption researchers make about how the environment affects identical and fraternal twins. Specifically, it is assumed identical and fraternal twins are subjected to the same environmental influences. If true, this would mean any differences noted between their concordance rates could only be due to their genes and not the environmental influences.[47] You can read about the problems with this *equal-environment assumption* as well as other weaknesses of genetic research in far more detail elsewhere.[48] I'll just briefly explain the more important points.

Identical twins not only share 100% of their genes, but contrary to the equal-environment assumption, they also share a unique set of environmental influences not experienced by fraternal twins or non-twin siblings. As identical twins grow up, their parents tend to treat them similarly, dress them in the same clothes, give them matching names, and talk proudly about their similarities. People outside the family contribute to this as they marvel about the twins' amazing resemblances, which would add to the influence of their parents' attention and expectations, encouraging them to continue acting in similar ways.

In basic behavioral learning terms, the attention they receive for being similar would reinforce the continuation of similar behaviors and experiences. Also, social psychology research has shown that one's expectations of another can create the very behaviors expected.[49] Therefore, over time, twins are likely to develop similar ways of interpreting events, interacting with others, and experiencing emotions. This would have a significant effect on whether or not they develop similar problems later labeled as "mental illness."

In contrast to identical twins, fraternal twins share only 50% of their genes, just like non-twin siblings. But because fraternal twins are of the same age, they are likely to be more similar in appearance than non-twin siblings of different ages. This is especially true if the fraternal twins are the same gender. So fraternal twins are faced with the same kind of reinforcement and expectation effects as identical twins, but to a lesser degree. Again, this is in opposition to the equal-environment assumption, which claims identical and fraternal twins share similar environmental influences.

We would expect this environmental effect to lessen with non-twin siblings, although it is still there somewhat, particularly if the non-twin siblings are close in age and the same gender. Incidentally, this effect would also be expected to apply to a lesser degree between children and their parents since they can look alike and identify with the family and its culture, including all the values and customs of that family. Thus, we would expect a higher concordance rate between parents and children of a particular family than there is between families. And this "running in families" effect is exactly what we see.[50]

However, a higher concordance rate for identical twins than fraternal twins, a higher rate for fraternal twins than non-twin siblings, and a higher rate for family members than between families, doesn't necessarily signify a genetic cause. It is just as likely the result of being treated similarly, expected to act similarly, and rewarded for acting and thinking similarly to each other. This is particularly evident when we consider the fact that fraternal twins and non-twin siblings are the same in terms of their genetic makeup, yet fraternal twins' concordance rate for the problem labeled "schizophrenia" is nearly double that for non-twin siblings.[51] If this problem was caused by genetic anomalies, then fraternal twins and non-twin siblings would have a similar concordance rate. But they don't.

Therefore, these differences in concordance rates among identical twins, fraternal twins, and non-twin siblings, are probably in large part due to their different environments; in other words, the differences in their experiences. It doesn't support the notion of a shared genetic anomaly, defect, or predisposition to suffer from specific types of emotional distress, especially since no such genetic *pathology* has ever been discovered.

Members of a family, who are reinforced and expected to be similar to each other, will likely confront life circumstances in a similar way, and this would affect how they tolerate and react to life stressors. Sharing the tacit rules and values of a particular family culture would enhance this similarity. Thus, it would affect the risk of whether or not their problems get labeled "mentally ill" if they seek out professional help. This would especially be true if the professional is aware they are twins or siblings of the same family and believes in this genetic falsehood. She would therefore be more likely to use the same Industry label for both of the siblings, which overtime might then create a self-fulfilling prophecy by artificially inflating the concordance rates for twins in contrast to non-twin siblings.

Despite the false equal environment assumption, researchers still claim a genetic disease is responsible for emotional distress and problematic human behaviors by looking directly at genetic biomarkers. But as with the previous example of how language is used in research studies to imply brain activation patterns are signs of illness, it is also used to suggest the same thing about the genetic underpinnings of human functioning.

For instance, the Cross-Disorder Group of the Psychiatric Genomics Consortium published the results of a genome analysis of five Industry categories of significant problems in living. They found *slight genetic differences* between these people and others who hadn't been identified with those problems. The authors referred to these differences as "risk factors," "genetic liabilities," "polygenetic risk," and "polygenetic contributions."[52] Whereas they never outright say the genes are defective or diseased in some way, the wording clearly suggests they are real illnesses having to do with those supposed defective genes. When the National Institutes of Health (NIH), who financed the study, reported on the results, they called the genetic differences "glitches," "illness-associated variation," and "factors that cause these major mental disorders."[53] But, again, there is never any evidence presented to demonstrate defective or diseased genetic material.

Another, more recent, example of how language is used to falsely portray genetic variation as a defect is found in an article entitled, "Shared molecular neuropathology across major psychiatric disorders parallels polygenic overlap."[54] This article describes the purported genetic underpinnings of several types of common human problems related to emotions and behaviors. The authors use medical language as a disguise that conceals simpler and more humane non-illness problems. Just a quick look at the study's summary demonstrates this deceptive ploy:

> The predisposition to *neuropsychiatric disease* involves a complex, *polygenic, and pleiotropic genetic architecture.* However, little is known about how genetic variants impart *brain dysfunction or pathology.* We used *transcriptomic profiling* as a quantitative readout of molecular *brain-based phenotypes* across five major psychiatric disorders—autism, schizophrenia, bipolar disorder, depression, and alcoholism—compared with matched controls. We identified patterns of shared and distinct *gene-expression perturbations* across these conditions. The degree of sharing of *transcriptional dysregulation* is related to *polygenic (single-nucleotide polymorphism–based) overlap* across disorders, suggesting a substantial causal genetic component. This comprehensive systems-level view of the *neurobiological architecture of major neuropsychiatric illness* demonstrates pathways of molecular convergence and specificity [italics added for emphasis].

I'm certain most people glaze over about halfway through this summary and just accept the claim that medical science has a clear understanding of the genetic defects forming the basis of the human problems that get labeled "mental illnesses." But if you take the time to wade through the wording, remove all the medical and illness terms, and replace them with non-medical/non-illness terms still descriptive of what is being reported, you'll see it merely says:

> Problem behaviors and experiences have a genetic foundation. However, we don't know much about the relationship between genes and those behaviors or experiences. We examined cellular gene activity to see how those genes differed for different behaviors and experiences. We discovered genetic differences and similarities among behaviors and experiences, suggesting they have a genetic foundation.

This is just circular commentary disguised as the scientific discovery of a genetic illness. The language implies illness, but the substance lacks any evidence of it. In actuality, the only thing it points out is that genes vary depending on the particular type of problem the person is having. This is similar to how brain scans and neurochemicals vary for those same problems. But we already knew human action and experiences will be represented by signature gene expressions. Gene expression, or activation, is triggered by environmental conditions. This activation occurs at the cellular level and "tells" the cell what to do.

But gene expression is not the same as gene malfunction or any other kind of genetic defect. Similar to unique brain scans and neurochemical variation, unique genetic expressions have nothing necessarily to do with verifying something as a disease or an illness. If we use the athletic analogy, as before, we can clearly see gene expression is not the same as illness. For instance, genes are expressed during physical exercise, but we wouldn't use that fact to conclude exercise is an illness.[55] In fact, genes are expressed in unique ways during all behavior.[56]

When we examine the results of these studies in more detail, we can see a linguistic disguise that gives the impression of the scientific discovery of genetic anomalies that cause distressing emotions and behaviors. But when we look behind the linguistic smoke and mirrors, we can see more clearly that these genetic studies are merely pointing out the fact that signature gene activity coincides with those forms of distress. This is neither a surprise nor a contribution to understanding the meaningful basis of those human problems.

Biology vs. Pathology

Perhaps the most important thing to emphasize is even if these lines of research (neurochemicals, brain scans, and genetics) demonstrated that distressing human problems were a direct effect of a person's neurochemical or genetic biology, it still would not be evidence of illness or disease. Yet this is a topic about which the guardians of the Myth and those who rebel against it frequently get locked into in a seemingly never-ending argument.

The reason it seems never-ending is both sides are correct. But their argument is a red herring. The guardians of the Myth present ample evidence that distressing problems and behaviors are accompanied by biological happenings in the human body, both in the brain and otherwise. Those who rebel against the Myth respond that, instead, those problems are about perceptions, desires, emotions, and values, in other words, psychology. And round and round they go. But they are both missing the point. The point is not whether or not these human problems have a biological underpinning or a psychological reality. It is whether they are pathological. In other words, this red herring distraction shifts the attention away from the crucial question of whether they are matters of real health and illness.

As far as we know, biology is required in order for a person to have experiences and take action, and dead people do not suffer from these distressing problems. Therefore, it is clear underlying biology allows all human activities and experiences to happen, including those tagged with "mental illness" labels. In this sense, we could say those problems are, in fact, biological, just as we could say walking and playing baseball are biological. But this is irrelevant to the question of pathology. Everything we can experience or do is possible only because of the biological structure and functioning of our bodies and our ability to experience that bodily action. This includes crying, thinking about your favorite color, reading, thoughts of suicide, and writing this book.

Realizing this truism only points out that we are biological organisms that remain alive and function through our body's ongoing biological processes. There are many biologically sustained human features, but they are not considered matters of disease or illness. I've already used the analogies of walking, talking, exercising, and playing baseball as behavioral examples. But there are more. For instance, eye color, hair color, height, skin color, and body structure are physical examples that are biologically and genetically determined to a very large degree. But that doesn't make them diseases or illnesses, or even problems for that matter.

Even if it were shown that people with particularly low abilities had correspondingly unique neurochemistry, brain scans, or genetics, this still would not mean they were illnesses. There are plenty of biological factors that are known to vary among people, and they are correlated with human abilities. For instance, people with shorter legs would probably be worse at jumping and running than people with longer legs. Likewise, people with shorter fingers would likely be worse at playing the guitar and piano than those with longer fingers. But it does not logically follow from this that poor abilities at jumping high, running fast, or playing a musical instrument are illnesses. Such abilities based on biological differences merely reflect the natural variation of those skills among human beings.

Natural skill variability alone is not a reason to conclude that lower abilities (or higher abilities) are signs of illness. They may be problems and create a sense of unease or unwell, like how low attention skills can negatively affect academic performance or how poor athletic skills can negatively affect sports performance. But they are not illnesses. To be a literal illness, the biology involved must be damaged or malfunctioning. Disease, not problems or natural biological variation, is the only reasonable province of the medical profession.

As stated at the beginning of this chapter, the problems the Industry calls "mental illness" were not discovered, and they are not diagnosed through the identification of disease processes that cause symptoms. Instead, they were invented as labels to describe unwanted and inconvenient people, many times for the purpose of controlling them and making them less annoying to others. The Industry has worked hard to imply otherwise. Still, those very real problems have nothing to do with real illness or disease. They are about moral judgments regarding the appropriateness of behaviors and experiences.

Chapter 3

Psychological Testing

Testing for Mental Illness?

By now you might be disputing what I said in the last chapter about not having laboratory tests to detect what the Industry labels "mental illness." After all, we have lots of psychological tests that can do the job, don't we? Actually, we don't. Despite the overabundance of psychological tests, none of them test for illness. They are not like blood tests that confirm excessive blood glucose levels or throat culture tests that confirm the presence of streptococcal bacteria. In other words, psychological tests do not detect evidence of disease in a person, thus, they don't test for illnesses.

Psychological tests aren't tests in the medical sense. When I went through my doctoral training, we were specifically cautioned not to call them tests. The preferred term was psychological *instruments*, in order to avoid the false implication that they detect disease or illness. Instead, they are one of three things: (1) measures of a person's cognitive performance (such as intelligence tests and neuropsychological batteries), (2) complicated opinion surveys about a person (such as personality tests and rating scales), or (3) speculations about allegedly unconscious traits and interests (such as the Rorschach "ink blot" test and Thematic Apperception Test). Nevertheless, just for simplicity sake, I'll continue to call them "tests" in this book.

One popular assessment of cognitive performance is the Wechsler Adult Intelligence Scale (WAIS).[1] It consists of several subtests that measure a variety of intellectual skills including visual processing speed, auditory working memory, visual perceptual reasoning, and verbal comprehension.

We interpret the person's performance on this test as a reflection of theoretically inborn intellectual capacity, or intelligence quotient (IQ). An analogy would be a test of physical capacity that asks a person to run, jump, throw, and lift weights. We could score that person on her performance to get an idea of her inborn physical capacity in several subareas. That capacity could be enhanced through training, but there will be a maximum level or ceiling dictated by her physical structure.

The same goes for the IQ test, but it is a measure of intellectual, not physical, capacity. Just as with physical skills, one's intellectual capacity can be increased to some degree through training (tutoring), but there will be a maximum capacity dictated by his neurological structure. There is natural variation for both physical and intellectual capacity, meaning there will be an average level of capacity for the population as a whole and as we deviate from that average, either higher or lower, there will be fewer and fewer people with those levels of capacity.

In this way, IQ scores show how a person compares to the average for his age group (the average IQ is 100). IQ is a good estimate of academic readiness, or how well a person will do with school-based tasks. This is similar to how a physical capacity test would be a good estimate of one's athletic readiness. But the WAIS doesn't assess all types of intellectual or cognitive skills. For example, it doesn't assess artistic, theatrical, or musical skills.

But don't forget that despite its value in assessing academic readiness, neither the WAIS nor any other psychological instrument like it tests for pathology, defect, disease, or illness. They assess demonstrated performance. Of course, if a person has brain damage or some other type of neurological defect, her IQ scores might be negatively affected. But when a person has low IQ scores, this alone does not warrant a diagnosis of brain damage. Instead, brain scans such as the computerized axial tomography (CAT) scan are the laboratory tests used in determining if such brain damage exists.

A person's history can also provide evidence of brain disease, even if brain scans fail to detect it (remember, technological limitations might prevent a scan from detecting damage that is truly there). For example, if a person's IQ changes drastically after suffering a head injury, that is evidence that the trauma damaged the areas of the brain involved in cognition. It is reasonable to use abruptly appearing peculiar behaviors and loss of mental functioning like this after such an incident to suspect there is brain damage.

But diagnosing a neurological defect or deficit because of a low IQ score alone would be like diagnosing muscular dystrophy because a person couldn't lift heavy weights or cerebral palsy because a person couldn't run fast. Absent evidence of the bodily pathology associated with muscular dystrophy and cerebral palsy, low abilities at weightlifting or running are just that – low athletic abilities. Similarly, absent evidence of brain pathology, low cognitive ability is just low cognitive ability.

People who have very low IQ scores, and who may have been designated in the past as mentally retarded, are not necessarily ill. We all vary in our cognitive capacity just like we vary on any human characteristic, such as height, weight, and how athletic we are. Further, there is no natural separation between different levels of cognitive capacity. Instead, the dividing line between average levels and below average levels of cognitive capacity is arbitrary. Cognitive skill variation and the potential practical problems that might result are not synonymous with disease or illness. It is inherent in the human condition. It might very well present the person with practical limitations, such as low academic performance and self-care skills, but it is not the same as illness.

Nevertheless, it is commonplace for psychologists to use low IQ subtest scores as signs of illness. For example, in cases where a person has average verbal comprehension and visual perceptual reasoning scores, but low scores in auditory working memory and visual processing speed, it has been interpreted as a sign of the problems labeled "attention-deficit/hyperactivity disorder." The low working memory and processing speed scores are presumed to reflect a brain defect that impairs the person's attention capacity. As another example, when a person has low verbal comprehension scores but average or higher visual processing speed, auditory working memory, and visual perceptual reasoning scores, this has been interpreted as a sign of a "learning disorder." The low verbal comprehension scores are believed to reflect some type of defect in the areas of the brain involved in learning verbal information.

But these interpretations are based on the questionable assumption that scores should be consistent across all types of cognitive skills for those who are free from the problems called "mental illness." Once again, though, this is not sound logic. Whereas differences in scores like this could reflect underlying brain malfunctioning that affects a particular subset of cognitive skill, such as how frontal lobe trauma might affect a person's ability to pay attention or damage to the thalamus might impair a person's visual processing ability, it isn't necessarily true in all cases when certain subtest scores are lower than others. Further, in cases where those brain regions are damaged, the resulting problems wouldn't be "attention-deficit/hyperactivity disorder" or "learning disorder" anyway. They would be real neurological illnesses.

Differences in IQ scores could merely reflect intrapersonal natural variation of skills; in other words, one's relative strengths and weaknesses of cognitive skills. These differences aren't necessarily due to brain malfunctioning. There is natural variation of cognitive skills within each person, as well as different histories of learning opportunities and the development of processing strategies for different IQ subtest areas.

The same thing is the case with physical skills. Physical skills are not consistent across the board. A very fast runner, for example, might not be as good at jumping high, even though both physical skills require the use of the legs. Also, that fast runner might not be as good at weightlifting. While there certainly are people who seem to be athletically skilled across the board, this isn't always the case. Similar to physical skills, a person very skilled at auditory memory might not have the same level of skill regarding visual perceptual reasoning, verbal comprehension, or visual processing speed. A true medical test would be needed to determine if neurological malfunctioning was affecting these physical and cognitive skills.

In addition to tests that measure cognitive performance, a second type of psychological test consists of personality inventories and rating scales. In essence, these are just very complicated opinion surveys either about the person taking the test or about others whom the person knows. One popular and widely used example is the Minnesota Multiphasic Personality Inventory (MMPI).[2] The MMPI asks people to give true or false responses to hundreds of statements such as "I don't like mornings" (not an actual item on the test). Based on these responses, scores are derived for several psychological issues, such as hypervigilance, despair, anger, and fears.

The resulting computer-generated report of MMPI scores looks impressive with lots of statistics and graphs. However, in my experience, it provides little useful information about a person *in addition to* what can be learned by just talking to him and reviewing his history. It rarely has any practical usefulness in terms of helping someone in distress, or in making a prediction about a person's future behavior. The apparent statistical precision of the MMPI is a smokescreen and, more importantly, it doesn't test for illness.

Several years ago, I used the MMPI, among other tests, to assess the psychological suitability of applicants for the Air Force Office of Special Investigations. After doing so for a while, I recommended we discontinue the practice and stop wasting the money, as it rarely gave us any useful information we didn't already know about an applicant from her background investigation. The one exception was when an applicant's MMPI scores were severe. In that situation, rejecting the applicant was a safe bet, just because of the extreme scores. But most applicants' MMPI scores were not severe, they were only suggestive of problems. Further, the applicant's history trumped the test results. There were times when the MMPI suggested a possible problem, but the applicant's history did not reveal any such problem. In those cases, after taking a second look at the history to make sure we didn't overlook something, we ignored the MMPI results, as was reasonable to do.

Standard official guidelines for interpreting MMPI scores caution against using the scores alone. They must be used in combination with the person's history, current problems, and observed behaviors, in making conclusions about that person's mental status. But if this is so, what is the value of the test results, other than possibly to formulate questions, narrow the scope of further inquiry, and to challenge a person who is thought to be omitting or withholding information? If the test results are consistent with one's history of emotional problems and behaviors, then they are largely redundant. If, on the other hand, the test results are inconsistent with that history, then they are doubted.

I have used the MMPI and other personality inventories more recently in my private practice and in different kinds of assessments, such as fitness for duty and child custody evaluations. In doing so, I experienced the same thing as I did in the military. The results of these tests looked impressive and fascinated the people asking for the evaluation, but they typically failed to provide any useful information that would assist in making decisions, in addition to what was already known. Many times, test results that are consistent with the person's history are said to increase our confidence in making an assessment. But there is no way to determine the absolute level of that confidence. Do the test results increase our confidence from 10% to 12%? Or is it more like 10% to 90%. We just don't know.

To make matters worse, the interpretation of MMPI results, as well as many other psychological tests, are couched in loose probabilistic terms such as, "John's scores are similar to people who experience obsessive thoughts," or "Mary's responses to the MMPI suggest an unsophisticated denial of common psychological problems." The scores are not definitive enough to know whether or not those things are actually true for John or Mary, making one doubt the statements' value. In short, the probabilistic nature of the statements makes them consistent with most any condition – "maybe you are, maybe you aren't." Loose pronouncements like these are also used in horoscopes in order to make them sound like they apply to anyone who reads them:

> You *may not* have been taking very good care of yourself *lately*, Capricorn. The planetary aspects are encouraging you to be *a little more* disciplined in your lifestyle.... *Anything* you do for yourself today *could* have very quick, healthy effects[3] [italics added for emphasis].

The MMPI and WAIS are called *objective* types of tests. This means they claim to be objective, rather than subjective, measures of psychological phenomena. The idea is since the input and output are specific and quantifiable, the results are somehow more precise or trustworthy. On the other hand, there are other types of psychological instruments called *projective* tests. These are tests that ask a person to respond to ambiguous stimuli, not explicit questions. The evaluator then makes judgments about the meaning of the person's responses and how they reflect underlying psychological problems. In other words, the person's responses are theorized to project or reveal unconscious psychological issues not readily apparent on the surface.

The best-known example of projective tests is the Rorschach "ink blot" test.[4] It is a series of cards, each of which displays a randomly created and symmetrical image, similar to how one might splash ink in the center of a piece of paper, fold the paper in half, and then open it back up. Each card is shown to the person and she is asked what the image looks like. Her responses are then interpreted in a variety of ways. Over the years, there have been attempts to make the Rorschach less subjective and more like the objective tests with standardized administration guidelines and methods of interpreting the person's responses.

Prior to the 1970s, there were several methods used and this led to contradictory interpretations and questions about the test's legitimacy. But in 1973, these competing methods were synthesized into what became the authoritative standard through the end of the 20th century.[5] Still, criticisms about the reliability and validity of the Rorschach and other projective tests persisted after that time.[6] In an attempt to correct this, a new standard made its debut in the first decades of the 21st century as an advertised improvement over previous ones.[7] Time will tell whether it is.

Regardless of whether a test is a measure of cognitive performance, objective assessment of a person's opinions, or projective speculation about a person's unconscious world, no test can provide precise scores of any psychological phenomenon, such as one's IQ or level of despair. This is because all tests have a *standard error of measurement.* In other words, they can only provide a range of scores that probably includes the true score. For example, a person's IQ of 113 would be reported as, "John's IQ was estimated to be 113. There is a 95% chance that his true IQ is between 108 and 118." This means there is a 5% chance that John's true IQ is below 108 or above 118, but we just don't know by how much or in which direction. If we want a more precise estimate of John's true score (a smaller range of scores), then the confidence we will have in that more precise estimate is necessarily lower (e.g., 85% instead of 95% confidence). On the other hand, if we want a higher level of confidence, the range of scores would necessarily increase (e.g., 103-123). As the confidence increases, the precision necessarily decreases.

Most importantly for this discussion, the main problem with all psychological tests, whether objective or projective, is they do not detect disease or malfunction like real medical tests do. At best, they are probabilistic estimates of one's skills, desires, beliefs, fears, and other concerns.

Screening Tools

Because full psychological tests are costly and take a lot of time to administer, score, and interpret, there has been a turn toward *screening tools*, such as those that claim to identify emotional and behavioral problems in kids at school, and like the ones you see in the pamphlets at your doctor's office. As an example, the American Academy of Pediatrics (AAP) recently urged that all teenagers be screened for "depression."[8] The National Alliance on Mental Illness (NAMI) similarly endorses the use of these screening tools. They said:

> Mental health screenings are a key part of youth mental health. Approximately 50% of chronic mental health conditions begin by age 14 and 75% begin by age 24. At the same time, the average delay between when symptoms first appear and intervention is 8-10 years. Mental health screenings allow for early identification and intervention and help bridge the gap.[9]

There are high-tech forms of screening tools also being advertised. For instance, researchers at the University of Vermont recently tested a wearable sensor that claims to detect emotional problems in young children who do not show any outward signs.[10] They said, "There is a critical need for fast, inexpensive, objective, and accurate screening tools for childhood psychopathology." It is said the sensor takes only 20 seconds to detect these hidden problems and it is 81% accurate. These screening tools are shorter, far easier to administer to large groups of people, and less expensive than full psychological tests. Their purpose is to identify people who might benefit from professional assistance but who haven't yet come to the attention of the Industry.

As a demonstration of how they work, I completed a 14-item online screening tool for "autism."[11] It took me only a few minutes and I responded to the items as truthfully as I could, remembering what it was like for me as a child as well as what it is now like for me as an adult (incidentally, I completed it twice, with about nine months in between, and the results were consistent). It concluded that I was in the "Autism possible" range. It said that I:

> ...have symptoms associated with an autism spectrum disorder diagnosis. People who've scored similarly to you on this screening measure will often meet the diagnostic criteria for autism or Asperger syndrome, a milder form of autism.

Note how the statement is probabilistic and it is couched in medical terms. This gives the equivocating impression of "maybe you are, maybe you aren't." But are my results on this screening tool an accurate portrayal of an illness that I have? Perhaps the conditions and features subsumed under the label "autism" are merely a set of preferences, behaviors, and experiences atypical among the general population, but that have nothing to do with illness. Perhaps they don't even cause problems for the person. Even if they are problematic at times, can they also be beneficial? Is it a problem or a benefit when people who are labeled "autistic" pay keen attention to detail and demand rigid routines? Maybe throughout our lives we just naturally manage these things, just like we manage all individualized preferences, urges, and behaviors. But are they really signs of illness and something requiring medical forms of intervention in order to reduce the "symptoms"?

Once a person is given a label like this, it is easy to look back into the past for all kinds of examples that fit with the label and "confirm" the screening results. I was never identified as an "autistic" child. But can you imagine what would have happened if I was screened with one of these tools when I was young, and a psychiatrist told my parents I was "autistic"? They most likely would have bought into the belief that it was an illness and I had it. They would have then "understood" why I memorized all the state capitals and the names of dinosaurs, and why I frequently sat alone on my bedroom floor for hours leafing through the volumes of the *World Book Encyclopedia.* It is also likely that any other kind of unusual or problematic behavior I displayed would have been similarly interpreted.

From that point forward, I would have been at risk of being thrust into a psychiatric pipeline and treated by my parents, my doctors, my teachers, and my friends as an "autistic" child. This would have inadvertently encouraged the adoption of behaviors fitting this diagnostic category and, perhaps worst of all, affected my sense of self and my beliefs about the possible paths available to me in life. Remember, social psychology research shows us one's expectations of another can be self-fulfilling.[12]

But for someone who is, according to this screening tool, on the "autism spectrum," I've done surprisingly well in my life and much of my success has to do with interacting with others – the exact opposite of what would be expected of a person labeled with "autism." It is true that I have experienced interpersonal discomfort at times, periodically harbored doubts about my social skills and judgment, and I have always valued time alone in more cerebral pursuits. But if, at a young age, I was told this was because I was "autistic" – that "autism" was making me feel and do these things – my parents and I would have had an "explanation." We might have just accepted it and resigned ourselves to my life as an "autistic" person. Of course, considering my inquisitive nature at the time, I would have also tried to learn as much as I could about this "condition," further reifying it in my mind.

But this didn't happen to me and throughout my life I tried to tolerate those uncomfortable feelings when I was around others, to keep an eye on how much alone time I spent, and to push forward with interpersonal connections, nonetheless. But how can I have done as well as I have if I have an illness called "autism"? Luckily, I wasn't diagnosed as such and I have never received any kind of "treatment" for it. I was once prescribed belladonna and Dilantin for hyperactivity. Fortunately for me, another doctor told my mother to stop giving me these drugs because of how dangerous they could be. Do you think I had "attention-deficit/hyperactivity disorder" instead?

A serious downside of these quicker and less expensive screening tools is they result in a very high number of *false positives*. This means that most people who are identified with them do not actually suffer from the problem for which they are screening. To see just how harmful this can be, let's examine it in more detail. The false positive problem happens with anything occurring infrequently or that has a *low base-rate*, such as the prevalence and incidence of "autism" or any other problem that has been labeled a "mental illness." Screening for any of these low base-rate occurrences, even with very accurate screening tools, will necessarily result in large numbers of false positives. For those of you interested, there is a detailed statistical explanation of how this happens at Appendix C.

According to the Centers for Disease Control and Prevention (CDC), around 3.2% of children and adolescents have been labeled with "depression."[13] Assuming this rate is an accurate count of the childhood problems described by that label, it means 32 out of every 1,000 children and adolescents would be experiencing those problems. This would be considered a low base-rate occurrence. A screening tool with 80% accuracy, which is considered "reasonably good for a screening instrument,"[14] will correctly identify 26 of those 32 kids. It will fail to identify six of them. These are the false negatives. Many people believe this is the chief problem with screening tools that are less than 100% accurate. Specifically, in this case, those six kids who might benefit from help would not be identified.

But I propose the far greater and more dangerous problem is that of the 968 out of 1,000 kids who are not having problems, the screening tool would wrongly identify 194 of them, nonetheless. In other words, only 26 of the 220 total kids identified with the screening tool would actually be experiencing those problems. One hundred ninety-four of them (88%) would not be. The significance of this cannot be overstated. It means out of every 10 kids identified with the screening tool, nearly nine of them wouldn't be experiencing the problems, but they would still be potentially subjected to the stigma of being labeled "mentally ill" and treated as such. This would likely include the prescription of toxic psychiatric chemicals and even possibly electric shock.

There are about 74 million children under the age of 18 living in the United States.[15] If all of them were screened with an 80% accurate tool, millions would be falsely identified. And if you are skeptical about whether our children would really be at risk of these kinds of harmful screenings on a large scale, just remember that the American Academy of Pediatrics recently urged that *all* teenagers be screened for "depression."[16]

With lower base-rate problems, there will be even more false positives. For example, the National Institute of Mental Health (NIMH) estimated that between .25% and .64% of the population experience the problems that get labeled "schizophrenia."[17] This means if we screened people with an 80% accurate tool, 98% of those identified as "schizophrenic" would be false positives! In other words, 98 out of every 100 people identified with this tool wouldn't be suffering as such, yet they would still be at risk of being targeted by the Industry and its "treatment." As base-rate decreases, false positives necessarily increase.

The only way to solve this false positive problem (other than to do away with screening tools, which is what I recommend) is to broaden the definition of the particular problem being screened, in effect increasing the base-rate for the problem. For instance, if the definition for "depression" was "feelings of sadness," then the screening tool would have one question: "Have you ever felt sad?" It is very likely that all people would respond "yes," and so there would be no false positives as the base rate would be 100%. But that would be absurd.

And what of those people who are falsely identified with a screening tool? What if they disagree and protest about it, claiming they have no such problems? Remember anosognosia mentioned in the Introduction? It is the alleged condition when people don't realize they have the problem. These people are at risk of being accused of having poor insight and judgment, which would just be seen as another "symptom" of the problem. It would be used as further rationale for erroneously branding them anyway and subjecting them to the Industry's onslaught.

Even more troublesome, what if a parent complains about his child being wrongly identified with a screening tool and resists placing that child into the hands of the Industry? We have already seen what can happen –

the parent is at risk of being accused of child neglect and having the child removed from the family because the parent's actions are seen as withholding necessary "medical treatment" for the child.[18] This is a parental double bind: regardless of whether the parent agrees or disagrees with the screening results, the child will potentially be harmed, either through unnecessary psychiatric "diagnosis" and "treatment" or through removal from the parent's custody.

Some might minimize the false positive problem by suggesting unnecessary interventions wouldn't be harmful. But they would be very wrong. In addition to the financial burden, which can be quite high, these interventions can also stigmatize people, which affects how others treat them. They can also negatively affect one's sense of self-worth. If told that a scientific instrument identified them as being "mentally ill" and in need of "treatment," don't you think it could lead to a self-fulfilling prophecy, especially for a child?

Intentionally or not, these screening tools also widen the Industry's market by identifying more and more people as targets of their services, which can further exacerbate any existing problems and even create problems that didn't exist in the first place. Psychiatric iatrogenesis, or how the "treatment" causes the "symptoms," has been known about for quite some time but is generally ignored.[19] Perhaps this is the reason why "autism diagnoses" (and other diagnostic types) have skyrocketed in the last 40 years. According to the Autism Science Foundation (ASF), one out of every 10,000 children was identified as "autistic" in the 1980s. Now, one out of every 68 children is identified.[20]

What is happening here? Are the problems labeled "autism" really on the rise? Or, are the diagnostic criteria for it becoming more inclusive, increased attention paid to it through the use of screening tools resulting in more people being branded with the label, and so-called "treatment" for it creating the very problems described by the label? The ASF gives part of the answer. They state:

> It is problematic to compare autism rates over the last three decades, as the diagnostic criteria for autism have changed with each revision of the Diagnostic and Statistical

> Manual (DSM), which outlines which symptoms meet the criteria for an ASD [autism spectrum disorder] diagnosis.[21]

In the effort to soften alarm about what appears to be a dramatically rising rate, they nonetheless suggest at least one other reason to be alarmed. This is the Industry-generated and arbitrary expansion of this ambiguous problem's definition, which identifies more and more children, and further expands the potential market for the Industry.

Of further concern, the Centers for Disease Control and Prevention (CDC) apologetically pointed out that less than half of the children given this label are identified prior to age three. They said, "This suggests that many children may not be getting identified as early as they could be"[22] and other researchers recently recommended screening for this problem in children as young as 12 months old![23] Given the false positive danger of screening tools, this will necessarily result in an artificial increase in the incidence and prevalence of "autism" and an untold amount of harm to children.

These screening tools follow the medical model approach. In other words, screening efforts originated out of the medical profession's attempt to efficiently identify people who were not symptomatic, yet who still had the disease or who might be at risk of developing it.[24] But as pointed out in this book, the problems called "mental illness" do not involve true disease processes of the body. Therefore, it might appear at first glance there is nothing to identify with screening, and so applying it to those problems is inappropriate.

However, this medical model concept of screening has also been applied to other problems in society having nothing to do with true disease. For instance, it has been used in order to identify victims of domestic violence[25] and sexual assault,[26] as well as to predict one's risk of physical and sexual violence toward others.[27] In those situations, there is no bodily disease or defect that the screening is intended to identify. Instead, the screening's purpose is to identify people who experience certain problems or to predict their future actions. Therefore, the concept of screening can still be applied to emotional distress and problematic behaviors, even though such problems are not about disease of the body.

In addition to the significant problem of false positives, screening for emotional distress and troublesome conduct comes with another serious drawback. Specifically, there is no way to confirm if one's identification through screening is a false positive. When screening for real diseases there is a potential solution to the false positive problem. It is to conduct a more detailed examination of those people who have been identified with the screening tool. This is done with laboratory tests such as X-rays, CAT scans, and blood tests to determine if the disease is actually present. But with the problems labeled "mental illness," there is no follow up to the screening because there is no internal dysfunction to be detected. Full psychological tests aren't the answer either, not just because they don't detect internal dysfunction, but also because they are just more lengthy screening tools with their own limited accuracy rates and false positive problems.

It has been suggested that "sequential screening" can address this problem.[28] This is when a second screening tool is administered to those identified with the first one, effectively increasing the base rate of the second sample. In the previous example of screening kids for "depression," the base rate of the second sample would increase from 3.2% to 12%. So, a second screening tool with 80% accuracy would reduce the false positives from 88% to 65%. But this still means more than half the kids identified with the second screening would not be suffering from the problems that get labeled "depression." This is hardly a solution to the harmful problem of false positives.

The consequence of this overly inclusive screening process is that it contributes to the increasing moralization and medicalization of human diversity, the classification of human problems as diseases, the stigmatization of people who are so identified, and the harm that frequently comes to them. These screening tools can therefore create the very problems they claim to detect by falsely identifying people as ill and in the process, leading to an artificial inflation of the official incidence and prevalence rates for those problems. And any disagreements by the people being screened are just seen as further evidence that they are "mentally ill."

Psychological tests and screening tools do not reveal underlying human defects. They are not like blood tests that can analyze the amounts of minerals, triglycerides, and white blood cells that might be associated with disease. They are simply probabilistic interpretations of a person's demonstrated performance on a cognitive skill, surveys that ask for personal opinions, or professional speculations about a person's unconscious concerns. This exposes the fact they have nothing to do with assessing real illnesses or other such disease defects. Therefore, they cannot be used as that third step of a legitimate medical diagnostic process – laboratory testing. Further, they can falsely identify large numbers of people and subject them to the Industry's "assistance."

Chapter 4

The Essence of Abnormality

Abnormality or Immorality?

It must be remembered that the Industry's concept of "mental illness" is defined as abnormal mental functioning and behavior as reflected in the branch of psychology that deals with it - *abnormal psychology*. But there is far more to it than abnormality. Typically, there is also an element of ridicule or disgust that is inseparable from the abnormality, and that is revealed in sneering, yet hollow, exclamations such as, "He's not *right* in the head," and "Something is *wrong* with her." But why do people react like this toward others who are said to be "mentally ill"? We don't see similarly contemptuous comments about those who are diagnosed with real illnesses unless it is related to a moral transgression of some kind, such as with sexually transmitted diseases.

But how do we distinguish between this kind of normality (right) and abnormality (wrong)? If we dig down beneath the layers of medical disguise, we inevitably find the answer. The kind of abnormality associated with the Industry's ideas about "mental illness," and the commonly held disdain for it, is based on morality, not science. Whereas moral judgments may be necessary in a civil society, mental health professionals are not the experts in morality. Instead, morality is the dominion of other social institutions like religious and legal systems.

What I mean by this, and what I'll show in what follows, is no natural boundary exists between normal and abnormal human behaviors and mental functioning. So, the only thing to use in determining the dividing line between so-called "mentally healthy" and "mentally ill" people is one's moral judgment about the appropriateness or inappropriateness of how those people think and act. This is vastly different from real illness abnormality, which is about the thresholds between safe and dangerous bodily conditions. In other words, real illness determinations are based on scientific judgments about abnormal vs. normal bodily functioning. Abnormal bodily functioning threatens the person's physiological viability. With real illness, abnormality is usually synonymous with pathology.

But with the problems that get labeled "mental illness," the threshold between normality and abnormality is based on values regarding the appropriateness of actions and experiences, not dangerous bodily conditions. The question is about right or wrong, good or bad, appropriate or inappropriate, which is only figuratively referred to as "healthy" or "sick." How else could we make such determinations about the appropriateness of these things other than relying on morality? It comes down to the question of whether people *should* behave or experience things in certain ways. This clearly applies to how the Industry assesses people. But those among the general public also judge themselves when they experience troubled times – "*should* I be this sad about life?"; "*should* I drink this much?"; "*should* I have these strange beliefs?"

This leaves us with the question of whose sense of morality do we use in determining what conduct is wrong or what experiences are inappropriate? Since ideas of morality are ultimately matters of individual personal values, the Industry is left with a very flimsy foundation for assessing abnormality. Its professionals are supposed to be scientific experts, not moral experts. So how do we justify our current role of identifying inappropriate ways of living, discouraging them, and enforcing appropriate ways? The answer is we can't, unless we abandon our scientific foundation and take on a more sanctimonious and authoritarian one, which is exactly what's happening. Purely by license and title, Industry professionals are placed into the ridiculous position of being medico-moral-police experts but performing this role under the fraudulent cover of medicine and then supposedly in the best interests of the person being targeted.

This is probably why there is so much inconsistency and disagreement within our professions about the line between normal and abnormal. Each professional must ultimately rely on personalized morality in making that judgment call. Official diagnostic guidelines are an attempt to remedy this, but as will be seen later in Chapters 5 and 6, those guidelines are written in such vague terms that they fail to do so. Furthermore, the guidelines are based on Industry leaders' moral views about what things are abnormal, inappropriate, wrong, bad, or "sick," and the process of developing the guidelines, as well as the content contained in the guidelines, reflect this moral foundation.

Without an authoritative scientific guide in determining abnormality, one might think the Industry would collapse like a poorly built house of cards. Nevertheless, it has continued on for more than two centuries despite this and it has become one of the most powerful institutions of moral control. Given its foundation in morality, it can be considered the modern-day priesthood masquerading as medical science.

We might find widespread agreement about abnormality in extreme cases. For instance, most people would consider it abnormal for a 12-year-old girl to unexpectedly go on a shooting rampage at school because of the shared sense of bewilderment and injustice when such tragic events occur. But we get far less agreement about the abnormality of more common human behaviors, such as when a person talks to an invisible God. Most would say this is normal even though some might say it is delusional, and therefore, abnormal. Depending on the particular God with whom the person claims to be talking (Christian, Muslim, Satanic, Roman, alien, Olmec), and the religious views of the person doing the judging, the level of agreement about whether this is abnormal might vary significantly. Further, one's assessment of this behavior would drastically change just by replacing God with an imaginary friend. Then it would be considered delusional, but only for adults, not children.

Further, consensus about abnormality would be greatly affected by what that God (or imaginary friend) tells the person to do. If God tells the person to have faith or to tithe 10% of his income, most people would be unconcerned and see it as normal. But if God's instructions were to kill a child, many would lean toward seeing that as abnormal even if the person did not carry out the act, despite the Biblical story of Abraham and Isaac. The point is that any level of agreement or disagreement about mental and behavioral abnormality does not rest on science or critical thought. It is exclusively about individual moral judgments and a loose set of professional moral guidelines about what are abnormal, inappropriate, wrong, bad, or "sick" experiences and conduct.

One's level of social functioning is sometimes used as the threshold criterion in determining abnormality. In other words, if the problem significantly interferes with school, work, and other social obligations, it is considered abnormal. But even with this, we are still left with the difficulty of determining how much interference in social functioning is required before a person is considered abnormal. How do we gauge a reasonable level of social functioning? One way would be to ask the person affected to see whether he considers his level of social functioning acceptable. But unfortunately, that doesn't happen often in the paternalistic Industry where individual desires and values are typically ignored. Instead, professionals think it is their job to make that moral judgment for him. Whereas dire examples might gain widespread agreement, such as when the person is miserably homeless, the only way to base that judgment of another is to use our moral standards about appropriate social functioning, which leaves us with the original problem.

Are Statistics the Solution?

The Industry has tried to give the impression of a scientific foundation by defining abnormality from a statistical perspective. The simplest way to do this is to determine how atypical, or infrequent, something is. For instance, if we surveyed 1,000 people and asked if they wear tissue boxes on their feet in order to avoid germs, like the billionaire aviator Howard Hughes did,[1] we are unlikely to find many who do. This particular behavior doesn't happen often (there are other, more common, germ rituals such as excessive handwashing and sterilization of phones). We must keep this in mind. Statistical abnormality regarding human distress is defined by how infrequently it occurs – the more infrequent, the more abnormal. It isn't based on pathology or bodily conditions that threaten physiological viability.

Wearing tissue boxes on one's feet and the obsessive fear of contamination without them would be considered extremely abnormal from a statistical perspective because not many people do it. But even more common behaviors can be considered abnormal. For example, there are very few people who hear voices when no one appears to be talking to them, but probably more than the number who wear tissue boxes on their feet. And there are even more, but still a minority of people, who are registered as members of the Libertarian or Green political parties.

This raises the question of how infrequent would something have to be in order for it to be considered statistically abnormal – .5% of the population, 1%, 15%? Further, which people do we examine when arriving at that frequency? All people? All men? All women? Just adults? Only children, only Christians? These questions bring us right back to using moral judgments to decide on an answer. How else would an Industry professional determine the statistical threshold between normal and abnormal (infrequent) behaviors? In other words, what rationale or justification would we have in saying anything less than a certain percentage of a particular group of people is abnormal and anything happening more than that percentage is normal? Also how do we justify deciding what group of people to measure in order to determine that percentage?

When we have a question about abnormality regarding issues that cannot be answered with a simple yes or no, like we can when asking whether one wears tissue boxes, we must first identify an arithmetic average for a large group of people. Then we must determine how far away from that average each person is before we can decide whether he or she is statistically abnormal or not.

In statistics, the average is called a *measure of central tendency*. This means it is a midpoint description best representing everyone in a group with one number. See the figure on the next page.[2] This shows what is called a *normal distribution*, or bell curve, of any characteristic or condition. Nature has it that if we measure a large number of people on most any phenomenon, the result will be represented by this kind of bell curve.

Let's say this represents the normal distribution of male height in the United States. The horizontal line represents inches, going from shorter on the left to taller on the right. The vertical height (no pun intended) of the curve is the number or frequency of men who are that tall at each measurement point along the horizontal line. The higher the curve, the more men there are of that height. The center, marked 0, is the highest part of the curve. It represents the most frequent, average, mean, norm, or normal, height. In this particular example of male height, it corresponds to about 69.1 inches.

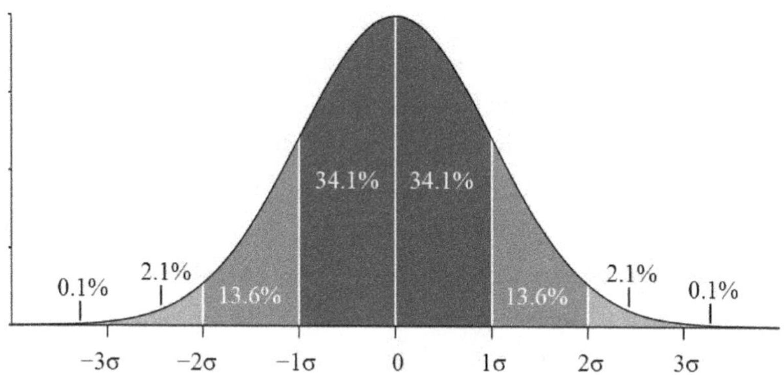

The curve is also marked in *standard deviations* with the Greek letter sigma (σ). Standard deviations merely show how much an individual's height, shorter or taller, deviates from the norm or average. That's why the average is marked 0 – it doesn't deviate from itself. That is also why the σ designations are positive to the right (taller than average) and negative to the left (shorter than average).

Because of the natural characteristics of any normal distribution, about 68% of the group will be within one standard deviation of average. In this example, nearly 7 out of 10 men are within one standard deviation of the average, or normal, male height of 69.1 inches. The dark shaded area includes these men. Men who are within two standard deviations of the average height (include the lighter shaded area) make up a little more than 95% of the total group. You can see this leaves less than 5% (the lightest shaded area) of all men, who are more than two standard deviations from the average height. Thus, in the example of male height in the United States, about 95% of all men are between approximately 63.3 inches and 74.9 inches tall.

The more we go away, or deviate, from the average, either taller or shorter, we get more and more abnormal, or infrequent. Remember, the less frequent something is, the less normal and the more abnormal it is. This is reflected in the origin of the word: from the Latin *ab*, meaning "off" or "away from," and *norma*, meaning "rule" or "pattern." But we find ourselves stuck again in that familiar dilemma. That is, how far away from average is abnormal?

As I already explained, when it comes to real disease and illness, this threshold between normality and abnormality is based on how the deviation from the norm threatens physiological viability. That threshold is not fundamentally a statistical issue; it is a viability issue. Even though the threshold might consist of a range and not an exact point, as with blood pressure and triglyceride levels, abnormality for real illnesses is mostly agreed on and can be determined through medical science. On the other hand, there is no authoritative scientific answer to this question for emotional distress and troublesome behaviors, other than to say it is when the problem threatens the person's social functioning, which we saw earlier is a vague standard for a threshold between normal and abnormal.

For instance, a 7-foot tall man might have social functioning problems because of the typical 7-foot doorway structures in our culture. But why would we call that pathological, diseased, or ill? Further, notwithstanding that statistical abnormality, the same man might be a great basketball player. The context matters. In this case, is abnormal height a problem of social functioning? Or, is it beneficial? Think about how this applies to one's level of interpersonal relatedness, emotional sensitivity, attention to detail, or self-esteem. At what level is social functioning jeopardized? The truth is all levels have their costs and benefits, just as with height.

Further, who gets to decide adequate social functioning? Of course, if people want help in becoming more socially viable on their own terms, that is one thing. But it is quite another when Industry authorities or family members demand changes in social functioning when the person himself disagrees and is quite satisfied living the way he does, except for the complaints of those close to him. And, once again, remember the concept of anosognosia and how it places a person into a Catch-22 situation. If he doesn't agree with those judging his social functioning, his disagreement is often interpreted as evidence of his abnormality, not a demonstration of his right to self-determination.

I was once asked to evaluate and "help" an elderly gentleman who was brought to me by his adult children. He reluctantly accompanied them to the session. They reported that his social functioning was impaired as he lived with one of them in a basement apartment and rarely engaged with the rest of the family or left to go outside. His children were convinced that "depression" was making him isolated. But he disagreed with them. Except for the complaints of his children, he said he felt quite satisfied living his solitary life and was functioning well, even in the face of some existential fears. Nevertheless, they wanted him to do otherwise and labeling him with "depression" was how they justified to themselves that he was living inappropriately and that his desires were abnormal. They were not happy when I refused to continue seeing him because of his lack of consent. They wanted me to make a moral judgment that he was abnormal and to do something that would make him normal, so they could feel better about the situation.

To see better how this statistical threshold problem applies to matters related to emotional distress, let's look at the normal distribution of sadness. We would see the same bell curve as with the earlier example of height if we plotted 1,000 people and their level of sadness (or fears, or suicidal thoughts, or excitement, or alcohol consumption). There will be an average, or normal, level of sadness for the entire group and as we go further from the average, or norm, there will be fewer and fewer people who have either higher or lower levels of sadness.

At what point does this become abnormal sadness? The only technical answer possible is any score that deviates at all from the norm(al) is abnormal. With such an outlook, this would mean any sadness score that isn't the exact average score is, by definition, abnormal. It deviates from the norm. And in any particular group of people, it is quite probable that no one will have the exact score as the statistical average for any phenomenon. This would lead to the ridiculous conclusion that everyone in the group is abnormal!

Consider the following hypothetical scores of a random sample of 20 people who rated their level of sadness on a scale from 1 to 9:

2	5	1	9	7
8	4	3	1	1
9	9	1	2	2
5	1	9	7	8

The average of these numbers is 4.7, and you'll notice that none of the participants has that score. Actually, only four of the 20 have scores that are even within two points of this average. Still, it would be absurd to say every one of them suffers from abnormal sadness. Likewise, it would be ludicrous to say any man who isn't exactly 69.1 inches tall is of abnormal height. So, if we saddle ourselves with the task of determining abnormal sadness, we have to decide how much of a deviation from the average level of sadness is required before one is considered abnormally sad. Therefore, we are left with making a moral judgment, again, about how much sadness is appropriate in certain situations and when it crosses the line to become abnormal, inappropriate, wrong, bad, or "sick" sadness.

Developers of psychological tests arbitrarily set these normal-abnormal thresholds ostensibly as guidelines for interpreting a person's test results. But they are not based on natural boundaries between safe and dangerous conditions, as they are for real illnesses. These thresholds are based on subjective moral judgments about how far one must deviate from the average on a variety of psychological issues before being considered problematic and, therefore, abnormal.

For example, the Conners Rating Scale,[3] which assesses people for the problems included under the label "attention-deficit/hyperactivity disorder," uses one standard deviation from average as the first threshold between normal and abnormal attention skills. Given the statistical features of a normal distribution, this would mean when using the Conners Rating Scale, 84% of people would be considered normal and 16% would have abnormal attention skills. The MMPI mentioned in the last chapter uses one and one-half standard deviations above the average as the threshold into abnormality. This would mean with the MMPI, 94% of all people would be normal, leaving only 6% as abnormal on a variety of psychological issues (the MMPI rejects the idea that low scores are abnormal). The threshold for assessing a "learning disability" in some states is a two standard deviation difference between a person's IQ scores and academic achievement scores, meaning even fewer people would be considered abnormal.

Notice as the threshold between normal and abnormal gets closer to the average, more and more people are considered abnormal. It is not surprising, then, that some psychological tests use a threshold closer to the average. Abnormality used this way can act as a marketing tool as it increases the number of people who would be considered abnormal and potentially fall within the influence of the Industry.

On the other hand, some thresholds are used for the opposite reason. Increasing the threshold for "learning disability" assessments decreases the number of people identified as abnormal, and thus, reduces expenditures for school accommodations by reducing the number of students who qualify as "disabled." In these situations, financial, political, and bureaucratic interests, and not medical science, drive the decision about the normal-abnormal threshold.

Any answer to the question of what is abnormal, then, other than saying it is anything deviating from the exact average, which we saw would be ridiculous, requires a judgment call as to just how far from the average one must be in order to be considered abnormal. Therefore, statistics don't help in avoiding these moral judgments when trying to determine the abnormality associated with human distress.

There are two other issues that further complicate this problem of determining statistical abnormality. The first is how do we decide what sample of people to measure in order to arrive at the frequency or average? For instance, if we measured the height of every adult and not just men, we are going to get a lower average. This is because it includes women, who, on average, are shorter than men. Including women will change how abnormal any one person will be than when we just measured men. If we included children, the average will be even lower because, on average, children are shorter than adults.

Imagine how this affects the determination of abnormal sadness. If we only studied people who lost a loved one within the past month, their average level of sadness would certainly be far greater than it would be for a random sample of all people. Yet, the people in this grieving group could still be considered normal, even though their scores would be far higher than the average of a non-grieving group. So, the sample of people we use in determining the average can greatly affect whether or not a person is considered abnormal. And deciding what sample to use is – you've guessed it – based on a moral judgment about which people are similar enough to each other for the purpose of determining an average that best represents all of them.

A second complicating issue is the desirability of the thing being measured. IQ scores, for example, will show the same kind of bell curve as seen earlier. But we only interpret low IQ scores as negative, not high IQ scores, even though they are equally statistically abnormal. Someone with an IQ of 130, and in the very superior range of intelligence, is exactly as statistically abnormal as someone with an IQ of 70, who is in the borderline range of intelligence. They both are two standard deviations from the average. The same is the case when we assess a person's attention capacity. High scores are desirable, not low scores.

Yet the reverse is true when it comes to sadness and many other phenomena related to mental functioning and behaviors, such as those measured by the MMPI – low scores, and not high scores, are desirable. So, does the normality and abnormality really matter? In this case the answer is no. What matters is how we value the thing being measured, and this brings us right back to our starting point of using moral standards to make that value judgment about what is normal or abnormal.

Therefore, not only are moral judgments involved in deciding how far from average one must deviate in order to be considered abnormal, they are also the basis for judging which sample of people to include when determining the average in the first place, and whether the characteristic being measured is desired. The more you think about it, abnormality seems quite elusive. In fact, I would argue it is actually quite meaningless. It really doesn't matter how much someone deviates from the average or how infrequently something happens. What matters is whether we think it is a good or bad thing. And that is a moral judgment.

Chapter 5
Classifying Immorality

Searching for Deviance

Despite the inherent moral basis of determining mental and behavioral abnormality, as detailed in the previous chapter, the Industry still goes about deciding which personal experiences and choices are deviant enough to be considered inappropriate and, thus, worthy of being classified a "mental illness." To repeat, these judgments are not like the scientific medical judgments about real health and illness intended to prolong or enhance biological living. Instead, they are judgments driven by moral interests about the appropriate ways to live but they are disguised as healthcare. In other words, they are questions about *how people should act, think, and feel.* In this way, diagnostic categories have been created and discarded over the years depending on the prevailing moral winds of the time.

For instance, in the early 19th century, an illness called *drapetomania* was said to be the reason why slaves wanted to run away from their masters. Another one, *dysaesthesia aethiopica*, was said to be the cause of their laziness.[1] One could imagine slave owners must have been very worried that these two "mental illnesses" were contagious and would cause an epidemic of slaves protesting their bondage and seeking their freedom.

Whereas these were considered legitimate psychiatric diagnoses then, it is now obvious to us they were wholly based in the blatant racist morality of the times. And, as with present day diagnoses, they did not refer to any defects that were causing the problems. They were merely labels assigned to people who had thoughts and behaviors deemed inappropriate by those in power. Both were eventually discarded as pseudoscience.

Another example of a diagnostic category that is based in morality is "autism." In her book, *Asperger's Children: The Origins of Autism in Nazi Vienna,*[2] historian Edith Sheffer explained that scientists in 1930s Nazi Germany wanted to identify children who were disconnected from the community. In particular, they were concerned about young people who were disinterested in joining groups such as the Hitler Youth. The Nazi leadership concluded that it was abnormal for these children to be so socially reticent and that something was "wrong" with them. They enlisted the help of pediatrician Hans Asperger to study the problem. Building on early 20th century concepts of "autism" as something akin to "schizophrenia," Asperger eventually proposed a diagnostic category called *autistic psychopathology*[3] as the cause of their social inhibition. The Third Reich was very concerned these children were a drain on their system and a threat to the Aryan gene pool. Based on Asperger's work, dozens of the children who he labeled were euthanized.[4] Unfortunately, this diagnostic category continues on, not in his name anymore, but as "autism spectrum disorder."

Further examples of morality-driven diagnoses live on in more modern times. Homosexuality, for example, was classified as a "mental illness" until 1973 when the American Psychiatric Association (APA) polled its members during its annual convention and found a majority of them *believed* it wasn't an illness anymore:

> In 1973, the American Psychiatric Association (APA) asked all members attending its convention to vote on whether they believed homosexuality to be a mental disorder. 5,854 psychiatrists voted to remove homosexuality from the DSM, and 3,810 to retain it. The APA then compromised, removing homosexuality from the DSM but replacing it, in effect, with "sexual orientation disturbance" for people "in conflict with" their sexual orientation. Not until 1987 did homosexuality completely fall out of the DSM.[5]

According to an article in *Behavioral Sciences*, "This resulted after comparing competing theories, those that pathologized homosexuality and those that viewed it as normal."[6] Doesn't it seem strange that there would be competing theories by serious scientists about this? Claiming this change resulted "after comparing competing theories" makes the decision sound scientific when in fact it was a moral one. It was based on a vote of

APA members and how they felt about it, and just those who attended the convention that year. What is astonishing is that nearly 40% of those who voted still believed homosexuality was inappropriate, abnormal, and an illness. They believed it; they didn't have any evidence.

We would never see the medical establishment arguing over whether cancer, diabetes, hypertension, emphysema, or blood clots are illnesses. It would be absurd to call a vote of the American Medical Association (AMA) members in order to decide if these things should be considered illnesses. And we wouldn't hear comments like, "...those that pathologized blood clots and those that viewed them as normal." There certainly wouldn't be a 60-40 split among them about the illness nature of blood clots or those other physical ailments. There might be debate as to the nature of the pathology, but not about whether it is pathology.

Furthermore, the statement from *Behavioral Sciences* also demonstrates how mental and behavioral abnormality and pathology are conflated, further revealing the moral nature of these judgments. It contrasts "...those that *pathologized* homosexuality and those that viewed it as *normal*" [italics added for emphasis]. But pathology and normality are not opposites. The opposite of pathology is health. The opposite of normality is abnormality. As pointed out in the previous chapter, when human behavior happens infrequently enough it might meet the definition of statistical abnormality, but that is not the same as pathology. In real medicine, pathology and abnormality are usually synonymous.[7] However, this is not the case with the various problems of human distress that get labeled "mental illness."

It is interesting to note that even though homosexuality was no longer considered an illness after this time, those same people who had earlier been "diagnosed" as homosexual could still be pathologized with "sexual orientation disturbance" or "ego-dystonic homosexuality," which reflected the understandable social difficulties and prejudices in living a gay lifestyle, especially openly.

But let's get back to other examples of how these diagnoses are moral judgments and not based on a scientific identification of illnesses. In her book, *They Say You're Crazy: How the World's Most Powerful Psychiatrists Decide Who's Normal*,[8] psychologist Paula Caplan, Ph.D., described the example of "masochistic personality disorder," which was eventually abandoned in the 1980s after activists argued it was discriminatory against women – it was. The category was intended to describe people who appear to allow others to abuse them in one way or another. In practice, this mostly applied to women.

To quell the protests, the name was changed to "self-defeating personality disorder" in order to remove the negative connotation of the term "masochistic," without changing any of the criteria. The Industry tried to suppress continued protest by suggesting the category not be included in the sections of official diagnoses but in an appendix reserved for conditions for "further study." This was done, but practitioners were still permitted to use the label to classify people masochistic. In effect, nothing changed.

An incident during the negotiations over this proposed category further demonstrates it was about morality and not science or medicine. During one particular meeting, which included the task force chair's wife, a social worker, they discussed the proposed criteria ("symptoms") of the category. When a specific criterion was suggested, the chairman's wife said the "symptom" sometimes applied to her. In response, the chairman removed it from the list.[9]

Another, more recent, removal of a category from the official diagnostic manual was "Asperger's disorder," the very one with its origins in 1930s Nazi Germany as explained earlier. According to a review of the category leading up to the latest revision of the Industry's diagnostic guidelines:

> In these 12 university-based sites, with research clinicians selected for their expertise in ASD ["autism spectrum disorder"] and trained in using standardized diagnostic instruments, there was great variation in how BEC [best-estimate clinical] diagnoses within the autism spectrum (ie, autistic disorder, PDD-NOS, and Asperger syndrome) were assigned to individual children….It is not surprising that clinicians often feel strongly that their distinctions among the various ASD diagnoses mean something. However, although patterns within and across the sites were clearly discernible, they were idiosyncratic and complex.[10]

How is this possible if "Asperger's disorder" is a real illness? It demonstrates those "clinicians selected for their expertise" were not using science to identify people with a real illness. Instead, they were using their own moral ideas about what behaviors are inappropriate enough to be considered part of the category, and not the remainder of the "autism spectrum." That is why there was "great variation in how BEC diagnoses within the autism spectrum…were assigned to individual children" and why the diagnostic patterns were "idiosyncratic and complex."

After this category was removed from the diagnostic guidelines, its criteria ("symptoms") were incorporated into the category of "autism spectrum disorder." This gives a greater sense of illness to the problem without anything other than the name changing. The "Asperger's disorder" category was always considered a milder form or "high functioning autism." Now, those who were so labeled will be called the full-blown term, "autistic," casting them in a more problematic light. In fact, researchers have even suggested doing away altogether with the phrase "high functioning autism" because, "[b]y continuing to use this term, we may be inadvertently perpetuating a cycle that denies people access to services and support that they need…."[11] The removal of the diagnostic category of "Asperger's disorder" and the phrase "high functioning autism" will result in more children being seen as "in need" of the potentially harmful medical interventions of the Industry.

I'll mention one last example of a morality driven diagnostic category. In May 2019, in response to political pressure, the World Health Organization's (WHO) legislative body ratified a proposal to reclassify "gender incongruence" (also called "gender dysphoria" and commonly known as "transgender") in the *International Classification of Diseases* (*ICD*) so it would no longer be considered a "mental illness."[12] This is a clear example of how political pressure and changes in moral views, and not science, dictate whether or not something is labeled an illness.

The advocates of this change claimed it "...was taken out from the mental health disorders because we had a better understanding that this wasn't actually a mental health condition and leaving it there was causing stigma."[13] But we don't identify real illnesses this way. Instead, we study the problem to determine what is causing the symptoms. It is only after we have a good theoretical hypothesis for, or actually find, the bodily defect responsible for the symptoms that we dub it an illness. We don't merely claim we have a "better understanding" of it without having any scientific evidence or critical reasoning to back up that understanding. It seems "a better understanding" in this case meant they just thought it was of political value to do it that way.

Further, keep in mind "gender incongruence" was not completely removed as an *ICD* illness with the WHO's vote. Instead, it was only removed from the *ICD* section on "mental illnesses." Yet, it was added to a new section entitled "conditions related to sexual health." This was done supposedly in order to "...reduce the stigma while also ensuring access to necessary health interventions...."[14] It is there along with sexually transmitted infections and premature ejaculation. But how does removing it from the "mental illness" section and placing it into this section of the *ICD* guidelines reduce the stigma? And why would we need a separate category identifying conditions that need "necessary health interventions" only transgender people suffer, unless it is because of their transgender status? Doesn't this just worsen and perpetuate the stigma?

These are noteworthy examples that demonstrate the problems called "mental illness" have nothing to do with real illness. Instead, they are category labels invented for administrative and bureaucratic purposes, but they are disguised as medical diagnoses. They are used to designate things abnormal, inappropriate, wrong, bad, or "sick," and that deviate from ill-defined norms. In other words, they moralize individual differences and problematic reactions to living. They are not illnesses. Furthermore, as explained in the previous chapter, there is no scientific basis for identifying these norms or what is a significant deviation from them.

For instance, what is inappropriate or abnormal thinking? Do you have to think or believe things very differently from other people in order to be thinking in an abnormal manner? Different from which people? How much different? Must your thoughts cause you social and interpersonal problems? Or is it sufficient that they are only upsetting to you when no one would notice by seeing you function? How about if they are only upsetting to other people but not to you? Is impaired judgment a sign of abnormal thinking? And how do we define impaired judgment? Does impaired judgment mean when you take action without sufficient cause? What is considered a sufficient cause?

How about behaviors? Is it inappropriate and abnormal to smoke cigarettes, drink coffee, drink alcohol, or take drugs? Does it depend on whether the substance is illegal? How much of a quantity would it take to reach the normal-abnormal threshold? Does your reason for using these chemicals matter? What reasons are legitimate? What amount of social interference must the drugs cause before being considered abnormal? Can the daily use of prescribed psychiatric drugs constitute a "mental illness" similar to how the daily use of illegal drugs does? If so, why? How about other problematic behaviors? Is it "mentally ill" when a person exhibits road rage? Is violence a sign of "mental illness" or just criminal behavior?

What are inappropriate and deviant emotions? Is it an abnormal condition when you are in distress or despair? Or is it only inappropriate and abnormal if you are feeling these things when others around you are not? Is it abnormal to hold a grudge against your spouse for something she said that hurt your feelings? Does it matter how long you stay resentful? What are valid reasons for being upset? Are emotions inappropriate only when they lead to problematic actions? If so, why?

The Industry has no authoritative science to answer these questions. Instead, when it comes to working with people struggling with life problems, its professionals typically use their own personal moral values or the Industry's vague conventional wisdom contained in diagnostic guidelines, to interpret these issues, but they pass them off as professional medical expertise and science.

The Official Guidebook of Immorality

Despite having no scientific foundation, the Industry still insists on identifying numerous categories of inappropriate personal actions and experiences, or abnormality, in the *Diagnostic and Statistical Manual of Mental Disorders (DSM)*.[15] The *DSM* is intended to be the standard for differentiating between normal forms of human distress and abnormal, therefore diagnosable, problems. As mentioned earlier, there is also the *International Classification of Diseases* (*ICD*),[16] published by the World Health Organization (WHO), which the *DSM* mostly mirrors in terms of the *ICD*'s section on "mental illness." Therefore, my comments here about the *DSM* also apply to that section of the *ICD*.

The *DSM* is mockingly by some, yet reverently by others, called the "psychiatric bible." Whereas I think this nickname is appropriate, as the manual is merely a collection of moral pronouncements, the name also unfortunately implies some kind of legitimate scientific authority. The *DSM's* publisher, the American Psychiatric Association (APA), says it is "an authoritative volume that defines and classifies mental disorders in order to improve diagnoses, treatment, and research."[17] Unfortunately, it does none of these things. The *DSM*'s only value is it provides bureaucratic efficiency for the Industry in its crusade to medico-moralize life. In its opening pages it starts with this puzzling disclaimer:

> Although DSM-5 remains a categorical classification of separate disorders, we recognize that mental disorders do not always fit completely within the boundaries of a single disorder."[18]

It seems odd that this authoritative tome of abnormality that forms the basis of the Industry admits at the outset that the diagnostic guidelines it presents do not define separate illnesses. Instead, the different categories contained in it not only have such blurred boundary lines that they substantially overlap, they also are so inclusive as to define most any human problem. Can you imagine the medical profession claiming this about diabetes, cancer, and kidney failure?

In a further act of confusion, the *DSM* uses the term "mental disorder," which is often called a *weasel word* for "mental illness" or "mental disease." But why substitute the term "disorder" for "illness" and "disease?" We don't typically refer to cancer, diabetes, and heart disease as "physical disorders." Why would we do so in the *DSM* if they are real illnesses? Why isn't the manual's title the *Diagnostic and Statistical Manual of Mental Illnesses*?

The only reason would be the *DSM* authors realized the categories in it were not really identifying true illnesses. But they didn't want to be up front about such an admission since that would be a serious threat to their very existence. After all, they see themselves as "healthcare" professionals whose livelihoods depend on the existence of illnesses. So, by using the term "mental disorder" they can stay consistent with the fact that there is no evidence of real illness without completely abandoning their medical approach to classifying inappropriate behaviors and experiences.

For each category in the *DSM* there is a checklist defining it, but the checklist items are misleadingly called "symptoms." This makes them sound medical and matters of illness. However, in fact, the items are nothing more than everyday problematic thoughts, feelings, and behaviors, not true symptoms or biomarkers of real diseases that can be detected with laboratory testing. It is the same as if we referred to the details of horoscope readings and fortune cookie sayings as "symptoms" of the people they describe.

The *DSM* method of diagnosing human problems has been called the "'Chinese menu' approach [that] allows for a substantial amount of individual variation of disorder expression while still capturing individuals who share common clinical features, and *hopefully*, the same disorder"[19] [italics added for emphasis]. This statement attests to the ambiguous nature of the categories and how they can be descriptive of a wide range of quite common and overlapping human problems that have nothing to do with illness.

Arguably the most confusing thing about the *DSM* is the very definition it gives for "mental disorder":

> A mental disorder is a *syndrome* characterized by *clinically significant disturbance in* an individual's cognition, emotion regulation, or behavior that reflects a *dysfunction in* the psychological, biological, or developmental processes underlying mental functioning. Mental disorders are *usually* associated with *significant distress* in social, occupational, or other important activities. An *expectable or culturally approved response* to a common stressor or loss, such as the death of a loved one, is not a mental disorder. *Socially deviant behavior (e.g., political, religious, or sexual) and conflicts that are primarily between the individual and society are not mental disorders unless the deviance or conflict results from a dysfunction in the individual*, as described above[20] [italics added for emphasis].

I remember the first time I read this definition. I felt like I was watching a shell game, desperately trying to keep my eye on the pea. The other thing that quickly came to mind was that scene in Star Wars when Obi Wan Kenobi does the Jedi mind trick as he waves his hand at the stormtrooper:

> Obi Wan: You don't need to see his identification.
> Stormtrooper: We don't need to see his identification.
> Obi Wan: These aren't the droids you're looking for.
> Stormtrooper: These aren't the droids we're looking for.

The same kind of servility happens in the Industry, but it is not because of the power of the Force or the Dark Side, but the power of medical model language. Professionals bow to the *DSM* and repeat the mantra of "mental illness," regardless of its unscientific and illogical foundation as revealed in this definition. Even though it says "mental disorder" is a "dysfunction in the individual," nothing is ever presented in the manual to demonstrate this dysfunction *in* the person. This is not surprising since, as I've said many times before, there has never been any such scientific evidence of pathology discovered despite the decades of searching for it.

Look at some of the other terms in this definition. For instance, the term *syndrome* is a medical sounding term that implies illness. If the term "mental disorder" is considered a weasel word as I said earlier, "syndrome" can be considered a *skunk word.* It smells of a crafty attempt to further blur and broaden the boundaries of "mental illness" by introducing another vague, but still medical sounding, word that misleadingly implies illness without saying so outright.

The definition further confounds things by using the phrases "clinically significant" and "significant distress" ostensibly to identify a threshold level of seriousness that would separate abnormal mental functioning from other forms of normal distress that are not considered disordered. But, how does one determine this? One way would be to say any problem a person brings to the attention of a *clinician* or to a *clinic* is, by definition alone, *clinically* significant and therefore a matter of significant distress. Or, more cynically, a problem can be considered clinically significant and of significant distress if in the mind of the clinician it is clinically significant and of significant distress! In short, each clinician must use personal ideas of significance and distress in order to make a judgment about inappropriate or abnormal levels of distress. There is no logical or scientific guideline for it.

Then, consider how the *DSM* excludes "expectable or culturally approved" responses. Why is this? Isn't an illness an illness regardless of cultural norms? If somebody in Bangladesh has cancer and they move to Canada, does the cancer go away? The answer is no, cancer is cancer, no matter where you live or what is expectable and culturally approved at that location. Cultural considerations do not change the reality of real illnesses.

As an example of "expectable or culturally approved" situations, the *DSM* gives a token nod to the grief commonly experienced when a loved one dies. But we must keep in mind there are many kinds of behaviors and experiences other than bereavement that would be considered expectable or culturally approved responses but based on more nuanced ideas of cultures.

Let us take religious cultures as an example. Is it expectable or culturally approved to believe in a God you cannot prove exists, or is it a symptom of "delusional disorder"? If one hears God speak, is this person spiritually sensitive, or is she hallucinating? Does it matter if the belief is not widely accepted? How many followers must a religion have in order to make its beliefs legitimate and not delusional? Is the Pagan belief that spirits inhabit all things in nature expectable or culturally approved? How about the ancient Greek belief that Apollonius was taken up into heaven while still alive, or the Mormon belief that God gave Joseph Smith seer stones so He could reveal His commands to Joseph conveniently in private? Are these legitimate beliefs, similar to those held by mainstream Christians that each person has a spirit inside them that survives the body's death, that Jesus literally rose from the dead and ascended into the sky, and that God gave Moses the 10 Commandments in private on a mountaintop? Or are they delusions?

Did the members of the 1980s Branch Davidians in Texas suffer from an illness or were they just very devout followers? How about the Islamic terrorists who attacked the United States on September 11, 2001 in the hopes of pleasing Allah? What about the followers of Jim Jones in 1978

Guyana or the kamikaze pilots of World War II? Crazy or committed? If all religious beliefs are exempt from being considered illnesses, then why? If not all of them, then how do we know which ones are expectable or culturally approved? Where is the line between legitimate beliefs and delusions?

Consider political cultures. Is being willing to die for a cause expectable or culturally approved? Would Mahatma Gandhi's near-to-death fasting be considered a legitimate political action that was expectable or culturally approved by his supporters, or was it a reflection of some type of self-defeating illness? How about being willing to kill other people for a political cause? Would Gandhi's assassin be considered "mentally ill," or just a zealot acting in expectable or culturally approved way in the eyes of his culture? When conventional military members kill the enemy during war and express gleeful pride in doing so, are they displaying "symptoms" of "psychopathy" or "antisocial personality disorder"? Or are they acting in ways that are expectable or culturally approved by the military and national cultures to which they belong?

How about when terrorists kill? Is the purposeful targeting of innocent civilians for political purposes any different in "mental health" terms from purposefully carrying out conventional military action that is certain to horribly maim and kill thousands of noncombatant civilians, including children? Why aren't the terrorists seen as patriots acting in line with expectable norms and approval of their political culture, similar to how 18th century American revolutionary war fighters are seen as patriots?

What about cultures not typically seen as cultures? During the last few decades, a popular Internet and smart technology culture has sprung up and changed the technological landscape of communications, entertainment, and business workings of the world. Is spending hours and hours on the Internet and personal computer devices considered an addiction or is it expectable or culturally approved behavior within that culture just like excessive television viewing dominated prior decades?

What about maintaining nearly exclusive communication with people via email, text, and internet-based social platforms, rather than letter writing, phone calls, and meetings in person? How about the apparent trend away from formality, proper grammar, and spelling in these electronic forms of communication? Are these signs of some kind of lackadaisical illness or are they expectable and culturally approved behaviors as seen from within that culture?

How about a time-related culture? Was it expectable or culturally approved in the antebellum era of the United States to have slaves, and to horribly mistreat them? Or was it a symptom of a sadistic illness? We have already seen that when slaves were lazy or tried to escape their masters, they were considered "mentally ill." Were they? Was it expectable or culturally approved in 1940s Germany to persecute and kill Jews and to think one's racial and ethnic makeup was superior? Or was it reflective of "narcissistic personality disorder"? How about the beliefs and actions of Ku Klux Klan members who rose up in revolt after the Confederacy lost the United States Civil War, leading straight to their present day attempts to return society to an ethnically and religiously "purer" status?

These questions about expectable and culturally approved behaviors demonstrate just how useless the *DSM* is in identifying and classifying human problems as illnesses. Most behaviors can be seen as expected and approved if viewed from within the subculture the person is from, and not expected or approved if viewed from another subculture. Therefore, one could argue nothing is a "mental illness" because it would be expectable or culturally approved by some subcultural perspective, even as narrow as a family or peer group. But at the same time, anything could be a "mental illness" if it is seen as deviant from another subcultural perspective.

If the response from the Industry is that we should only consider conventional cultures, then why? Again, as with the other issues already noted, this demonstrates the *DSM* is nothing more than a compendium of moral judgments about people's conduct and emotional distress. It is not a medical manual of illnesses. It is a reflection of the authoritarian power vested in the Industry.

The last sentence in the *DSM* definition is bizarre and confusing. It claims, "socially deviant behavior (e.g., political, religious, or sexual) and conflicts that are primarily between the individual and society" are not "mental illnesses." But since everything in the *DSM* is some kind of socially deviant behavior or conflict with societal norms, this caveat would dictate nothing in the manual is a "mental illness." However, immediately after this proviso, it claims these deviant behaviors and conflicts can still be "mental illnesses" if they are a "dysfunction in the individual." But this is exactly what the definition starts out saying they are in the first place. In essence, this last sentence is making the absurd argument that a mental illness is not a mental illness unless it is a mental illness!

When using the *DSM*, nearly anything can be considered an illness. The manual portrays common human struggles in such ambiguous and probabilistic terms that it can describe just about anyone in the midst of any kind of life situation. This is exactly how horoscopes and fortune cookie proverbs are written. They are so vague and general they can appear to describe any person who reads them. Regardless of your actual zodiac sign, think about how this description from today's horoscope can fit you:

> You *may* find it hard to relate to others verbally.... You *may* have everything figured out in your head, but the words get in the way as soon as you share your ideas. Talking with someone else *may* add confusion instead of clarity to the situation. The other person's energy *seems* to affect your perceptions. Stay grounded despite your frustration[21] [italics added for emphasis].

Or, look at this fortune cookie message that came with my wife's Chinese take-out order two days before she met me. Was this a valid prediction of our meeting?

> An introduction will alter your plans.

In the *DSM*, there are checklists of so-called "symptoms" that describe various forms of human emotional and behavioral problems. Clinicians are supposed to use these checklists in order to categorize people who come to them for help, as well as during ongoing work with the person in order to determine if the nature of the problem changes, if additional problems develop, or if the problems subside. As an example, the following are the checklist criteria for a "major depressive disorder,"[22] one of the most common conditions:

A. Five (or more) of the following symptoms have been present during the same 2-week period and represent a change from previous functioning; at least one of the symptoms is either (1) depressed mood or (2) loss of interest or pleasure.

> Note: Do not include symptoms that are clearly attributable to another medical condition.
>
> Depressed mood most of the day, nearly every day, as indicated by either subjective report (e.g., feels sad, empty, hopeless) or observation made by others (e.g., appears tearful). (Note: In children and adolescents, can be irritable mood.)
>
> Markedly diminished interest or pleasure in all, or almost all, activities most of the day, nearly every day (as indicated by either subjective account or observation.)
>
> Significant weight loss when not dieting or weight gain (e.g., a change of more than 5% of body weight in a month), or decrease or increase in appetite nearly every day. (Note: In children, consider failure to make expected weight gain.)
>
> Insomnia or hypersomnia nearly every day.
>
> Psychomotor agitation or retardation nearly every day (observable by others, not merely subjective feelings of restlessness or being slowed down).
>
> Fatigue or loss of energy nearly every day.
>
> Feelings of worthlessness or excessive or inappropriate guilt (which may be delusional) nearly every day (not merely self-reproach or guilt about being sick).
>
> Diminished ability to think or concentrate, or indecisiveness, nearly every day (either by subjective account or as observed by others).
>
> Recurrent thoughts of death (not just fear of dying), recurrent suicidal ideation without a specific plan, or a suicide attempt or a specific plan for committing suicide.

B. The symptoms cause clinically significant distress or impairment in social, occupational, or other important areas of functioning.

C. The episode is not attributable to the physiological effects of a substance or to another medical condition.

> Note: Criteria A-C represent a major depressive episode.
>
> Note: Responses to a significant loss (e.g., bereavement, financial ruin, losses from a natural disaster, a serious medical illness or disability) may include the feelings of intense sadness, rumination about the loss, insomnia, poor appetite, and weight loss noted in Criterion A, which may resemble a depressive episode.

Although such symptoms may be understandable or considered appropriate to the loss, the presence of a major depressive episode in addition to the normal response to a significant loss should also be carefully considered. This decision inevitably requires the exercise of clinical judgment based on the individual's history and the cultural norms for the expression of distress in the context of loss.

D. The occurrence of the major depressive episode is not better explained by schizo-affective disorder, schizophrenia, schizophreniform disorder, delusional disorder, or other specified and unspecified schizophrenia spectrum and other psychotic disorders.

E. There has never been a manic episode or a hypomanic episode.

Note: This exclusion does not apply if all of the manic-like or hypomanic-like episodes are substance-induced or are attributable to the physiological effects of another medical condition.

Specify:
With anxious distress
With mixed features
With melancholic features
With atypical features
With mood-congruent psychotic features
With mood-incongruent psychotic features
With catatonia. Coding note: Use additional code 293.89 (F06.1). With peripartum onset
With seasonal pattern (recurrent episode only)

There are many procedural and conceptual problems with this checklist, as well as others in the *DSM*. What happens if there are only four instead of five items from criterion A? Why would that matter so much as to disqualify it as a "major depressive disorder"? How about if the episode only lasts for 12 days? What is so special about 14 days? Why is the definition of weight gain at least 5% of one's body weight in a month? And how did the *DSM* authors arrive at these thresholds?

Notice the verbal sleight of hand in the note in A, the wording of C, and the note in E. They caution not to include symptoms belonging to "*another* medical condition" [italics added for emphasis]. This implies "major depressive disorder" is also a medical condition, when it isn't. Further, it is impossible to determine the seriousness threshold required to make an item apply to any one particular person. For example, what does "nearly every day" mean? How about "diminished ability," "recurrent thoughts," and "inappropriate guilt"? How do we decide these things?

More importantly, professionals do not take the time to wade through these burdensome checklists and obsess over which category is the "correct" one out of the many that might apply. In practice, most professionals who work with people on a daily basis rarely ever look at the *DSM*, other than when they are going through training, complying with research protocols, or as I am doing now in writing about it. As a matter of practice, most practitioners use just a few favored categories, and pick the one that seems most representative of the problems the person is experiencing. But they don't refer to the manual each time to make sure all the complex details are in order.

The *DSM* Is Harmful

In scientific terms, the *DSM* is neither reliable nor valid. First, it has poor *reliability*.[23] Reliability is when an assessment tool provides the same results regardless of who uses it to assess a particular person. Ideally, we wouldn't want an assessment of a person's problems to be based on the assessor's subjective opinion. Instead, we want it to be based on science. The *DSM* fails in this regard, as reflected in the lack of expert consensus regarding "Asperger's disorder" and the *DSM*'s own admission it doesn't identify distinct problems. The guidelines in the *DSM* are so imprecise they can produce wildly different decisions, depending on who uses the manual.

Second, the *DSM* also has poor *validity*. Validity is when an instrument actually identifies the thing it says it is identifying. As has been mentioned several times already, the thing it says it is identifying is not really illness. *DSM* labels merely describe different kinds of greatly overlapping problems, but not different kinds of distinct and separate illnesses.[24] These problems with the reliability and validity of the *DSM* are similar to the problems described in Chapter 3 regarding screening tools and the danger of false positive results. So, using an unreliable and invalid tool like the *DSM* can significantly harm people who are being classified with it.

The latest version of the *DSM* was published in 2013 and it has received such severe criticism that the Task Force Chair of the previous

DSM edition, Allen Frances, M.D., discouraged professionals from buying and using it. He said the *DSM* was so "dangerous in its product that many mental health professionals may choose not to use it.... My advice - don't buy DSM 5, don't use it, don't teach it."[25] Curiously, though, Frances strongly contrasted the *DSM-5* with his *DSM-IV*, saying his edition was "scrupulously scientific," despite there being little substantive difference between the two manuals.[26]

Two years before the publication of the most recent edition of the *DSM*, an international effort had already been underway to examine its weaknesses. Initially, the British Psychological Society (BPS), representing over 70,000 members,[27] registered its criticism of the proposed revision of the manual by providing input to the publisher, the American Psychiatric Association. The BPS said:

> The putative diagnoses presented in DSM-V are clearly based largely on social norms, with 'symptoms' that all rely on subjective judgements, with little confirmatory physical 'signs' or evidence of biological causation. The criteria are not value-free, but rather reflect current normative social expectations [morality]. Many researchers have pointed out that psychiatric diagnoses are plagued by problems of reliability, validity, prognostic value, and co-morbidity.[28]

Subsequent to the BPS's complaint, the Society for Humanistic Psychology (SHP) drafted an open letter in opposition to the *DSM* and posted it at an internet petition site. The petition eventually received over 15,000 endorsements from individuals and more than 50 organizations, including 16 divisions of the American Psychological Association. However, despite the strength of the SHP petition, the American Psychiatric Association summarily rejected their requests to address the *DSM*'s problems. The American Counseling Association (ACA) also submitted a petition to address these very same problems, but without success. The SHP subsequently organized the Global Summit on Diagnostic Alternatives, bringing together dozens of scholars and practitioners to search for scientifically defensible alternatives to the *DSM* that would correct its weaknesses.[29]

In an attempt to address how these reliability and validity problems affect professionals' ability to provide ethical services, and as the Executive Director of the International Society for Ethical Psychology and Psychiatry

(ISEPP), I petitioned five American professional member associations for guidance.[30] Eight other organizations[31] critical of the Industry joined me in signing the petition.

Members of these professional associations are ethically prohibited from using unreliable or invalid tools in their work. Ideally, they would therefore abandon the *DSM*, as well as the mirror document the *ICD* ("mental illness" section). However, if they did, people who want to use their health insurance benefits[32] to pay for services might not be able to afford professional help since health insurance companies require a person to be given a *DSM* label before they will pay the claims for services. This puts those association members in an ethical double bind. If they use the *DSM*, they are being unethical because it is an unreliable and invalid tool. But if they abandon it, their actions could be considered just as unethical because they would be preventing many people from using health insurance benefits to pay for crucial services.

Unfortunately, only one of those professional associations responded after more than two years of my urging them to do so. This was the American Psychological Association (perhaps because I was one of their members at the time and they were encouraging me to renew my membership). Regarding this important ethical dilemma, their Chief of Professional Practice said:

> I can appreciate that this is an important issue to you, and I hope that I can be of service by offering clarity and a conclusion. The APA will not be making a comment on this issue now, nor in the foreseeable future.[33]

This response is unacceptable, as one of the primary purposes of the APA is to ensure its member psychologists act in an ethical manner. Also, remember that 16 APA divisions endorsed efforts to address the problems with the *DSM*. Why wouldn't the association's leadership do the same? APA's policy regarding this ethical dilemma as reflected in their response appears to be "the buck stops somewhere else." This failure of leadership and ethical oversight was my motivation for not renewing my membership with them, as it made me wonder what value such membership could possibly be if the association wasn't going to address one of the most fundamental ethical dilemmas facing its members. It was also my reason for sending the following reply, which received no further response from them:

> If I understand you correctly, you are informing me that the APA refuses to address one of the most ethically troublesome issues plaguing mental health professionals. This is quite disappointing, given that the APA is supposed to be "the leading scientific and professional organization representing psychology in the United States" ... Further, your Ethics Office is said to be "a resource to members and the Association in addressing new ethical dilemmas as psychology grows and evolves as a discipline" ....If I am correct in my understanding, how does the association retain any legitimacy or acceptable reputation regarding ethical matters and support to the profession? The *DSM* is the foundation of the classification of "mental illness" and it is admittedly flawed from a scientific perspective. Besides being unscientific, it also harms and stigmatizes untold thousands of people with its fallacious labels. What are we to do, given this ethical dilemma that jeopardizes all psychologists' ability to comply with basic ethical standards?[34]

Other dissident professionals have likewise registered their complaints about these concerns with the *DSM*, and far before the publication of the latest edition in 2013. One psychologist in particular, Paula Caplan, Ph.D., was a consultant on two working groups in the late 1980s organizing and preparing the publication of an earlier edition of the *DSM*. During that time, she was alarmed at how unscientific, arbitrary, and harmful the process was. It was one of pathologizing emotional distress and individual differences, without having any sound foundation for doing so. Frustrated by the Industry intransigence and belittlement of her complaints, she eventually resigned in protest and published her experiences.[35] She later faced continued resistance from the Industry about these ethical problems.[36]

Another dissident professional attempted a more severe tactic. In 2003, activist and retired social worker Mickey Weinberg organized a hunger strike in Pasadena, CA. Called the Fast for Freedom, it was an attempt to draw widespread attention to the lack of any foundational science behind the Industry, including the categories of "mental illness" in the *DSM*.[37] It was carried out by six individuals who are critical of the Industry, supported by a scientific panel of renowned psychiatrists and psychologists. The strikers demanded that the American Psychiatric Association (APA), the National Alliance on Mental Illness (NAMI), and the United

States Surgeon General provide scientific evidence for the claim of "mental illness" as a biologically-based brain disease that can be reliably detected and diagnosed with laboratory testing (the validity and reliability issues explained earlier).

Unfortunately, the Industry's response to the strikers' demands was without substance. The APA sent a patronizing and evasive letter to the strikers, later rebuked by the scientific panel members who pointed out it didn't address any of the demands. NAMI told the strikers their efforts were "ill-considered" but likewise didn't provide the evidence requested. The Surgeon General never responded. During the fast, some of the strikers met in person with APA representatives, who refused to address their demands, merely claiming an abundance of evidence without specifying it. The fast officially ended after three weeks without any further response by the Industry, other than a final APA reply that was condescending and again avoided any direct answer to the strikers' concerns about the validity and reliability of *DSM* diagnoses.

Some professionals address these ethical problems with the *DSM* by fully explaining them to consumers who are seeking help and then getting their consent to continue. Those professionals also frequently use relatively mild labels, such as "adjustment disorder," so as to minimize any potential harm that can result. However, *any DSM label* in one's record can jeopardize many things. These include employment suitability, security clearances, military service, health and life insurance eligibility, parenting and adoption rights, and parole and probation actions. These are the problems I know of firsthand that are being experienced today.

I worry that as our private lives are increasingly subjected to the prying eyes of government and industry, we could also see a *DSM* label being the basis for denying other things like housing and financial eligibility and acceptance at colleges and universities. It seems they are as harmful as criminal conviction records. Given the moral basis for how they are attached to people, this is not surprising. In essence, they are little more than derogatory judgments of people who face very common and understandable human struggles.

More problematically, labelling someone this way can be harmful to her own sense of identity, worth, and power, and thus what she believes about her capabilities and potential choices in life. This is especially true if she believes the label reflects an innate personal defect in how she functions, just like how the *DSM* says it is "a *dysfunction in* the individual" [italics added for emphasis]. In other words, she believes something is wrong with her inherent makeup and is either extremely difficult to correct or can't be corrected.[38]

Furthermore, having a diagnosis can affect how other people interact with the person. Not only do laypeople tend to keep their distance from someone who has been diagnosed "mentally ill," even professionals' perceptions are negatively affected when interacting with someone who has been labeled, regardless of their behavior. In other words, professionals view and treat people based on the label they've been assigned, not necessarily based on their actions or stated desires.

A classic study (the Rosenhan study) showed just how powerful this effect is.[39] In this study, eight volunteer "pseudo-patients" contacted 12 different psychiatric hospitals on the east and west coasts of the United States and pretended they were hearing voices. Based only on their report of hearing voices, they were all diagnosed with a "mental illness" and admitted to the hospital. The pseudo-patients had been instructed to then act as they ordinarily would during the rest of their time in the hospital. It was up to them to convince the hospital staff they were no longer "ill" so they could be discharged, except they were not to reveal they were part of a ruse. After admission, they told the hospital staff they no longer heard the voices, were not troubled by any distressing emotions, and they were cooperative with daily hospital procedures.

It might not be surprising that one can fake "mental illness" like this, and that professionals might be cautious when someone admitted to a hospital later claims they are no longer troubled. But the important thing about this study was that the hospital staff interpreted many of the pseudo-patients' ordinary behaviors as "symptoms." The mere act of labeling them had a great effect on the interpretation of their behaviors and how they were treated. This study demonstrates the powerful effect *DSM* labels have on professionals' perceptions and treatment of people, and it shows how loose the diagnostic decision-making process is, as very ordinary behaviors can be interpreted as "symptoms."[40]

Perhaps the most damning thing about the *DSM* is that the very leaders of the Industry from which it comes have publicly disparaged it. In 2012, one year before the publication of the latest *DSM* edition, the Director of the National Institute of Mental Health (NIMH), Thomas Insel, M.D., blogged:

> Terms like "depression" or "schizophrenia" or "autism" have achieved a reality that far outstrips their scientific value. Each refers to a cluster of symptoms, similar to "fever" or "headache." But beyond symptoms that cluster together, there should be no presumption that these are singular disorders, each with a single cause and a common treatment.[41]

He later cast additional doubt on the *DSM* by saying its "weakness is its lack of validity" and the categories in it are "based on a consensus…not any objective laboratory measure."[42] To emphasize, these criticisms of the foundational document, the "psychiatric bible," of the Industry came from the person who was the Director of the NIMH when the latest edition of the *DSM* was published. It would be difficult to find a more respected Industry authority.

Others have made similar public criticisms about the *DSM*. One of Insel's predecessors, Steven Hyman, M.D., said the *DSM* is "totally wrong," "an absolute scientific nightmare," "a fool's errand," and that it has "wasted human capital and industry funds."[43] In further criticism of the *DSM*, he described it as containing "widely accepted but fictive diagnostic categories…."[44]

In 2010, Allen Frances, M.D., alarmingly said during an interview with *Wired Magazine*: "There is no definition of mental disorder. It's bullshit. I mean you just can't define it."[45] One would wonder how Frances could actually believe this, as he was the Task Force Chair of the previous edition of the *DSM*, which was clearly based on the assumption that "mental illness" can be defined!

So here we have luminaries of the field saying the *DSM* is not valid, it is a fool's errand, and the very concept of "mental illness" is bullshit. Yet the *DSM* continues to be used as the basis for morally judging people's behaviors and experiences, but it hides these judgments behind a medical mask, and millions of people around the world are harmed by it. It forms the basis of the Industry's power to arbitrarily designate people defective and dangerous, incarcerate them, and forcibly drug or shock them without the protections of due process of law.

I've discovered that few people realize if you have a problem, any problem, and you seek out assistance from the Industry using your health insurance benefits, you are going to be diagnosed with a "mental illness." This is because, as I said earlier, health insurance companies will not reimburse the professional's time spent during the office visit or subsequent visits without the professional first diagnosing you. And keep in mind the diagnostic guidelines are so horoscopic and vague that any problem you happen to have will fit some type of *DSM* category.

Some professionals will diagnose you even if you are not using your health insurance benefits. This is because they believe that emotional distress and troublesome behaviors are real illnesses and so they think a correct "diagnosis" is what dictates proper "treatment." This makes me wonder whether the prevalence and incidence figures for "mental illness" are inflated to the point of being meaningless. It also makes me wonder whether there is a real distinction between the so-called "mentally ill" and "mentally healthy."

Most people appear to find comfort in believing they are not "mentally ill"; they are not like "those" people. But if they seek out professional assistance for any problem, they are going to be diagnosed as such. And depending on the personal proclivities of the professional, the diagnosis might be quite severe. Remember, the *DSM* is not a reliable tool. What you are diagnosed with depends a lot on the person doing the diagnosing. Many of you would be surprised to know you already meet the criteria for some *DSM* diagnostic category. The only difference between you and the ones already labeled is you haven't yet asked for professional help. But that doesn't mean you aren't "mentally ill."

Further, harmful *DSM* labels can follow people throughout life, especially if they start out in the Industry's pipeline, bouncing from doctor to doctor, and from which they will have a very hard time exiting. And the longer they stay in that pipeline, the more at risk they are of being diagnosed with labels of increasing severity. This is because the conventional wisdom says the longer a person continues in "treatment," the more deep-seated and serious are the problems. And since these problems are not really illnesses that can be cured, this sets people up for the risk of being in the system perpetually.

Other Classification Systems

Other systems have been suggested as replacements for the *DSM*, but they still suffer from similar problems. I'll mention three of them. One is called the Hierarchical Taxonomy of Psychopathology (HiTOP).[46] It proposes to use a dimensional rather than categorical approach to identifying emotional and behavioral problems. While it might correct some of the shortcomings of the present *DSM* categorical structure, it nonetheless falls short. Its weakness is two-fold: (1) as with the *DSM*, it still regards human struggles as pathological and; (2) despite envisioning human distress on a continuum instead of separate categories of diagnoses, it still retains the main moral decision-making challenge of determining normal from abnormal human experiences and behaviors.

First and foremost, the HiTOP continues to use a medical model approach and the concept of psychopathology. It must be remembered the term "psychopathology" is figurative language at best and disinformation at worst. But the HiTOP continues to perpetuate this scientifically empty hypothesis of emotional distress and problematic behaviors as illnesses and it still couches those problems in language that implies illness (e.g., pathology, patient, symptoms, syndromes, clinical, illness, comorbidity, diagnostic, etiology, pathophysiology, etc.).

Moreover, the HiTOP might actually increase the extent to which natural human struggles are considered illnesses, even more than the *DSM* does. For example, its researchers say, "Dimensions are psychopathologic continua that reflect individual differences in a maladaptive characteristic across the entire population (e.g., social anxiety is a dimension that ranges from comfortable social interactions to distress in nearly all social situations)."[47] But how can "comfortable social interactions" be considered a "maladaptive characteristic," and entire dimensions of human experience be "psychopathologic continua"?

So, in continuing to use the medical model, but absent any evidence of biomarkers that identify the supposed pathology, the HiTOP remains a pseudo-medical endeavor and suffers many of the same weaknesses of the *DSM*. It claims pathology but it must rely on moral judgments, not science, to identify it, even in a figurative sense. Given the lack of evidence of literal pathology, who determines whether something is figuratively pathological?

The HiTOP's second weakness is it retains a focus on distinguishing between abnormal and normal human experiences. Thus, it still saddles itself with that familiar moral judgment problem of determining the threshold between normality and abnormality. This is the exact opposite of what the HiTOP was intended to do. It is said, "This quantitative approach responds to all aforementioned short-comings of traditional nosologies. First, it resolves the issue of arbitrary thresholds and associated loss of information."[48] But if the task is to differentiate between normality and abnormality, there will always be a morally-based arbitrary threshold. This problem is reflected in the following statement:

> A common concern with dimensional classifications is whether they are applicable to clinical settings, as clinical care often requires categorical decisions. Indeed, actionable ranges of scores will need to be specified on designated dimensions for such a classification to work effectively in clinical practice.[49]

But how do we determine the difference (or range) between normal and abnormal human experiences and behaviors? As pointed out before, in real medicine this decision is based on the extent to which the pathology threatens the physical viability of the patient. But we do not have that with emotional and behavioral problems because they do not affect the physical viability of people, any more than how other common behaviors not thought of as illnesses (well, at least not yet) might affect physical viability, such as with the high risk recreational pursuits of football, boxing, and hang gliding.

A second alternative to the *DSM* is the proposed *Classification and Statistical Manual of Mental Health Concerns* (*CSM*)[50] that came out of the work of the Global Summit on Diagnostic Alternatives mentioned previously. This is a humanistic attempt to de-medicalize and de-pathologize the existing *DSM* system. Its goal is to remove the medical disguise. Much of its framework does a very good job at this.

One benefit of the *CSM* is it focuses attention on the problem and not the person. This is consistent with the idea that human reactions to difficult situations are natural and expected ones, not signs of "dysfunction in the individual," as is stated in the *DSM*. Of further benefit, the labels used in the *CSM* to categorize different forms of human distress are presented in straightforward everyday language, not medical language. For instance, a proposed category that would include people who suffer from the traumatic experiences of war or other catastrophes would be called "challenging life situations" and not "post-traumatic stress disorder."

However, the *CSM* still has significant problems that continue to perpetuate the medical model of human distress. The first is that while it eschews the concept of "mental illness," it still retains the problematic medical model concept of "mental health." But how can the medicalizing concept of "mental illness" be removed from the *CSM* classification system while the equally medicalizing concept of "mental health" be retained? It seems if the absence of significant human distress were considered "mental health," then, by definition, the presence of those forms of distress would be considered "mental illness." One cannot exist without the other any more than the words "up" and "down" can exist without the other. In order for one to have meaning, the other must exist.

The *CSM* developers' answer to this problem is they intended a different meaning than the traditional sense of "mental health" implied in the *DSM*. They point out that distressing human experiences and behaviors can have an effect on one's physical health and, thus, the professionals who would provide services to alleviate those forms of distress would be considered part of the allied health professions working toward the end goal of improving physical health. In this sense, the term is intended to signify that *mental* distress affects physical *health*, thus, "mental health."

However, this distinction between two different types of "mental health" will likely be confusing to the lay public and possibly to professionals as well. It will continue the powerful effect language has on casting non-medical and non-healthcare counselors, psychologists, and therapists as members of the Industry. This can fool people about the nature of the services they provide and, therefore, the nature of the problems being addressed.

With this definition of "mental health," the same reasoning could be applied to corporate safety officers, as their role is to reduce workplace accidents through their interaction with employees, thus improving physical health. What prevents this from being interpreted as "safety therapy" and those safety officers as allied health professionals? This would be stretching the definition of this particular form of "mental health" and allied health professionals too far. It is likely that other occupational professionals whose work affects employees' physical health could also be problematically viewed this way.

Another rationale for retaining the concept of "mental health" in the *CSM* is:

> Currently we have such enormous organizations as the National Mental Health Association and its state and regional affiliates, the NIMH, university and college programs offering degrees in Mental Health Counseling, and States offering certifications in this field. Psychologists, social workers, counselors, and psychiatrists regularly refer to themselves as providing services under the umbrella of "mental health service providers." For these reasons, "A Mental Health Concerns Classification System" maintains the concept of "mental health," but within its system it defines its use in a way that is *just enough* different so it can be comfortably and realistically accommodated into the many large organizations currently using it[51] [italics in the original].

This is a politically expedient move. It is intended to ensure existing Industry systems accept the *CSM* and not see it as too much of a challenge to the medical model. But it will likely result in the same problem with defining counselors, psychologists, and therapists (and safety officers) as healthcare professionals. It will cause confusion regarding the precise meaning of "mental health" and, further, it defeats the purpose of developing a classification system for human distress that tries to eliminate the medical disguise. The *CSM* developers recognize that "[p]eople have a hard time dealing with ideas that strike them as too radical"[52] and this is the primary reason they retain the concept of "mental health."

In addition to the conceptual complications regarding the meaning of "mental health," a second potential problem with the *CSM* has to do with informed consent. The *CSM* proposes two classes of "mental health" concerns. The first consists of those concerns people have about themselves. An example would be if I am losing interest in life and therefore seek out assistance on my own. The second class consists of other people whom someone has concerns about. Examples are when a spouse, parent, court, probation officer, or employer demands someone seek out services.

But nothing is mentioned about the voluntary or involuntary nature of this second class of "mental health" concern. Would the *CSM* be applied only when the target person fully consents to the services? If the person does give full informed consent, then why have the second class? Why wouldn't that person be considered part of the first class? If they don't agree to services, then they are not giving informed consent and any attempt to force them would be unethical. Plus, how would we know whether the person "agreeing" is merely placating those who are making the demand, meaning they aren't truly agreeing?

A final alternative system to the *DSM* that I'll mention is a project by the National Institute of Mental Health (NIMH). It is fundamentally different from the first two examples in that it isn't intended to avoid the medical model. Quite the contrary, it is an attempt to shore up the medical and illness interpretation of human emotional and behavioral struggles. Given doubts about the validity and reliability of the *DSM* system, the NIMH announced it would shift away from research that is based on its diagnostic categories.[53] This doesn't mean the *DSM* was abandoned completely. It was just abandoned by the NIMH, but it still continues to be widely used most everywhere else within the Industry.

Setting out in a different direction, this new NIMH program is called the Research Domain Criteria (RDoC), which is aimed at uncovering real demonstrable biological pathology that underlies emotional and behavioral distress. This program will rely on brain scan technology, genetics, and other medical science, and it proposes to help understand these problems from a biologically bottom up perspective. I applaud this effort if it genuinely focuses on finding real bodily pathology and not just real bodily differences. Remember what I said in Chapter 2: the bodily differences shown in brain scans, neurochemicals, and genetic expressions are not the same as bodily pathology and, thus, cannot be used as evidence that the problems are really about health and illness.

Yet despite this principled effort, NIMH's very attempts present it with a dilemma. If the search for real brain pathology succeeds in confirming these problems are actually caused by biological pathology, then why would they continue to be known as "*mental* illnesses"? If they are all eventually found to be caused by such pathology, wouldn't we then discard the concept of "mental illness" completely and let the real medical specialties such as neurology, nutritional science, and immunology handle these real bodily illnesses? And if some of them cannot be verified as being caused by bodily pathology, then we wouldn't continue to call them illnesses and instead recognize them as non-illness human struggles and those who try to help them as non-medical, non-healthcare professionals.

These three proposed alternatives to the *DSM* are an attempt to correct its shortcomings. Whether they succeed in some way as a replacement for it has yet to be seen. Regardless, it is quite clear the psychiatric bible has a significant problem. Its creators admit "mental illness" cannot be precisely defined, but still define it in a mystifying way, and spend nearly 1,000 pages in an unreliable and invalid manual of moral judgments, laying out hundreds of instructions hardly anyone uses, on how to diagnose someone with the condition that cannot be defined and just might be bullshit. Still, thousands and thousands of Industry professionals around the world rely on the diagnoses in this manual every day, branding an untold number of people with its fallacious and stigmatizing labels, driving them into a psychiatric pipeline they may never escape, and controlling their very lives in a way that is more unjust than a kangaroo court in a third-world dictatorship. As long as we continue to look for ways to classify human behaviors and experiences as pathological, but without evidence of bodily disease, we will fail because there are no such things.

Unless alternatives to the *DSM* are completely detached from the medical model, devoid of medical jargon, abandon the attempt to morally judge the appropriateness of human conduct and experiences, and include a firm commitment to individual self-determination, they will continue to be at risk of suffering the same problems as the *DSM*. That is, human problems in living will continue to be cloaked in a medical disguise, professionals will continue to be forced into the position of morally judging people's experiences and behaviors, and individual desires and autonomy will continue to take a backseat to the power of the Industry.

Chapter 6

Life as Illness

Medicalizing Suffering

In the beginning days of psychiatry, the problem it dubbed "mental illness" was without form. It was essentially an undifferentiated phenomenon and all that was known about it was the person appeared to be suffering from something strange. But there was no identifiable cause that could explain the suffering. In 1812, Benjamin Rush, considered to be the father of American psychiatry (and who was also a signer of the Declaration of Independence), published *Medical Inquiries and Observations Upon the Diseases of the Mind*[1] as the infant profession's first textbook. With this, the medical model and medicalization of human suffering formally began in the United States. Prior to this time, questions about extreme distress and problematic behaviors were mostly understood as the consequences of spiritual and religious deficiencies. Rush thought medical science was a better answer. It is ironic in the opening pages of his textbook, he hoped "that this work may be the means of lessening a portion of some of the greatest evils of human life."[2] As it turned out, though, some of the greatest evils are found within the medical model he initiated.

Other competing models arose in the 19th and 20th centuries to explain extreme emotions and behaviors. As an example, Sigmund Freud and his followers proposed a psychoanalytic model of psychological suffering that claimed it was the result of difficulties controlling the unconscious, dealing with problematic relationships, and failures of psychological development early in life. Similar psychosocial explanations sprouted forth in the attempt to explain how psychology in social contexts accounted for human emotional and behavioral struggles.

Incidentally, even though these competing psychosocial theories focused on social and psychological influences and not on biology, many of them still maintained the idea that the problems were forms of personal *pathology*. This notion of psychological or psychosocial pathology, while rejecting the idea of biological pathology, still proposed emotional and behavioral problems as manifestations of defective personal processes rather than natural and expectable human reactions to life challenges.

Whereas these psychosocial theories have continued on into the present day, by the mid 20th century, the medical model clearly assumed the reigning position within the Industry. The dominance of this medical model was bolstered by the invention of psychiatric drugs in the 1940s and 1950s, and later in 1980 by the codification of biological psychiatry in the third edition of the *Diagnostic and Statistical Manual of Mental Disorders* (*DSM-III*).[3] This edition of the *DSM* was a substantial change from previous editions as it was the first to use specific diagnostic criteria similar to medical diagnostic guidelines. A review of the change brought about by the *DSM-III* noted:

> Prior to the DSM-III, psychiatry was dominated by psychoanalytically trained psychiatrists who eschewed the ideas of Kraepelin [biologically oriented psychiatrist of the late 19th century]. These psychoanalysts saw little value to clinical diagnosis for working with psychotherapy patients. In contrast, the main authors of the DSM-III were the leaders of a group that have become known as the neo-Kraepelinians.... Outcasts within American psychiatry during the 1950s and 1960s, these individuals took over the DSM-III. In doing so, the neo-Kraepelinians attempted to bring psychiatry back to its medical roots. The ideas of the neo-Kraepelinians also fit well with the transition in treatment focus from psychotherapy to the use of medications.[4]

Thirty-two years after the publication of Rush's textbook on psychiatry, his fledgling profession formed the Association of Medical Superintendents of American Institutions for the Insane (AMSAII).[5] This was a professional member organization with the purpose of sharing "their experiences to each other, cooperate in collecting statistical information relating to insanity, and assist each other in improving the treatment of the insane."[6] The organization changed its name in 1892 to the American Medico-Psychological Association (AMPA).[7] It is interesting to note this name change reflected an emphasis on combining medicine and psychology not implied in the organization's original name.

The new name echoed Rush's 1812 focus on applying the medical model disease concept to the mind, not the body. In essence, it was an attempt to apply medical science to the psychology of the mind. In 1921, the AMPA changed its name, this time to the American Psychiatric Association (APA).[8] The APA remains today's leading professional organization dealing with the diagnosis and treatment of "mind diseases" and, moreover, it has become a very powerful lobbying group that helps to maintain the Industry's reign. This name change retained the profession's medical and psychological focus but with just one word, "psychiatric." The origin of the word comes from the Greek *psykhē* (mind) and *iatreia* (healing), preserving the organization's interest in applying the medical model to "diseases of the mind." So, at its foundation, even though psychiatry is considered a medical specialty, it didn't have its primary focus on the human body like all other medical specialties. Its focus has always been on the immaterial mind.

In reviewing the history of the medical model classification of human suffering,[9] the American Psychiatric Association (APA) noted that in 1840, just prior to the formation of the AMSAII, there was only one formal category tracked by the U.S. census. This was "idiocy/insanity." Over time, the Industry has identified additional kinds of suffering and labels for these newly invented "illnesses." Understanding them for what they were – emotionally upsetting and significant problems in living – didn't fit with the pathology-oriented medical model. So, the search was on for more and more different types of "mind diseases."

Despite this early diagnostic expansion, just three categories would have been sufficient. I would call them: *Up*, *Down*, and *All Around.* People who are very excitable or obsessed are Up; those who are in the depths of despair are Down; and those who are very confused, disoriented, and disconnected are All Around. Although these somewhat lighthearted labels obviously weren't the official labels chosen at the time, they do accurately describe the most basic forms of human distress.

In fact, the earlier mentioned psychiatrist Emil Kraepelin (1856-1926) presented a similar description of these basic conditions in the late 19th century, although using medical-sounding terms. He differentiated between *dementia praecox* (my All Around) and *manic-depression* (my Up and Down) as the two main categories.[10] The difference between his and mine is that he understood them as matters of true illness caused by some kind of disease process. On the other hand, notice the three categories I've chosen are not in medical language. Up, Down, and All Around are simple, non-medical, non-disease descriptors of everyday problems we all face.

Over the years, since the original classification of these problems by Kraepelin and others, there has been a frenzied effort to subdivide them into a multitude of different, finer-tuned categories of "mind disease." This proliferation of precise medical sounding diagnostic terms that followed the birth of the medical model of psychiatry in the early 19th century have acted as the disguise concealing what are, in actuality, non-medical human troubles – Up, Down, and All Around.

The APA pointed out that by 1880, there were seven categories of "mental illness" for which statistics were collected during the U.S. census: mania, monomania, dipsomania, melancholia, paresis, dementia, and epilepsy.[11] Mania, monomania, and dipsomania would correspond to my category of Up. The latter two of them are obsessions with something: a fixed idea and alcohol, respectively. Melancholia corresponds to my Down. Paresis, dementia, and epilepsy belong to the medical specialty of neurology and it doesn't make sense to include them within the realm of the problems called "mental illness." Still, these last three were used to describe thinking and behavior that would today be considered some form of psychosis, and so would fall within my All Around category.

Eventually, in 1952, the first edition of the *Diagnostic and Statistical Manual of Mental Disorders* (*DSM-I*)[12] was published with an official collection of 128 categories of "mind disease." This is nearly one new category each year since Rush's textbook was published. Between 1952 and 2013, the Industry continued to further expand the number of categories through the publication of six more *DSM* editions. In just over six decades, the *DSM* grew from a 132-page *DSM-I* to a whopping 947-page *DSM-5*. The number of "mind disease" categories had ballooned to 541.[13] That is more than six new categories per year.

Edition	Diagnoses	Pages
DSM-I (1952)	128	132
DSM-II (1968)	193	119
DSM-III (1980)	228	494
DSM-III-R (1987)	253	567
DSM-IV (1994)	383	886
DSM-IV-TR (2000)	383	943
DSM-5 (2013)	541	947

There are other sources that disagree over the exact number of diagnoses in each edition, based on how the subtypes of each are counted. Nevertheless, it is clear that regardless of which source is queried, the diagnostic categories have radically increased in number and scope, essentially encompassing all conceivable problems of human living into some type of disease entity. But despite this explosion of diagnostic specificity, subdividing diagnoses any further than my Up, Down, and All Around descriptions serves little purpose, other than to create the illusion that the *DSM* is a medical catalogue that facilitates precise understanding and diagnoses of several distinct kinds of "mental illness," and thus, more fine-tuned "treatment." In all honesty, though, we could do just as well today by using my three diagnoses of Up, Down, and All Around.

Treating the Name

Medically minded professionals claim that subdividing human suffering and getting the "correct" diagnosis helps in determining what to do in order to "treat" the person. Whereas it is important to pay attention to the specifics and individualized emotional and behavioral problems that manifest with different people, and then to address those problems, the specific diagnostic terms with which they are called are not useful in helping people who are suffering.

Still, those who buy into the Myth sometimes fret quite a bit over which diagnosis is accurate, making it appear as if they haven't heard the news about the *DSM*'s unreliability and invalidity as mentioned earlier, or the *DSM's* own admission that "mental illnesses" do not always fit completely within the boundaries of a single category. Quibbling over which

DSM diagnosis is correct is like debating whether someone is a Capricorn or Aquarius. The Zodiac sign doesn't matter. Experiences and actions do.

Unlike the diagnoses for real illnesses, *DSM* categories do not refer to defects in a person, even though the *DSM* says they do. They are merely descriptions of what the person is doing and feeling. As explained in more detail in Chapter 2, a diagnosis for a real illness points to the bodily defect that causes the illness and so appropriate treatment critically depends on the correct diagnosis. But since there are no defects that cause the problems that get labeled "mental illness," the diagnosis is irrelevant for purposes of helping the person. In other words, a *DSM* diagnosis doesn't point to a defect that causes the problem. It just names the problem.

This is especially evident when we consider the fact that there are a limited number of interventions available to psychiatrists and psychotherapists. Psychiatrists typically prescribe drugs that can be roughly classified as two basic types: uppers and downers. Calling them antidepressants, antianxiety, antipsychotic, and mood stabilizers, is more of a marketing tactic than a true description of their chemical properties or effects. Prescribing one over another is mostly a trial and error process, not one dictated by precise medical rules or how each chemical affects the brain. There are no drugs tailored for a particular problem, notwithstanding what the advertisements say and even though different psychiatrists and patients will anecdotally claim certain drugs work better than others with certain types of problems.

This lack of psychiatric chemical specificity is revealed in the fact that drugs in one class are frequently used for problems in another class. For instance, so-called antidepressants are used for "anxiety," antipsychotics are used to "assist" with "depression," antianxiety and stimulant drugs are used for "depression," and anticonvulsant and blood pressure drugs are used for psychiatric reasons. It is also why antidepressants can cause suicidal thoughts and "depression" and antianxiety drugs can cause agitation and "anxiety" (see Chapter 9). Which drug works the best is based mostly on what each person taking the drug feels, not the drug's chemical properties or what the drug is advertised to do.

Along similar lines of falsely claiming certain psychiatric drugs target specific types of problems, the developers of medical marijuana are claiming it is being grown to target specific "symptoms."[14] This is just ridiculous. Regardless of how the plants are bred and genetically altered, the substance has its effect on so-called "symptoms" through its general psychoactive properties. In other words, it gets you high and some varieties can get you higher and possibly different kinds of high than others. It is the high that helps with problems of varying kinds, from physical pain to fears. Even if the psychoactive effects work better on certain problems than others, this doesn't mean they are targeting true symptoms of an illness. Think about it – if you are fearful, the stimulant effects of cocaine are not going to work very well. On the other hand, marijuana and alcohol can help ease the fear, at least temporarily. We have medical marijuana. Why not "medical alcohol"?

While we're on the topic of alcohol, we might as well consider how wine can help with these problems. People differ in their preferences for wines because of taste and inebriation effects. A colleague[15] of mine jokingly suggested we look at wine the way the Industry portrays otherwise illicit drugs as psychiatric medicines. Imagine, "medical Malbec." Varieties can be produced for different levels of alcohol, sugar, acids, and flavors ostensibly to quell different emotional problems. We can prescribe Merlot for despair, Pinot Grigio for panic, Shiraz for excitability, and Port for cognitive confusion. But if those prescribed pairings don't work to your satisfaction, just pick the ones that do. That's what prescribing doctors do with psychiatric drugs. People are individuals and so they do not all experience psychoactive chemicals in exactly the same way.

Along similar lines as psychiatric drugs, psychotherapy is not based on the diagnostic names given to the person. It is based on an understanding of the specific problems the person is complaining about. Basically, this kind of work is a process of talking with someone in order to explore and help her better understand the problems she faces in life and to identify possible solutions. It is not a process of the precise application of a "treatment" to target specific "symptoms." How could it be if the diagnostic categories themselves (which contain the "symptoms") are so unreliable and invalid? See more about psychotherapy in Chapter 11.

We Are Always Sick

A sampling of the most recently anointed categories in the latest edition of the *DSM* demonstrates its astounding medicalization of human life. In 2013, the following problems officially became "mental illnesses":

- Mild neurocognitive disorder[16] – The Alzheimer's and dementia thresholds were lowered in order to create this category. The American Psychiatric Association says this new category "provides an opportunity for early detection and treatment of cognitive decline before patients' deficits become more pronounced and progress to major neurocognitive disorder (dementia) or other debilitating conditions."[17] This means almost any cognitive problem can now be diagnosed as a mental disorder, especially in the elderly.

- Disruptive mood dysregulation disorder[18] – Childhood temper tantrums. Yes, you heard right.

- Binge eating disorder[19] – Overeating at least once a week for at least three months. Considering the Centers for Disease Control and Prevention (CDC) estimated 72% of United States adults in 2015-2016 were overweight or obese,[20] this is going to be a very profitable diagnosis.

- Unspecified and other specified mental disorder[21] – If something doesn't meet the full criteria of a category, like "major depressive disorder," it can still be diagnosed as a disorder, but it is just referred to as "unspecified depressive disorder" or "other specified depressive disorder." In essence, this is my suggestion of the Up, Down, and All Around categories. "Unspecified Down" has a nice ring to it, doesn't it? The difference between the unspecified and other specified categories and my three are mine do not claim to refer to illnesses.

These new *DSM* categories clearly demonstrate the manual is like a fishing net that is made larger and larger with each new edition but with smaller and smaller holes. It increasingly ensnares more human problems as illnesses to the point that any human difficulty can be "diagnosed." The manual is a very effective marketing tool for the Industry, second only to the medical language used in talking about non-medical human struggles.

This is a process of turning life into illness. In following these *DSM* guidelines, hundreds of thousands of Industry professionals around the world unwittingly become agents of moral control, and marketing representatives for the Industry, while they and the consuming public mistakenly think they are medical specialists diagnosing and treating illnesses.

If you think the overabundance of unreliable and invalid categories in the *DSM* is bad, there's an even more dangerous issue that puts people at risk of being labeled and controlled by the Industry. This is the concept of *prodrome* or *latency*. In other words, it is not uncommon among Industry professionals to speculate a person is "mentally ill" even without meeting the *DSM* criteria for the problem because it is said to be latent or in the prodromal stage.[22]

This means the "illness is in you," but it is dormant and hasn't yet revealed itself – it is asymptomatic. People with these allegedly latent problems are at risk of being assessed with screening tools (which we saw in Chapter 3 are grossly overinclusive and harmful) so they can receive "preventive treatment." This kind of thinking is convenient for the Industry because it portrays quite ordinary and non-problematic human experiences and actions as predictors of "illnesses." So, when you are feeling fatigued, it might be said you have "depression" but it is in a prodromal stage, and you would benefit from a prescription of Prozac to prevent it from becoming full-blown.

In addition to how these all-encompassing and latent ideas muddy the waters and make just about everything fit some category of "illness," there is more confusion. Many Industry professionals make a distinction between "*serious mental illness*" (SMI) and all other "mental illness." But there are no clear guidelines on just how they make this distinction. Those who use this split between serious and not-so-serious problems merely point out extreme examples of people in distress and call it SMI. This is no different from calling people "crazy" when their actions are misunderstood or atypical.

But it turns out the SMI concept was a political and bureaucratic move, not a clinical or professional one. In 1992, Congress asked the Secretary of Health and Human Services to define SMI so the federal government had a better way to allocate precious federal grant funds to the states for "mental health" services.[23]

This sounds reasonable, but a closer look reveals a problem. The federal government's definition of SMI conceivably included any diagnostic category because the key difference between SMI and all other kinds of "mental illness" was whether the problem "…substantially interferes with or limits one or more major life activities…."[24] It didn't matter what the specific problem was called. Since the *DSM* definition of "mental illness" already requires "…significant distress in social, occupational, or other important activities,"[25] this leads to the absurd conclusion that all *DSM* categories meet the government's definition of SMI! Therefore, distinguishing between SMI and all other forms of "mental illness" is meaningless since there would be no distinction.

Of even more concern, the *DSM* has another section describing more problems in addition to the sections outlining all the officially anointed categories. For some reason, these problems did not warrant the formal designation. Incidentally, health insurance companies do not pay for services intended to help with these less-than-illness problems. This section is called *conditions for further study*.[26] It includes problems deemed worthy of future consideration of possible inclusion as official categories. No sound rationale is given in the *DSM* for why they are not already included – well, at least not yet – other than it was the consensus of the *DSM* committee members that they are somehow different than the formal categories. Among the conditions for further study are things like "attenuated psychosis syndrome," [27] caffeine use disorder," [28] "neurobehavioral disorder associated with prenatal alcohol exposure,"[29] and "Internet gaming disorder."[30]

The first of these conditions, "attenuated psychosis syndrome," saw a controversial backlash when it was proposed as a new category in the current *DSM* edition. This is another example of the latency idea I described earlier. It was proposed as a way to identify people who exhibited signs thought to be predictive of the later development of a formal category, even though they did not show current signs of that category. The criteria for this proposal were:

> At least one of the following symptoms is present in attenuated form, with relatively intact reality testing and is of sufficient severity or frequency to warrant clinical attention
>
> Delusions
> Hallucinations
> Disorganized speech

Symptom(s) must have been present at least once per week in the last 1 month

Symptom(s) must have begun or worsened in the past year

Symptom(s) is sufficiently distressing and disabling to the individual to warrant clinical attention

Symptom(s) is not better explained by another mental disorder, including: Depressive or bipolar disorder with psychotic features and is not attributable to physiological effects of a substance or another medical condition

Criteria for any psychotic disorder have never been met.

Note how difficult it would be to determine "attenuated form," "relatively intact reality testing," and "sufficient severity or frequency." But more problematically, do you know any teenager who doesn't meet these criteria at some point, especially in the "attenuated" form? You'll notice these things are describing the typical adolescent who is experiencing the craziness of troublesome thoughts, confusion, and doubts about the future as he leaves the nest and considers an independent life. But this is disguised behind medical-sounding language to appear as a health matter.

Because of the controversy, the American Psychiatric Association (APA) announced it would withdraw the proposal as a formal category and only include it in the conditions for further study section. But it wasn't removed. Even though it is, in fact, now listed in the conditions for further study section as promised, it was also surreptitiously added within the subtypes of the official diagnosis of "other specified schizophrenia spectrum and other psychotic disorders."[31] Our teenagers can now be formally diagnosed with it.

The rest of these conditions for further study are just weak attempts to expand the jurisdiction of the Industry. Caffeine use disorder? Are they serious? It has been estimated that 85% of the United States population age two and older consume at least one caffeinated drink per day.[32] Given the inherent difficulty of judging inappropriate use and significant levels of distress, can you imagine how this would create a huge new market for the Industry? By the way, notice the condition is not called "caffeine *abuse* disorder." This essentially lowers any threshold that would have distinguished between the ideas of use and abuse.

"Neurobehavioral disorder associated with prenatal alcohol exposure" is just another attempt, like I described earlier with Parkinson's and Alzheimer's diseases, of including real medical problems in the *DSM* in order to give the overall sense of pathology to non-illness problems also in the manual. This proposed condition is clearly about how alcohol use during pregnancy can affect the physiological development of the fetus and, consequently, later post-birth developmental milestones. It doesn't belong in the *DSM*. It belongs in the guidebooks for obstetricians and pediatricians.

Including "Internet gaming disorder" makes me wonder why the earlier editions of the *DSM* did not include conditions like "letter writing disorder," "radio listening disorder," "television watching disorder," "car cruising disorder," and "hanging out with friends disorder." These are all things young people sometimes do excessively as part of their maturation and socialization process, and all people do especially during the startup of a new technology. Advancements in Internet capabilities offer increasingly realistic and interactive forms of available recreation and entertainment.

It is clear we are all faced with the challenge of managing the amount of time we spend on recreation and entertainment, in addition to work, sleep, and other daily human activities. This challenge increases the chances that personal obligations and commitments might be negatively affected by devoting excessive time to these activities. But they are not illnesses.

I remember in the early 1980s when we received the first batch of Z-100 computers where I worked. For the first several months, not much work got done while we played with these new machines and their "amazing" features. This was pre-Windows green-screen technology. Despite how primitive it was compared to today's technology it was nonetheless fascinating to us. We could have been diagnosed with some kind of "gaming disorder" then, even though the Internet didn't yet exist.

Our "game" was to write complicated programs to make bubbles and stick figures appear on the computer screen. And sometimes we were able to use the rudimentary database software to create "to do lists" to keep track of tasks for which we had deadlines. The system would automatically sort those items by due date, start date, or alphabetically by task name. But, given there was only one computer for about five of us, it took far too much time to do this than when we just maintained a box of 3 x 5 cards for each task due.

A multitude of "mind disease" names have evolved over the last two centuries. They are either official diagnoses or included under the rubric of conditions for further study. Regardless of which, they have grown from simple descriptions of troublesome human experiences and behaviors into hundreds of different medical model categories that are neither distinct problems nor illnesses. This explosion of unjustifiable diagnostic specificity and the medicalization of human living have done nothing but confuse and mislead us about meaningful and natural human reactions to the challenges of life. Over the years, this diagnostic fetish has resulted in almost all human problems in living being caught up in the Industry's morality nets. And nothing is being thrown back.

Chapter 7

The Maintenance of a Myth

Worshiping the Experts

There is no evidence to support the notion of "mental illness" as true illness. At best, it is a figurative way to think about natural human problems and emotional distress, and at worst it is a fiction that forces prevailing moral standards on people and creates a financial market. But if this is the case, how is the Industry continuing as it is?

One reason is because of our respect for authority. Most of the time we rely on authority figures to decide what is true. We have to if we don't have access to certain information or if the information is so obscure it is outside our understanding of it. For instance, with some exceptions, lay-people tend to trust what doctors tell them and they follow the suggested treatment because they haven't been trained as medical doctors and they don't know the complex nature of medicine or how the human body works. Similarly, most people trust climate scientists about their area of expertise. This is because the lay public doesn't fully understand the complexities of the sciences involved in climate change.

While this reliance on authority clearly applies to the lay public, it also happens with Industry professionals, who usually accept the teachings of their professors in school, their mentors afterwards, and the published experts in the field. This is exactly what happened to me in my earlier days in the clinical psychology profession when I was ignorant about the lack of a scientific basis for "mental illness." I just went along with what I was taught in a conventional university's doctoral program and that included the unspoken assertion that problematic emotional reactions and behaviors were about real illness, just like cancer and diabetes. I believed what I believed because that was what I was taught to believe.

It wasn't until later in my training when I was introduced to competing theories and challenges to the medical model that I started to question what I originally learned from the authorities in my field. I looked for the evidence myself, and I saw none. I was lucky enough to have a mentor who encouraged critical thinking rather than blind acceptance of knowledge. Ironically, it wasn't until I took a more empirical, logical, and reasoned approach (the method ostensibly used in postgraduate training) that I was able to see past the smoke and mirrors and understand the concept of "mental illness" for what it is.

So, for layperson and professional alike, it is assumed the experts know the truth and it is important to trust what those experts say. But even though reliance on the experts can be useful, there is also danger in unquestionably accepting everything they claim. We must think critically and question them about how they know the information and how they arrive at their conclusions. Also, to the extent possible, we must research the information for ourselves. There have been numerous situations where experts outright lie, parrot the conventional but erroneous wisdom, or they honestly arrive at a mistaken conclusion.

Overreliance on experts, without questioning, can lead to a formal logical fallacy called the *appeal to authority*. The structure of this fallacy goes like this: (1) Dr. Smith is an authority on a particular topic (e.g., "mental illness"); (2) Dr. Smith says something about the topic (e.g., "depression" is caused by a chemical imbalance in the brain); and (3) What Dr. Smith says must be true because she's an expert (e.g., "mental illnesses" are real illnesses caused by chemical imbalances in the brain).

To guard against this appeal to authority fallacy, it is important for quality educational programs in the sciences to teach students *how to think*, not *what to think*. Instead of merely relaying knowledge to those students, educational institutions must teach them how to arrive at knowledge, using critical reasoning, empiricism, logic, and the scientific method. This kind of approach is the only way to defend against the appeal to authority logical fallacy. Schools that teach what to think, not how to think, are more like religious institutions that discourage independent and critical thought. This tension between authoritarian dogma and critical thinking is further explored in Chapter 12.

There are many reasons we fall prey to this logical fallacy. First, and probably the most important, is we consider ourselves novices on a subject, such as the problems that get labeled as "mental illnesses." Whether we are a patient, a customer, or a student, we look toward those in authority to guide us and teach us their areas of expertise. What makes things worse is many people don't care to fully know a subject in all its complexities and nuances. Instead, they'd rather those authority figures provide a simple "feel good" explanation. But the acquisition of accurate knowledge can be a complex and painstaking process, not a simple or easy one, and it many times results in "feel bad" explanations.

Second, we are reluctant to question the authority of teachers who have taken us under their wings so as not to disappoint them. This even applies to how patients are reluctant to question the opinions of their doctors. In many situations, especially during professional mentorship and training, the relationship with authority is cherished and the thought of losing that relationship keeps students compliant. And so, they continue on, learning from their teachers, hesitating to challenge their teachings, and continuing to accept without question what they say as true, at least on the surface.

Third, in many cases of professional mentorship, the student's livelihood rests on obedience to the mentor. The mentor provides a professional avenue for the student to establish a separate and to some extent independent professional path. Being too critical, especially of a narcissistic mentor, would surely threaten the student's livelihood and standard of living. This even applies to professionals who have completed formal education and training and are in the workforce. Supervisors, colleagues, professional membership organizations, and licensing boards pressure them to comply with the orthodox model of knowledge and not to question it.

Follow the Money

The appeal to authority logical fallacy is one way we can be fooled. But there is a far greater and insidious factor that helps to maintain the Myth.

This is the tremendous amount of financial incentive for the system to continue on unchanged. Drug companies spend billions of dollars each year to ensure the Industry's medical model stays alive because without it they would lose large portions of their markets and risk great financial damage. They frequently engage in questionable actions to maximize their profits and the billions of dollars invested are returned to them many times over.[1]

Furthermore, in addition to the drug companies, many other organizations' very survival depends on the Myth remaining accepted as true. These are professional member organizations, medical and clinical professional schools, health insurance companies, professional journals, and grassroots advocacy organizations. Most of these organizations receive substantial funding from the drug companies.

The online statistics portal Statista reported that in 2016, drug companies reaped nearly $14 billion in revenue for just the top nine psychiatric drugs sold.[2] According to Public Citizen, a consumer watchdog group, these drug companies paid roughly $1.5 billion a year in civil and criminal penalties for various disreputable activities during the 24-year period between 1991 and 2015, totaling about $36 billion. But this astounding amount of penalties was only 5% of the total profit realized by the top 11 performing drug companies during this same period of operation.[3]

A jury recently ordered Johnson & Johnson to pay a staggering $8 billion in punitive damages in just one case for marketing Risperdal to children, despite knowing about and hiding research that showed the drug caused gynecomastia, which is the development of female breast tissue in males.[4] The company will surely appeal this ruling. Still, this is an unusually high amount and a sign from the jury that Johnson & Johnson's actions were particularly reprehensible.

Regardless of the final award in this case, and the likelihood of future penalties assessed against them for nefarious actions, drug companies consider these just the costs of doing business, along with utilities, employee wages, and other typical budget items. Besides, these costs will certainly be passed on to consumers and the drug companies will continue to make billions as long as the medical model of human distress continues.

Perhaps even more revealing of their interest in perpetuating the Myth over actually developing effective drugs is that drug companies spend far more on marketing than they do on research.[5] This is atypical for large corporations. For example, in 2015, Johnson & Johnson, the company who lost the previously mentioned $8 billion case, spent more than double on marketing than on research: $17.5 billion vs. $8.2 billion. This demonstrates the priority they place in convincing consumers and prescribers to use their product, over the actual work they do in researching, testing, and developing the drugs to make sure they are effective and safe.

Drug companies market directly to consumers and, more profitably, to professionals who they hope will prescribe their drugs. The United States and New Zealand are the only two countries in the world that allow drug companies to advertise directly to consumers on radio, print media, Internet, and television. These advertisements typically contain misleading information about the benefits of psychiatric drugs and they significantly downplay their negative effects. These ads generate a multitude of requests made directly to primary care doctors by patients for the prescription du jour. Many of these commercial advertisements encourage people to, "Ask your doctor whether [insert drug name] is right for you." It was estimated the drug companies spent over $3 billion on these ads alone in 2012.[6]

A more alarming issue is that drug companies spent eight times that much on marketing directly to healthcare professionals.[7] The ways in which drug companies market their products to doctors have been widely criticized as constituting conflicts of interest.[8] It is tantamount to bribing doctors to prescribe their drugs and not another company's drugs. You've all seen the well dressed, young, cheerful, and attractive marketing representatives with corporate suitcases of drug wares in tow, and who seem to get in to see your doctor even without an appointment. You've also noticed the branded promotional pens, wall clocks, and notepads they leave sprinkled behind them as little trinkets of their visit. And, if you are at the office around lunchtime, you might see the free catered "training" luncheons for the doctors and their staff.

More troublesome are the free psychiatric drug samples left with the doctor. This gives the doctor the ability to entice patients who don't think they can afford it, or who would like a free trial of the latest and greatest drug prior to agreeing to take it indefinitely. This is like an illegal drug dealer giving a potential customer a free sample in order to get that customer interested and hooked on the drug in order to convert him into a steady paying customer.

But perhaps the most alarming drug company marketing scheme with doctors is to offer them the status of "thought leader" or "key opinion leader," who essentially acts as the drug company's spokesperson among the doctor's medical colleagues and patients.[9] These designated surrogates of the drug industry are also offered "educational opportunities" in the form of lavish trips to alluring places and authorship of "ghost written" research articles showing a particular drug's alleged effectiveness and safety.[10] Ghost writing is when the drug company representatives actually conduct the bulk of the research and write the article, but they offer named authorship to a prominent physician.

Drug companies are also well known for funding legitimate research conducted by universities and government agencies. But having substantial portions of research funding coming from the very drug companies who have a clear vested interest in positive outcomes constitutes a conflict of interest. This seriously places into question the legitimacy of subsequent results of such research. Furthermore, it was revealed that several prominent psychiatrists involved in this research failed to disclose millions in payments made to them from drug companies, casting doubt on their professional and academic independence.[11]

As if this wasn't enough proof of how financial incentives keep the Myth alive, the *DSM* committees that meet every so often to revise and publish the manual have members with financial interests in the drug companies' successes. A 2006 study showed 56% of all the *DSM-IV* panel members had one or more financial associations with drug companies that presented them with a conflict of interest. But far more damning was all of the committee members on the Mood Disorders and Schizophrenia and Other Psychotic Disorders panels had financial ties with drug companies.[12] These two panels oversee a sizeable portion of the *DSM* diagnostic categories. Despite the American Psychiatric Association (APA) instituting a financial disclosure policy for the committee members during the production of the most recent edition of the *DSM* (*DSM-5*), the situation had not changed.[13] With this in mind, what do you think the chances are these *DSM* experts would entertain the idea that "mental illness" is not really about illness and just a figurative way to describe human struggles?

Drug companies, as well as other agencies that have an interest in continuing the medical model of human suffering, have also invested a considerable amount of money in lobbying our elected representatives and government officials to maintain the status quo. In 2016, just four companies related to the healthcare industry spent about $179 million in lobbying the U.S. Congress and federal government agencies. These four were Blue Cross Blue Shield, the American Hospital Association, the American Medical Association, and the Pharmaceutical Research and Manufacturers of America. The last of these lobbying groups represents U.S. drug companies and they spent nearly $20 million in lobbying that year alone.[14] It has been reported there are two drug industry lobbyists for every representative in Congress.[15]

Lastly, grassroots and professional organizations, like the National Alliance on Mental Illness (NAMI) and the American Psychiatric Association (APA), receive generous annual funding from drug companies. NAMI received about three-quarters of its donations between 2006 and 2008, totaling $23 million, from drug companies.[16] The APA received almost $37 million from drug companies in 2006, which was 30% of its annual budget.[17] As with the *DSM* committee members and legislators, what do you think the chances are these grassroots and professional organizations would challenge the idea that emotional distress and troublesome behaviors are illnesses?

Despite the lack of a scientific foundation, the Industry remains alive and powerful because of its unquestioned reputation as an authority on the human problems that get labeled "mental illness" and because of the tremendous amount of financial incentive for it to continue. Is it any wonder why such a profitable and powerful Industry is able to maintain the reins of power and drive the Myth?

Chapter 8

Rebranding Immorality as Illness

Religious to Medical

Prior to the 18th century, when religious authorities firmly reigned in matters of philosophy and politics in the Western world, all types of problematic human experiences and conduct were commonly believed to arise from insufficient religious faith, rebellion against God's laws, and interference by demonic forces. The remedy was to strong-arm those who were "afflicted" with these problems into realignment with the Church's teachings, and if conversion wasn't possible, to eliminate them.

Consequently, history witnessed the terrible acts of the Inquisition and other tragedies where people were tortured and executed in order to "treat" their abnormal religiosity. Because the power of the state was based in Church dogma during that time, it was hard to distinguish between a religious heretic and a political opponent. It was also difficult to distinguish between religious leaders' genuine concern for the spiritual welfare of their flock on one hand and their dissatisfaction with political opposition on the other. Eventually, this stain on history faded in the 17th and 18th centuries as orthodox religion's political power gave way to reason during the Age of Enlightenment. However, this kind of parochial and political pressure didn't end, as the Industry took over as a new religion, persecuting its own heretics.

Philosopher and psychotherapist Robert Fancher, Ph.D., described how this transition occurred within the United States in *Cultures of Healing: Correcting the Image of American Mental Health Care*.[1] He explained that the earliest efforts to help people who were suffering from these significant problems in living were shouldered by the communities and families from which the person came. But a growing individualism in the 19th century, brought on by increasing urbanization and industrialization, threatened the central role of this type of community care. At the same time, many medical professionals (e.g., Benjamin Rush) increasingly adopted the view that emotional distress and troublesome behaviors were signs of *defects in the natural functioning* of the individual.

Enter psychiatry. These professionals came on the scene at a time when benevolent groups, such as the Quakers, had already pioneered a humane form of caring for individuals who were experiencing significant life challenges. They believed the various forms of emotional disturbance were the result of excessive stressors of modern life. So, their solution was to provide relief and rejuvenation by getting them back to the simplicity of nature in remote asylums away from urban centers. It served the dual purpose of a respite for them, as well as a respite for others who were bothered by their distressing problems. This kind of "moral treatment" took place in rural settings where productive labor, education, exercise, and nutrition were key elements of care.

In 1844, the emerging psychiatric profession formed the Association of Medical Superintendents of American Institutions for the Insane (AMSAII). With this organization's political clout, they worked hard to take control of the asylums in order to try out their medico-moral model of treatment for human suffering. However, the claimed "illnesses" being treated were not well defined, and so real treatment was nearly nonexistent. This professional stagnation worsened psychiatry's reputation in the eyes of the public, as well as in the eyes of other medical professions that were scientifically advancing. Consequently, the asylums became little more than cloistered and convenient places where troublesome people were indiscriminately dumped, mostly for being annoying to those in power.

Since little medical care was offered, inmates languished for years and the asylums basically became warehouses, not healing institutions like they once were, and the conditions within them deteriorated.[2] The AMSAII slowly lost political influence and became superficial. In 1892, the American Medico-Psychological Association (AMPA) was formed as a replacement organization to represent psychiatry with the hope of elevating its professional reputation as a respected scientific field. As mentioned in Chapter 6, this organization eventually became the American Psychiatric Association (APA) in 1921.

In the late 19th and early 20th centuries, there was another transition in how disturbed people were treated. Psychiatric care shifted from remotely located rural asylums to urban-based hospitals that were centers of general medical care, and whose various medical specialties had far better scientific reputations than the asylum psychiatrists. Further, psychiatry expanded its influence at this time by targeting emotional and behavioral problems not seen in the asylums. These were the "walking wounded" who periodically suffered from mild to moderate forms of distress that were not as devastating as the more severe problems common in the asylums. These lesser problems could be cared for in outpatient as well as short-term inpatient settings. This was psychiatry's chance to join the scientific ranks of other medical specialties.

However, notwithstanding these historical developments that brought psychiatry into the modern world, it was destined to fail. Whether in asylums or hospitals, the problems these embryonic psychiatrists were trying to treat had nothing to do with literal illness. Instead, the problems they identified were simply about painful emotions and bothersome behaviors and how those negatively affected the person or others in the person's life. So, despite the trappings of medicine, the only thing psychiatrists could do was to continue making moral judgments about the appropriateness of these emotions and behaviors, and then to warehouse those whose emotions and behaviors were deemed inappropriate. Further, any successful attempts at alleviating the person's angst had nothing to do with the application of medical science.

Psychiatrists don't make medical judgments or apply medical treatment because there are no confirmed or theorized disease processes that account for emotional distress and odd behaviors, and that don't already belong to other medical specialties. So, those who suffer have no disease or illness of the body, and it is nonsensical to medically treat "diseases of the mind," as will be seen in more detail in Chapter 12. Therefore, the 19th century conceptual shift was only a medical disguise that concealed the continuation of moral treatment. However, this time it was not the humane moral restoration such as that organized by the Quakers. Instead, it became the inhumane moral paternalism of the Industry.

Inpatient Psychiatry

Despite the appearance of a medical purpose, warehousing and moral control are still the primary functions of conventional inpatient psychiatry to this day. It is commonplace for people to be confined to psychiatric hospitals when they are thought to be at risk of suicide or violent behavior, although all too frequently without any firm scientific evidence to support such a conclusion. Sometimes they are confined only because they are labeled "mentally ill," and this is the sole reason for locking them up and forcibly "treating" them for the alleged illness. And remember, the *DSM* diagnostic rules are so vague and overly inclusive that all of us could be called "mentally ill" at many times in our lives.

Therefore, people are not hospitalized for the true purpose of being medically treated. It is merely to monitor and control them, at least in the short term, and then with only the appearance of ongoing medical care. This is usually done with psychiatric drugs that numb their emotional sensations and deaden their impulses to act. Sometimes electric shock is also used for the same purpose. But these two forms of so-called "treatment" are just modern-day chemical and electrical versions of asylum chains and straitjackets, all of which are ways to subdue people.

Notwithstanding this significant problem, hospitalization can sometimes offer a break from the torments of life when things get overwhelming. So, in this limited sense, inpatient facilities can serve a purpose, but at a great cost. This is because while they are in the hospital for relief from their daily traumas and stressors (like that offered by the original asylums), they are simultaneously subjected to the onslaught of potentially harmful psychiatric interventions. They can't get one without the other. Further, once they are released from the hospital, an attempt is made to keep them within the Industry's control and encourage them to continue complying with its moral ideas about appropriate ways of living, which typically includes the indefinite use of psychiatric drugs.

It would surely be a positive development if there were institutions and programs where people could find relief when things are overwhelming, but where they would not be harmed by the medical model. In fact, there have been such attempts to provide this kind of supervised residential assistance. The Soteria Project[3] was one. It was started in the 1970s by Loren Mosher, M.D., who was the Chief of the Center for the Studies of Schizophrenia at the National Institute of Mental Health (NIMH) from 1969 to 1980. The project was set up to help people who were having very difficult life experiences and who had been labeled with "schizophrenia," but it did so without the use of conventional hospital confinement and, most importantly, with very limited use of drugs. The project demonstrated increased effectiveness over conventional methods. Regrettably, Mosher's work was seen as a threat to the prevailing medical model and he was eventually removed from his position at the NIMH and funding for Soteria Project research was terminated.

Another program that offers a humane way of providing relief to people in the throes of emotional angst and disorienting experiences is Open Dialogue.[4] Developed in Finland in the 1980s, it is also based on a non-moralizing, non-medical, non-disease, and non-drug model. It focuses on a family and social networking approach to helping. It also emphasizes how language affects one's sense of reality, which dictates the meaning of emotional distress. It encourages an understanding of so-called "symptoms," not as indicators of illness, but as strategies in which people engage to survive and overcome very difficult and real-life circumstances. Its programs have spread to Europe and, less so, to the United States. It has shown promise, similar to the Soteria Project.

A third program of similar focus is Warfighter Advance.[5] It is the brainchild of Mary Neal Vieten, Ph.D., ABPP, a United States Navy officer who has ample experience with veterans and military members who've suffered the traumas of war. While Warfighter Advance isn't a residential facility per se, it still provides participants with a week-long break from one's daily routine in order to better understand the problems the Industry designates "post-traumatic stress disorder" and the harmful psychiatric responses by the Departments of Defense and Veterans Affairs. It is held at a rustic location along the shores of the Potomac River in southern Maryland. This idyllic place helps to "cleanse" the participants' hearts and minds as the program applies a novel approach. It is founded on the principle that traumatic war experiences trigger natural and understandable hypervigilance that is not an indicator of illness or defect. It is an indicator of meaning.

Therefore, Warfighter Advance is non-clinical, non-medical, non-drug, non-defect, and non-treatment oriented. It is focused on community support, the comfort of sharing experiences with those who have "been there," and education about the natural and adaptive ways we react to distressing experiences. Post-program alumni support group activities maintain the benefits derived after the week-long course is over. This program has been a literal lifesaver for hundreds of people who had been, and would otherwise still be, subjected to the inhumane and harmful onslaught of the Industry.

But programs like the Soteria Project, Open Dialogue, and Warfighter Advance are few and far between. This is likely due to the financial incentives mentioned in the previous chapter that discourage these projects before they gain popularity and acceptance, and therefore become a threat to the Industry. This leaves the prevailing medical model of psychiatric hospitalization the dominant option of respite available today. It is a process of confining people in order to keep them away from others, and while there, to test out dubious forms of so-called "medical treatment," similar to what happened in the 19th century asylums after the psychiatrists took over.

Whereas protecting society from people who are truly dangerous is an important function, it is not within the expertise of the Industry to do so. Instead, that is a role for the courts and legislatures within the guidelines of due process of law. There is robust psychological science those institutions can use in assisting them in deciding who is likely to be dangerous, and how to reduce that danger. But it is not medical science and it has little to do with true health and illness.[6] Further, dangerous people cannot be medically treated to make them less dangerous, unless we want to use incapacitating amounts of drugs so they wouldn't be able to function, but that would not be medical treatment of dangerousness. Rather, the drugs merely restrain them from acting on their impulses, similar to how chains and straitjackets work. On the other hand, there are psychosocial factors known to increase one's risk of being dangerous and managing those factors can reduce the person's risk. But this isn't a medical form of treatment either.[7]

Besides warehousing and controlling people, conventional inpatient facilities also include the attempt to teach those people how to live a so-called "healthier" life. They are given daily routines of activities, many of which can be superficial and meaningless. One large-scale study found only 50% of hospital staff time was spent with the patients, and only 4 to 20% of that time was spent in some kind of therapeutic work.[8] This means there typically isn't much therapeutic interaction between hospital staff and patients, as 90 to 98% of their total time at work is exclusively for administrative and bureaucratic purposes. Furthermore, the miniscule amount of therapeutic contact that does take place is frequently condescending.

When I was assigned to the psychiatric ward during my residency at a military hospital, there was a newly admitted person who isolated himself and cried frequently. This was quite unexpected of him as he was a senior enlisted member of the Air Force and he was nearing retirement after a successful career. The staff was perplexed and didn't know what to do to get him to stop crying and join the others on the ward. Remember, the focus of psychiatric treatment is to reduce "symptoms" and that is how they interpreted his crying and self-isolation.

Of course, he had been prescribed psychiatric drugs to "help" him stop these behaviors. Still, he persisted and resisted their interventions, refusing to cooperate with the daily regimen of activities. At best he was treated with benign neglect. At worst, he was seen as "crazy" and a disruption to the ward's flow of events. Clipboard-holding nurses and aides treated him like an unnamed part on an assembly line and ignored the possibility that something very meaningful was going on with him. They just wanted to take his blood pressure and rattle off checklist questions so they could diagnose him and process him into the ward environment. I think they labeled him with "schizoaffective disorder," one of the most serious categories. Once he was on the ward, they focused on what kind of "treatment" would stop his crying so he could join the rest in unison in what reminded me of herding cows from one place to another (wake up, breakfast, medication dispensing, group therapy, meeting with a psychiatrist, etc.).

I first met him in the dayroom where he was sitting in a corner by himself with his head in his hands. I walked up to him and asked what happened. He was surprised at the question as I was the first person to ask. He stopped crying and through tearful eyes told me his story. Just days prior to being admitted to the hospital, he had been quietly enjoying a day off when he heard several young people outside his window playing basketball and they made quite a bit of a ruckus that disrupted his pleasant afternoon. This simple encounter triggered the realization in him that a younger culture he saw as disrespectful of tradition was taking over from his. His career was ending, and he wondered if his commitment and contributions really made any difference. Faced with this existential threat, he began to question his entire life and whether it was worth anything at all. The pain was too much and he recoiled into a dark hole of despair, later being tagged "mentally ill."

I met with him several times to talk about this important development in his life. Whereas there was no clear answer to his dilemma, it allowed him to explore its meaning and how he could continue on after retirement and still find contentment and purpose. This was difficult to do as the very treatment he received in the hospital reminded him of the young people outside his window days earlier. He felt disrespected, as his senior enlisted status, decades of experiences, patriotism, and personal sacrifice were invisible on the ward. He was treated as just a number among many and this reminded him of how his culture of respect and tradition was dying. He did eventually come to a resolution, with a renewed sense of the future, and moved on with his life.

But typically, without some type of meaningful assistance while in the hospital, the best outcome one can hope for is to be discharged as soon as possible. For this reason, those who are hospitalized quickly learn the right words to say and actions to take in the hopes of gaining that release. Remember, the problems that get labeled "mental illness" cannot be verified with laboratory testing. So, psychiatrists must rely solely on what "patients" say and do in order to decide whether or not to discharge them. It is based on the psychiatrist's personal opinion, not science.

Yet, in far too many situations, people are held indefinitely just because they are in distress (and sometimes even when they're not in distress) and they've been tagged with one of the hundreds of horoscope-like problems in the unreliable and invalid *DSM*. And that's it. But what possible justification would there be for a medical professional to hospitalize someone against his will when he wasn't asking for help? If this is a justifiable role for them, why shouldn't these medico-moral-police also be rounding up others who haven't yet been identified, just for their own good, including many of their colleagues?

See the terribly inhumane case of Bill as an example of how very harmful this can be.[9] In June 2006, Bill mistakenly entered a residence he thought was a friend's and waited for the friend to return. When the true owner returned, Bill realized he was in the wrong residence. He tried to leave but the owner detained him and called the police. This summary of what transpired is presented as an example of how the Industry can harm. It is neither intended to denounce nor sanction Bill's actions.

Bill was subsequently arrested for criminal trespassing. He never engaged in any theft or violence while in the residence. In fact, he was just sitting and waiting when the owner returned. He had no other prior "mental health" or criminal history. Years later, Bill would reveal he was under the effects of psychedelic mushrooms when he entered the residence. He initially withheld this information out of embarrassment and fear of more severe punishment for the act. The mushrooms most likely affected his mental state at that time and contributed to his actions.

Bill decided to plead not guilty by reason of insanity (NGRI) (see more about the insanity issue in Chapter 15). He was released on bond and for the next two years the state fought against his plea. Bill subsequently underwent several state-ordered evaluations to address the question of insanity. In addition to the evaluations, he was prescribed psychiatric drugs during that time. The judge finally concluded he would accept the plea of NGRI despite the prosecution's objections.

Consequently, instead of being confined to jail, Bill was ordered into a group home where he was free to leave during the day but had to return each evening. The judge ordered him into the home ostensibly to protect the public, even though Bill did not have a history of violent behavior or other harm to the community. Further, how could such an order truly protect the public from him if he was free to leave during the day? The professionals who evaluated him during this time labeled him with "social phobia" and "polysubstance abuse."

Bill stayed in the group home for a year and during that time he was required to be monitored by a psychiatrist and take psychiatric drugs. During his stay, another resident made sexual advances and assaulted him. At one point during this time he became suicidal, but this was just seen as reason to increase the dosage of his psychiatric drugs. When Bill requested to be placed in a different home because of this harassment by the other resident, it was denied.

In September 2009, Bill was again assaulted, this time by someone whom he encountered while returning to the group home after an evening out with friends but whom he could not identify. This person physically and sexually attacked him before he could get into the home. Bill finally returned to the home that evening and reported what had happened.

Soon after, the resident who had earlier assaulted and made sexual advances toward him resumed his harassment and Bill came to believe this must have been the person who had assaulted him outside the home the earlier night. In retaliation, Bill attacked the resident and then asked for the police to be called. Bill was arrested for felonious assault and over the next five months he was alternately confined to a state hospital and jail while awaiting trial.

In January 2010, he was arraigned and entered a NGRI plea for the felonious assault charge. During that time between arrest and arraignment, he underwent psychiatric evaluations and continued to be administered psychiatric drugs. He also experienced frequent suicidal thoughts. After his plea, he was again found NGRI and confined to state hospitals for the next eight years and forcibly drugged against his objections.

While in the hospital, he was given two new labels: "schizoaffective disorder, bipolar type," and "personality disorder." Why weren't these detected earlier if they are true illnesses? And is it possible his natural reactions to the mistreatment, distrust, and victimization under the state's care led to behaviors later seen as the "symptoms" for these new labels? Bill's complaints about being confined and forced to take psychiatric drugs were considered "symptoms" of his "mental illnesses" (remember anosognosia?).

In November 2014, after considerable legal efforts by his family, they were successful in convincing the court to stop the forced drugging. It took Bill three more years of weaning off the drugs to finally be free of their effects. During his entire time under state care, he had been prescribed 11 psychiatric drugs at different times. In January 2018, after his family's continued efforts, Bill was finally released from the hospital, and this was without any claimed cure for his alleged "mental illnesses" or insanity. He is now trying to get his life back on track but, given his experiences of the unrestrained authority of Industry professionals and the legal system, he lives in fear of similar things happening to him in the future. Ironically, he seemed to have developed the problem the Industry calls "post-traumatic stress disorder" from the treatment he endured at the hands of the Industry.

This was a case of the Industry's abuse of power and the legal system placing far too much trust in the Industry's expertise, not to mention the claimed reality of "mental illness." Bill had no history of criminal, violent, or troublesome experiences prior to the 2006 incident. He was 26 years old when he mistakenly entered the residence and 37 years old when he was finally released from state control.

He lost nearly a third of his life only because he chose to plead NGRI to the original charge of criminal trespassing. That plea triggered an avalanche of Industry insults focused on the absurd purpose of "treating" him for insanity. But the so-called "treatment" with psychiatric drugs and confinement to the institutions served nothing more than to progressively worsen his mental functioning. Some of the drugs he was prescribed are known to increase the risk of aggressive and violent behavior, to include suicide – see the next chapter. But that fact was either unknown, ignored, or overlooked.

Bill was subjected to years of this process solely because he was labelled "insane" and "mentally ill" at the outset. As you can see, he suffered not only from the mistreatment at the hands of the Industry, but also at the hands of other people, culminating in becoming the victim of violence and developing suicidal urges. His natural reactions to the mistreatment were interpreted as just more "symptoms" that were used to justify continued involuntary confinement and drugging.

If it wasn't for his family's assistance, he might still be indefinitely confined to a psychiatric hospital. This is not an uncommon incident. How many other people are experiencing similar things, but do not have the support and resources Bill had? Sadly, Bill no doubt would have fared far better if he originally pleaded guilty to criminal trespassing.

Another example of this kind of paternalistic coercion by the Industry is the case of Jane.[10] Jane was enjoying a successful United States Army career of more than 10 years, having been promoted to the rank of Sergeant. She was a high functioning and psychologically stable individual with no history of emotional or behavioral problems prior to joining the military. As part of her Army service, she deployed to Iraq three times: 2004, 2007, and 2010. During her stay in Iraq, she worked long, stressful days, was deprived of adequate sleep, suffered from poor nutrition, and had to constantly cope with the trauma of a war zone. Also, while on leave in Paris, she was raped by a stranger. She returned to Iraq after this and, knowing the difficulty of prosecuting the rape in French courts, decided to let it go and try to cope with it on her own.

In response to these painful experiences, Jane suffered from flashbacks of the traumatic events, temporary disorientation, panic, emotional numbing, and sleep disturbances. Many times, particular sounds and smells would trigger these reactions. She also experienced visual and auditory hallucinations. These problems are typical of someone who has encountered extreme trauma and horror, things Jane had endured.

When she approached the military medical authorities for assistance, they told her she was suffering from a "psychotic disorder." They prescribed multiple psychiatric drugs and hospitalized her for extended periods of time. Jane's requests to participate in her care were dismissed by her psychiatric handlers, as were her complaints about how badly the psychiatric drugs were making her feel. It is important to note that many of her problems, including the flashbacks and hallucinations, occurred or worsened only after she started taking the prescribed drugs.

The Army eventually decided she couldn't remain on active duty, so they discharged her under a medical disability. After discharge, she continued to loyally take her psychiatric drugs and periodically meet with Department of Veterans Affairs (VA) and military practitioners. She also continued to be intermittently hospitalized. Claiming her problems were caused by "mental illness," instead of being the effects of the psychiatric drugs or the natural reactions to trauma, her doctors encouraged increased dosages and different trials of multiple types of drugs in combination. Jane was not functioning well and felt like a burden, at times having suicidal urges. At one point, when she failed to show for a scheduled appointment, the authorities thought this was proof she was a danger to herself and enlisted the assistance of the police to go to her house, detain her, and hospitalize her.

Later on, Jane was fortunate to hear about the Warfighter Advance program mentioned earlier. After participating in this program, she decided to wean herself off the psychiatric drugs (against the advice of her psychiatrists), obtained gainful employment, became a community volunteer, and served as a mentor to others who had experienced a similar fate as she did. Yet, even after this, the psychiatric authorities continued harassing her about her choices, even though she was managing quite well.

In late 2018, Jane contacted a local military nurse help line for medical assistance. In her own words:

> I told the woman on the phone my symptoms were pain in both ears that got worse with talking or chewing, occasional loss of balance, body pain especially in the torso area to include my back, spotted vision (sometimes my vision was cloudy or I could see flashes of lights or objects in an unusual way). I then said that sometimes it's hard to get out of bed and walk, and that no matter how much rest I get I am always tired/sleepy.

The nurse recommended Jane see a doctor within 24 hours and transferred her call to the local military clinic to schedule an appointment that day. At the appointment, a nurse and doctor examined her. During this time, they discovered she chose to stop taking the psychiatric drugs prescribed to her months earlier. The doctor challenged her on this decision and said it was a bad idea, urging her to resume taking them immediately. This was despite the fact that Jane explained to the doctor how beneficial it was to have weaned off the drugs. Nevertheless, Jane was then escorted to the psychiatric department.

During this processing, Jane was assigned a guard and she wasn't allowed to leave the facility. Her doctor consulted with a psychiatrist and returned, recommending she be admitted to the psychiatric ward where she could "get stabilized" on new psychiatric drugs. The psychiatrist interviewed Jane at length and asked how she was able to cope with the problems she had been experiencing without taking the drugs. Jane responded, "The same way I did with medication."

Nonetheless, as did the doctor, the psychiatrist lectured Jane about weaning off the drugs, that it was a bad idea, and recommended admission to the psychiatric ward in order to determine the "right medication." A third and fourth doctor entered the picture to persuade Jane into hospitalization and drugs. Despite this, Jane continued to protest and said she was neither willing to take psychiatric drugs nor be admitted. She again explained how well she had been functioning in life, other than the pain she was experiencing and for which she originally came to the clinic, and how terribly disruptive it would be to her life if she were hospitalized.

At one point in this standoff, one of the doctors told Jane she would not be allowed to go home unless she was "stable," which meant until she agreed to the doctors' demands. She was also told the psychiatric drugs would help with the pain. Further, they told her they would treat the pain if she agreed to take the psychiatric drugs too. Out of frustration, and in order to get her pain treated and leave the facility, Jane agreed. She was eventually prescribed antibiotics for an ear infection, and it was discovered she was suffering from low thyroid hormone levels, the effects of which are known to mimic the problem called "depression" and for which she underwent additional lab work. In truth, Jane had no intention of complying with their demands to take the psychiatric drugs.

Later that day, Jane received a call from the clinic saying they knew she didn't get the psychiatric prescription filled. They threatened to issue a "mental inquest warrant" to have her detained and returned to the clinic unless she came in voluntarily. She refused. Fearful of being seized by the authorities, she waited, but nothing happened that day. A few days later, her therapist (who she had been seeing but who was not involved in this fiasco until now) called Jane to verify their appointment in a few days. Jane told the therapist she was not comfortable returning to the clinic because of how she feared being detained there. The therapist tried to convince her to come to the appointment. Jane refused and felt compelled to flee the state and stay with friends at an undisclosed location in order to avoid being detained.

This is another egregious case of the Industry professionals operating as moral judges, treating people inhumanely, and forcing them into inhumane settings. Things were going well in Jane's life after she stopped consuming psychiatric drugs and left the influence of the Industry. This is not an uncommon occurrence. The psychiatric professionals attempted through lies and extortion to convince her to submit. The authorities even threatened to withhold medical treatment for her ear pain unless she agreed to be subjected to the harmful effects of psychiatric drugs and hospitalization. They also threatened her with arrest if she didn't agree. And this is medical treatment of an illness?

In both Jane's and Bill's situations, this is exactly what we would expect when we allow these professionals to decide what actions, thoughts, feelings, and beliefs are inappropriate. They follow the Industry's conventional wisdom, not medical science, in determining whom to treat this way, and they certainly have no respect for human dignity or self-determination.

They coercively deceive people into complying with their demands, even if it harms those people in the process. In their quest to correct immorality, they ironically create a morally questionable situation and operate contrary to their prime directive: *primum non nocere*; in other words, "first, do no harm." Just like the Church and state joined forces prior to the 18th century to identify religious moral opponents, the Industry and the state have joined forces in the present era to identify medical moral opponents.

Moral Basis of Psychiatry

The 19th century shift to a medical model of understanding human distress and upsetting behaviors suffered from a fundamental flaw at the outset. The psychiatrists who took over the asylums were trying to treat "diseases of the mind," not the body. The body was not their target as it is with legitimate medical specialties.

You might think their target is the brain because they keep searching there for "mental illnesses." But their search is a waste of time since diseases of the brain are the dominion of neurology, not psychiatry. So, if they ever did find "mental illness" in the brain, there would be no reason to keep calling it "mental illness." Instead, it would be an illness within the dominion of neurology.

Psychiatry's focus has always been the mind. Stop for a minute and think about how nonsensical this is. How can the mind, which has no substance or spatial location, be literally diseased, healthy, or ill? The same would go for the idea of diseased behavior. Mind is the sum of one's ongoing moment-to-moment experiences. Behavior is one's actions. Neither exists as something that can be diseased because there is no substance to be affected by disease. Only the body can be diseased. Yet this is how the Industry started – on the illogical idea of mind or behavioral disease.

So, since psychiatry has no literal disease to medically treat, the only thing left for them to do is morally judge people who think or act in ways they deem inappropriate. Subsequent attempts to change them are frequently coercive,[11] and they include "talk therapy," confinement to hospitals so they don't bother others, and the application of chemical, electrical, and surgical procedures that impair their natural ability to function as meaning-making emotional creatures.

It is one thing for people to decide *they want help* with significant problems and then to reach out for professional services of varying kinds, selecting those that are helpful. But it is quite another when Industry authorities decide *they must get help*, in particular, "help" that makes them easier to control and less annoying to others. In other words, this kind of help is intended to make their conduct and experiences more appropriate as defined by the Industry, but the problems are labeled illnesses. Sometimes, this even appeals to those who voluntarily seek out assistance. Claiming an illness (or demon) as the cause of their problems can give them a false sense of relief from the very difficult dilemmas of personal choice and change.

This focus on morality is also evident in how Industry professionals equivocate about the matter. Their message to you is: You have an illness – "it's not your fault" – you have been inflicted with a tragedy of nature. But at the same time, they distrust and suspect your motives and choices in life. They sometimes demand you admit you have a problem and take responsibility for your actions. They see refusal to do so as a "symptom" of your illness. But if it is a real illness, it wouldn't be a matter of personal choice and you wouldn't be able to change without their outside medical interventions.

Thomas Szasz, M.D., highlighted the moral basis of the Industry in *The Manufacture of Madness: A Comparative Study of the Inquisition and the Mental Health Movement.*[12] In it, he compared the present-day Myth (of "mental illness") to prior centuries' myth of witchcraft. He showed how both myths have threatened individual liberty by creating the illusion of an internal impurity that causes people to act in upsetting and strange ways. Prior to the 18th century, the Church declared the impurity to be demons. Since then, psychiatry has declared the impurity to be illnesses. Neither of these two ideas are scientifically legitimate. Instead, each is about the enforcement of morality-driven standards of conduct.

Both the Church and the Industry have wielded the full power of the state to control the citizens. Szasz termed the present day psychiatric-state power the "Therapeutic State."[13] Under the guise of medical science, it has been given the authority to do the same thing that a "Salvation State" did centuries ago under the guise of religious beneficence. That is, it morally judges people and subjects them to trials and convictions for their actions, but without the protections of due process of law afforded to defendants in criminal and civil trials. Further, just as in the cases of Bill and Jane, sentencing all too often consists of involuntary confinement to hospitals and mandatory psychiatric "treatment" that consists of the daily ingestion of toxic chemicals and sometimes electric shock.

Whether viewing society's complex and entrenched problems as caused by illnesses or demons, those in power can maintain moral control. They can focus on something wrong with the person rather than with larger and more meaningful societal factors that disturb the person. And in the process, they stigmatize and devalue the very people who are suffering. The real problems are left untouched.

We recently witnessed this tendency to invoke the idea of an internal impurity as an explanation for a mass shooting in a Florida school.[14] The gunman was a disgruntled and troubled youth who was earlier expelled from the school. He and his younger brother were adopted at birth. He witnessed his adoptive father die years earlier. Just six months before the shooting, his adoptive mother also died, leaving him and his younger brother to move in with friends of the family. These circumstances surely affected the shooter's motivation and actions, and they presented him with difficult challenges above and beyond the typical ones he was already experiencing as an adopted teenager and young adult.

Still, people remained raptly focused on blaming "mental illness." Some also talked about this as an act of evil, even Industry authorities, which is reminiscent of the days of religious control. However, as with other shooting incidents like this, the authorities have said not a word about the very real factors that put the public at risk of these kinds of horrific events.[15] This demonstrates the focus is on morality, not medicine, and certainly not science.

More problematically, though, they are missing the point and their actions will do nothing to reduce the chances of future violent acts like this from happening again. In fact, they will more likely increase the risk of these shootings because the typical response to these tragedies is "better mental healthcare," which means more paternalistic and coercive oversight of people's actions including the administration of psychiatric chemicals. Feelings of persecution and the use of drugs are risk factors for violence.[16]

A Crusade

All too often, many Industry professionals leave the role of helper. They cross a line and become coercive crusaders for optimal human living, despite the person's wishes. They think it is their business to correct "unhealthy" ways of being. They seem to be driven more by their own discomfort with others' distress and deviations, than by a genuine respect and desire to help others find life satisfaction on their own terms. They forget whose side they are on and they become agents of moral control, under the guise of medical science, rather than as assistants in a personal change process. Once this line is breeched, they lose track of respect for the values and perspectives of those they try to help, and they forget they are supposed to help only to the extent they are invited to help. Remember the foundational principle of informed consent?

All Industry professionals' codes of conduct contain provisions about respecting the people with whom they work. But this seems to be superficial. For instance, the American Psychological Association's (APA) Ethical Principles and Code of Conduct states in part:

> Principle E: Respect for People's Rights and Dignity
> Psychologists respect the dignity and worth of all people, and the rights of individuals to privacy, confidentiality, and self-determination. Psychologists are aware that *special safeguards may be necessary to protect the rights and welfare of persons or communities whose vulnerabilities impair autonomous decision making*[17] [italics added for emphasis].

For now, let's set aside the glaring ethical problem of diagnosing a person with an unreliable and invalid *DSM* condition and how that would jeopardize "respect [for] the dignity and worth of all people." Instead, just notice the italicized portion. Even though the very first mandate in this principle is to respect the dignity, worth, privacy, confidentiality, and self-determination of the people with whom they work, it also contains a euphemistic exception permitting psychologists to do the exact opposite. This is when the psychologist believes the persons' or communities' "vulnerabilities impair autonomous decision making."

What exactly does this mean and what scientific expertise does a psychologist (or any other Industry professional) have by virtue of training and education, in making that determination? I am a psychologist, and I know of none. The phrase "impairment in autonomous decision making" means an inability to choose actions independently and freely. But there is no evidence that something takes away our *ability* to freely choose. One's circumstances can provide the *rationale* for choices made, but those circumstances do not dictate or remove the ability to choose. See more about this in Chapter 15. This APA ethical principle gives psychologists the green light to do the exact opposite of what this principle claims to be protecting. It allows them to ignore the rights, dignity, privacy, confidentiality, and self-determination of people if the psychologist doesn't agree with their decisions; in other words, if the decisions are deemed inappropriate.

This might be helpful for children whom we deem unable to make significant life choices, and for adults who suffer from real illnesses like dementia or who are otherwise physically incapacitated. But it also can be applied to anyone the psychologist thinks is affected by "unhealthy" living. And that determination is a judgment based on the psychologist's moral values or the shared moral-institutional values of the Industry. There is no scientific basis for determining this kind of "impairment in autonomous decision making," yet, it is cloaked in language that aims to "protect the rights and welfare" of people.

In attempting to comply with the ethical principle of the APA, how would we assess impairment in autonomous decision making? Other than in the cases of children and incapacitated adults as mentioned earlier, the Industry's answer would be when a person is "mentally ill." But how do we know when to label a person "mentally ill"? The Industry's answer would be when the person's autonomous decision-making is impaired. This is just circular reasoning that attempts to defend a moral judgment. As with the issue of dangerousness, our legal and legislative systems and not the Industry should be resolving questions about the appropriateness of people's decision making.

The way it works all too often is Industry professionals take on a paternalistic moral role and they try to eradicate personal distress and "unhealthy" behaviors. They usually ignore the dignity, worth, and rights of the people they judge because of an alleged "vulnerability" that impairs their autonomous decision making. But they still believe those "impaired" people are responsible for their actions, even though the professional gets to decide what is best for them. They have no problem coercing and manipulating, along with help from friends and family, so they can restore people to "health," despite themselves.

To make matters worse, the conventional standards of optimal "mental health" are unrealistic. I saw an example of this kind of strained optimism in a pamphlet I was reading in a doctor's waiting room. The pamphlet was entitled, *What Everyone Should Know about Good Mental Health.*[18] The cover shows caricatures of an oversized man and woman sitting on the Earth, apparently as a symbol of power over earthly problems. The man and woman are grinning, and they are giving a "thumbs up." Inside the pamphlet, it says that people in good "mental health":

> Have a positive attitude – they look forward to the challenges of life. Feel good about themselves and others. Act responsibly in their work and in their relationships. When you're in good mental health, you expect the best out of life – and you're ready to make it happen![19]

Simply put, this cheerful hurrah is unrealistic. It is not possible to maintain this level of optimism for very long. But this would be expected of a system that values conformity over individuality and diversity, and appearance over substance. In such a system, everyone is expected to be the best, despite the impossibility of doing so since the "best" refers to only the very few at the top. Nonetheless, the impossible is made to appear attainable, causing quite a bit of distress for those who notice they are not reaching that goal. In other words, this pamphlet demonstrates when you define a goal in such extreme terms, and only a very small proportion of people can actually achieve it, you will create a large mass of people who won't reach the goal. Suspiciously, this ensures there is a large market of potential mental health consumers.

This manual is among the hundreds of similar kinds of pamphlets and brochures displayed in medical office waiting rooms for the patients to read while they're patiently waiting. But let's remember, consumers (the ones who are most affected by the Industry) mostly see these as authoritative standards for assessing "mental health" problems, not advertisements or marketing tools. Therefore, the messages contained in them are going to attract consumers' serious attention and trigger concerns about their "mental health."

Another example from my time in the military will illustrate this problem of unrealistic enthusiasm. Shortly before my retirement, I presented a paper on the psychology of terrorism[20] at a symposium for military "mental health" professionals. One day during the conference, a general addressed the group via a satellite video link. This was partly a pep talk to keep us going and believing our efforts were worthwhile, and partly a demonstration of the new video link technology at the time, which, by the way, did not work very well. The general looked and sounded a lot like the 1980s artificial intelligence TV host Max Headroom.

At one point, the general was talking about the professionalism and expertise of military psychologists, and he said something like, "We're the best we can be, and we're getting even better!" Now, maybe I'm a stickler for truth in advertising, but this sounded quite bizarre to me. How can we be the best, and get better? My recollection of elementary school grammar lessons tells me once you are at the best level, you can't get better – good, better, best. It isn't good, better, best, bester, bestest, and so on. This kind of exaggerated optimism was as rampant in the military then as it is in the Industry and other corporate systems now. In answer to insufficient resources, increasing stress, yet continued demand for more and more output, it is commonplace to hear quips such as "Have a can-do attitude," "Don't work harder, work smarter," and "Do more with less." But it is impossible to comply with these demands because they don't make sense.

It is like whipping a horse already running at top speed. You are unlikely to get the horse to run faster and, in fact, it will probably slow down, despite the whipping.[21] This doesn't even take into consideration how whipping is abusive to the horse. The same thing goes for human beings who are already at top speed in a world of increasing demands. Whipping them to do more is counterproductive and abusive. Instead of realistically recognizing our limitations as human beings, we are often pushed into an absurd situation where we are encouraged to surpass those limitations. In psychology, this is called "learned helplessness,"[22] where it becomes evident nothing will change despite one's earnest efforts and so the person eventually gives up in frustration, despite the continued pain.

But back to the pamphlet I was reading. The message in that pamphlet was just as absurd as the general's comment about doing better than best and what happens when you whip a horse running at top speed. It presents an unrealistically superlative and counterproductive goal of optimal living. The pamphlet also, by the way, demonstrates "mental health" has nothing to do with health or illness. It only talks about attitudes, hope, feelings, and personal responsibilities. These are all issues of moral standards of living.

It is misleading to tell people they can expect to be as "healthy" as the pamphlet portrays. It sets them up for more distress when these promises of such an extremely positive outlook cannot be maintained. This is an example of the idealistic and unrealistic nature of the Industry's moral ideas about how to live your life. Ironically, many Industry professionals would suspect you were in a hypomanic phase of "bipolar disorder" if you told them you were feeling the way the pamphlet defines good "mental health."

Suggesting this kind of lofty goal serves to perpetuate the belief in the Myth. If you think this is how you are supposed to be feeling, you may mistake normal shifts of emotions and changes in outlook as signs of illness. If you find you are feeling pretty good about yourself at times (which we all do), you respond with relief that you have achieved "good mental health." Then you happen to hit a bump in the road (which we all do) and begin to doubt your worth and abilities. You may not "have a positive attitude," or "look forward to the challenges of life," or "feel good about [yourself] and others," or "act responsibly in [your] work and in [your] relationships," or "expect the best out of life." And you may not be "ready to make it happen." Based on the pamphlet's description, you would be sliding into poor "mental health."

But later you find yourself back to where you were before; feeling like you are on top of the world with thumbs up and things are falling into place. Yet, life throws you a curveball once again. Now you feel even more distraught over not maintaining "good mental health" and you might wonder if a "mental illness" is causing these mood swings. If you constantly seek to maintain such an idealistic persona, you will always fail, and the more you try, the more you will find yourself on an emotional roller coaster of unfulfilled expectations.

Instead of this idealistic portrayal, real life is full of both anguish and joy, and a lot of gray area in between. When was the last time you really felt the way the pamphlet says you are supposed to be feeling in order to be in "good mental health"? And how long did it last? For me, at least, there have been only a few times when there wasn't something troubling, distressing, or upsetting going on in my life. This doesn't mean life is awful, or those troubles are devastating, or we must obsess about them. It just means with the good comes the bad.

For every benefit there is a cost; but for every cost there is a benefit. It is impossible to live life by avoiding the bad in constant search of the good. The forever optimist is just as vulnerable as the forever pessimist. If you try to live life by expecting and even demanding only the good, you will get blindsided by the bad. Someone once illustrated the absurdity of this kind of feverish and futile attempt to avoid the painful parts of life by saying it was like trying to get rid of the left by constantly turning to the right.[23]

Agents of Social Control

I have no objections with society trying to coerce people into behavioral conformity with its laws and standards of personal conduct in an attempt to maintain civility. Governmental agencies at all levels, acting on behalf of the citizens, understandably have interests in encouraging and sometimes coercing people to behave appropriately, and it is well within their role to manage social behavior toward that goal. This is what law enforcement, courts, and legislatures are all about.

But one would hope such social coercion applies only to behaviors and not emotions or thoughts. Also, it is important to candidly identify it as methods of social control as decided through political decision making, not by disguising it as some kind of benevolent healthcare. However, Industry professionals routinely pass themselves off as kind and caring assistants to people in anguish, while they are actually functioning as agents of social control. They make moral judgments about behavior and think it is their job to correct that behavior and the experiences associated with it through a corrupted version of healthcare, even against the person's will if necessary.

Some of these professionals are on the government's payroll, working for agencies in an attempt to control people or to help agency authorities make decisions about the application of legal remedies against those people. But they frequently conceal their adversarial role and instead present themselves as advocates for people. Further, they are not up front about the fact that they have no expertise as Industry professionals in making decisions about appropriate social conduct.[24]

In my time conducting court-ordered forensic evaluations, such as child custody cases, it was clear the court frequently deferred to Industry experts' recommendations about ultimate decisions, such as which parent to award residential custody and what kind of visitation arrangements were best. While I had the scientific expertise to address various issues regarding these matters, and to provide that evidence to the court, the final decision for any judicial process from a legal standpoint is the responsibility of the "trier of fact," which means the judge or jury. This is because the ultimate decision is not a scientific or expert conclusion. It is a moral judgment. Therefore, Industry professionals have no expertise in deciding, euphemistically referred to as "recommending" or "suggesting," those final actions.

Many in the Industry, who are not assisting the courts or governmental agencies, still have taken it upon themselves to do the same thing – make moral judgments about the best ways to live. But they talk about it in terms of health and illness, creating the illusion that things like anguish and misbehavior are illnesses or are caused by illnesses and their interventions can cure such illnesses, thus solving those problems.

Worse yet, they sometimes impatiently treat you like a criminal suspect or rebellious child rather than a fellow human traveler. Many times, they have a condescending attitude with you, without compassion, respect for your ideas and struggles, or your version of reality. If you don't agree with them and comply with their suggestions, they see that as a "symptom" (remember anosognosia?). And if you disagree too much by wanting to march to your own drummer, they may refuse to help you altogether out of frustration with your resistance, that is, if they don't try to involuntarily hospitalize you first.

They sometimes even make fun of you when you are not around. One of the most irritating experiences I had was during my residency training on an inpatient psychiatric ward. There, we attended daily morning meetings with the entire staff. The meetings were supposed to be a time to review the progress of people who were admitted to the ward, to plan future ways to help them, and to provide an educational opportunity for the residents to learn. But all too often, these meetings devolved into gossip sessions with staff members talking about the inmates and the "funny" things they did in the previous 24 hours. Obviously, those "funny things" were seen as "symptoms." Sometimes the person was brought to the meeting and made to sit in the center of a large circle of residents and staff, reporting on their progress and fielding questions from the circle of inquisitors. This reminded me of a zoo where onlookers gawk at interesting animals on display while the animals entertain ideas about how to escape.

As another example of this antagonistic attitude with consumers of Industry services, I had a very heartbreaking experience with a young woman who lost a long fight with brain cancer. It was easy to understand how much terror and despair she felt as she endured the deterioration of her body from the cancer as well as the treatments, the increasingly intense pain, and the certainty of a quickly approaching death. I worked with her for months to help her with this transition and to find some kind of meaning in it.

What saddened me the most about her situation was her cancer doctors persisted in labeling her with a "mental illness," and they appeared frantic in coming up with the correct diagnosis and "curing" it. I remember it was a toss-up between "bipolar disorder" and "major depressive disorder" – as if the problems labeled with either of these would be a surprise for someone dying of cancer. She was also reprimanded for taking too much of her opioid drugs, which was the only way she could escape the pain.

They repeatedly chastised her for not complying with "treatment" recommendations, which was some form of simplistic thought restructuring and psychiatric drugs they tried to impose on her. All she wanted to do was find peace during her departure from this world. I don't know if she ever did find peace, as her condition worsened to the point of being bedridden, mostly non-communicative, and unable to continue our sessions. Weeks later she died.

These medico-moral professionals believe they know if you need to have more patience, if you need to stop drinking, if you need to control your anger, or if you need to work less. They are quick to prescribe and proscribe all sorts of things. They may proclaim which spouse is more reasonable in a marital dispute, whether to accept a marriage proposal, or whether to ignore your boss's harassment and try not to rock the boat. They may tell you to stop coddling your adult children, to get more involved in the community, to be more assertive, or to take on a cause. They are very demanding in their attempts to get you to do these things, because that is what they believe you need to do, and they fret quite a bit when you don't comply with their "advice."

Some have even given up the profession because they have lost patience with people who seem to constantly complain about problems without doing something about them, of course, in line with what the professional suggests. They have forgotten that at the heart of our helping professions, there must be a deep respect and patience for you and your perspectives, and the realization each of us has a valid, yet possibly problematic, way of understanding and doing things. Further, they have forgotten we all get to decide our own destiny and so the decision about the best way to live must remain forever a personal one. They have found it irritating to be your companion on your journey through life. They would rather you just get over it and join them on their journey. Woefully, our professions have allowed, and even encouraged, the misconception that science has given the Industry the expertise to know what the appropriate (misleadingly termed "healthy") ways of living are and whether people who are not living in those ways need to change.

I often encounter situations in my private practice when the local courts, employers, or family members refer someone for an evaluation in order to find out whether they "*need* mental health treatment." They are disappointed when I explain to them that misbehavior is not a health matter, crime is not an illness, and I have no special expertise that allows me to decide what they need to do or how they should live their lives. It is clear that people can do things that cause a lot of turmoil. We can try to assist and work with them in order to help them change, but we must be careful not to give them the impression that we are qualified to know what they should do in those situations or what they need. That decision is entirely up to them.

Needs are secondary to desires. In other words, the only reason we say we need something is because we are extremely concerned about the consequences of not having it. But the important thing is what we *desire*, not what we *need*. This even applies to the most basic things. For example, if you do not mind dying, then you don't need to eat. And if you do not mind feeling the way you do, acting the way you are, and suffering the consequences of those things, then you do not need to change. The courts, employers, and family members might say you need to change, but that is based on their desires, not yours. You can choose to comply or not. There is no absolute necessity or cosmic requirement with which we all must comply. It depends on what we desire.

Despite all I've said, there are many who agree with the moral position Industry professionals have assumed in society. This includes knowing what you need, how you should feel about things, and how you should live your life. But there are no authoritatively correct answers to such questions because there is no such thing as a correct or "mentally healthy" way to be. Those are moral questions to be answer by each individual. See Chapter 15 for a more detailed examination of need vs. desire, ability vs. willingness, and how the recognition of these differences can enhance one's sense of contentment in life.

When asked to precisely define "mental illness," Industry professionals fumble over their responses. Some believe they know what it is, but they have a very difficult time putting it into words or really specifying its essence. They just claim to know it. But when pressed for that definition, they eventually throw up their hands in frustration and say something like, "I don't care, I just believe it" (someone actually said this to me once), or they point to the most recent edition of their diagnostic bible to justify their belief. But remember, the *DSM* was created without a scientific or otherwise sound foundation, so as such, it is not much of a scientific authority.

This kind of frustrating defensiveness is unnervingly similar to what happens when people are questioned and asked to defend their religious beliefs. They quickly become irritated with any kind of reasoned dialogue and eventually fall back on the divine infallibility of their respective scriptures to justify their views. This is because they hold on to their religious beliefs purely out of faith and loyalty to their leaders and dogma, not because of a scientific or critically reasoned approach.

These two methods of understanding the world, with religion and science, do not mix. One is not able to outdo the other because they start out with vastly different assumptions about the world and the best way to gain knowledge about it (see more about this in Chapter 12). Both modes are legitimate, but the point is the defenders of the Myth are more like religious believers than scholars or scientists. They have faith that "mental illness" exists as illness; they don't have any evidence like every other medical specialty does. And they cloak their faith in medical disguise.

The reasoning used centuries ago to convince the public that people were possessed by demons is the same used today to convince them they are possessed by "mental illnesses." Today's medical reasoning makes no more sense than yesterday's religious reasoning. It is ironic that in the last few centuries we have come full circle. Distressed and troublesome people were first viewed through religious lenses, then they were seen as little more than defective cargo to be warehoused and tolerated, and finally they are again viewed through religious lenses. But this time, the religion is the Industry, not the Church.

Chapter 9

Stop Complaining!

A Slap in the Face

Ever since psychiatry began as a new medical specialty in the 19th century, its one and only treatment goal has been *symptom reduction.* As explained in Chapter 2, this is because the problems that get labeled "mental illness" are not caused by underlying bodily disease or defects that can be treated. They cannot be addressed similar to how Synthroid can correct a hormone deficiency and chemotherapy can shrink a brain tumor. Therefore, the only thing left to do is to reduce the so-called "symptoms."

When we look at the checklists for the various categories contained in the *DSM*, we see they are mostly comprised of people's reactions to difficult life circumstances. Despite being called "symptoms," and even though they might be problematic and counterproductive, those reactions make sense. Furthermore, they are the natural things we do when presented with distressing situations, not true symptoms of illnesses. So, the attempt to reduce them through "treatment" is equivalent to preventing people from reacting to life challenges in sensible and natural ways.

For instance, one of the "symptoms" included under the label "generalized anxiety disorder" is excessive worry. This means the person is reacting to the fear of a perceived omnipresent threat. But this "symptom" can be better understood as a *complaint about life*. In other words, the person's reactions to difficult life circumstances reveal what he deems unacceptable. As another example, one of the checklist items for the problem called "depression" is a general sense of diminished interest. In other words, the person is complaining that life is meaningless. Thus, given that Industry "treatment" is focused on "symptom reduction," the goal is to silence these symptom-complaints.

Various forms of so-called "treatment" have evolved over the years. If you examine each and how they work, you'll see how language has been used to disguise them as medical procedures. However, they are merely different ways to stop people's complaints about life problems by stunning them into silence. This is like the proverbial "slap in the face" to quiet a hysterical person. When Industry officials claim these procedures "work" or are effective, they merely mean they are powerful enough to stop the person from noticing, thus complaining about, real and significant life problems.

One early method of stopping complaints was to induce *seizures and comas*. This was accomplished with excessive doses of toxic chemicals, which shocked the body into an unnatural state. It was thought this would be such a jolt the "mental illness" would dissipate in some way. It didn't work, except in the very short term, just like how a slap in the face only works in the short term to silence a person, but it never addresses the problems about which the person was complaining. Further, it is abusive and can aggravate the original problems.

Another form was *hydrotherapy*. This consisted of immersing or spraying cold or hot water on the person in order to stimulate the same kind of jolt. Sometimes the person was wrapped in mummy fashion in ice-cold wet towels. Again, other than silencing the person in the short term, this didn't have any lasting effect because it didn't address the sources of the problem. It merely exacerbated the person's distress in the long term.

Then, there was *rotational therapy*, or spinning the person while they were strapped to a chair. This was effective only in making the person vomit. Perhaps this was foreshadowing the nausea people commonly experience when they start using psychiatric drugs? But, again, this form of treatment was only effective in stopping complaints in the short term without addressing the problems the person was complaining about through the so-called "symptoms."

You can read about these and other early forms of barbaric "treatment" in the online magazine *Medscape*.[1] *Medscape* claims to be "the leading online global destination for physicians and healthcare professionals worldwide."[2] This means they endorse the orthodox notion of "mental illness" as illness and not just as natural complaints about life. Nonetheless, they refer to these earlier forms of complaint-stopping procedures as "outlandish." I wonder what their contributors think about the following, more modern, yet still cruel, forms of "treatment," or how their psychiatric descendants will think about them hundreds of years from now.

You are all familiar with the *lobotomy*, as was portrayed in the popular 1970s movie *One Flew Over the Cuckoo's Nest.* This is where a part of the frontal lobe of the brain is either removed or damaged. One type of lobotomy was performed with an instrument that looks like an ice pick and that was punctured through the back of the eye socket to get at the frontal lobe of the brain. Actually, a real ice pick was used to perform the first lobotomy in 1936.[3] It works, and in this case permanently, but only to turn the person into a zombie so they don't have the ability to complain anymore. This is because the procedure damages parts of the brain needed to find meaning in life problems.

You are also aware of *electricity* used to induce seizures. These are like the seizures caused by overdoses of toxic chemicals, but they are caused by electricity instead. The typical electroshock machine sends 750 to 900 milliamps of electricity through the brain.[4] By comparison, any electrical current over 75 milliamps through the heart is enough to cause death through ventricular fibrillation.[5] This is because electricity disrupts the heart muscle's natural electrical-chemical functioning and rhythm. Since natural brain functioning is also based on electrical-chemical processes, one must wonder whether and how the brain is damaged by this amount of electrical current.

Of course, all these procedures "work" in the sense that each is a "slap in the face" in order to get people to stop complaining about life – to reduce "symptoms." While most of the more modern forms are still considered legitimate procedures today, it is easy to discount earlier types as ill-informed or cruel. In medical terms, the "treatment is effective in reducing the symptoms of the illness." In more honest and humanistic terms, it is a "slap in the face" that traumatizes the person. She is stunned into silence and stops complaining about the problems in her life, at least temporarily. Yet, it never addresses the meaningful nature of the complaints.

Many think we've come a long way from earlier procedures and the more modern forms are safe and effective. But that would be a questionable assumption. It is true lobotomies are not performed these days, but there is a newer procedure similar to the lobotomy called the *magnetic resonance image-guided stereotactic cingulotomy*[6] that uses various methods to destroy portions of the brain naturally involved in emotional distress and troublesome behaviors. But why would we want to destroy parts of the brain that are not defective, other than to silence the person by preventing him from using them? This is exactly what the lobotomy did.

You might think that while we still have electroshock in our arsenal, it is used sparingly. In actuality though, we are witnessing a comeback of professional interest in electrifying the brain, even for children. This is accompanied by the claim that it is a safe, effective, and an underused procedure,[7] ignoring the fact that it can result in memory loss and other cognitive impairments.[8] Interestingly, memory loss and cognitive impairments are exactly its intended "therapeutic effect." You can't complain about life when you forget or get confused about the problems about which you were complaining. In lay terms, it traumatizes the brain, but just in a different way than how lobotomies and cingulotomies do. But why would we subject the brain to such a potentially damaging jolt of electricity when there is no identifiable brain defect to treat, unless our purpose is merely to stop the person's complaints ("symptoms") by preventing his brain from functioning as it naturally does?

There is also a procedure similar to electroshock that is used for opioid addiction and other significant life problems. It is called *deep brain stimulation* (also used to treat real diseases like Parkinson's and epilepsy).[9] It involves placing electrodes into particular regions of the brain in order to deliver an electrical current. Whereas it apparently doesn't destroy brain matter like the cingulotomy does, and it doesn't deliver as high of a current as does electroshock (only around 10-20 milliamps[10]), it still prevents the brain from functioning naturally. Thus, the person cannot experience things like addiction cravings, obsessive thoughts, and despair. The advocates of deep brain stimulation echo a familiar but flawed theory. They claim it corrects a chemical imbalance in the brain, even though it actually disrupts natural neurochemical functioning. Further, some of the negative effects of this procedure are ironically the development of "[d]epression, hypo-mania, euphoria, mirth, and hypersexuality."[11]

Theoretically, we could use procedures like any these chemical, surgical, and electrical ones to prevent just about any human experience or behavior that we deem inappropriate. Of course, such "treatment would work." But it would be better described as "human behavioral-experiential engineering," not "treatment."

Psychiatric Drugs

In no less of an assault on the brain, psychiatric drugs are a "slap in the face" just like the preceding forms of so-called "treatment." And, they are by far the most common one. All of them are toxic chemicals prescribed for the simple purpose of interfering with the way brain cells naturally function during difficult times. This chemical disruption prevents people from fully noticing the natural emotional fluctuations in life, and thus, they are less likely to complain about the meaningful circumstances that trigger those emotional reactions. Depending on the dosage, some of them can also interfere with voluntary body movement.

In fact, psychiatric drugs can be seen as a slow-motion version of induced seizures and comas, hydrotherapy, rotational therapy, lobotomy, electroshock, cingulotomies, and deep brain stimulation. They are a slap in the face just like these other forms, but just not as abruptly. And alarmingly, the Industry's own research has shown psychiatric drugs worsen one's outcome over the long run.[12]

As of 2013, one out of every six adults in the United States was taking some type of psychiatric drug.[13] Using U.S. Census data, which estimated there were about 249 million adults in 2013,[14] this equates to over 41 million adults taking some form of psychiatric drug for emotional or behavioral problems. In contrast, the National Institute on Drug Abuse estimated only 24.6 million people age 12 and older that same year used illicit drugs within the past month.[15] Because the figure for psychiatric drug use is only for adults, but the figure for illicit drug use also includes children between 12 and 17, the actual discrepancy between psychiatric and illicit drug use is even greater.

Something is wrong with this picture. On one hand, the Industry strongly and routinely encourages the use of psychiatric drugs as a solution for emotional and behavioral problems. But on the other hand, it vilifies (even calls them "mentally ill") those who resort to illicit drugs on their own for the same purpose, even though there are only about half as many people using illicit drugs as there are using psychiatric drugs.

I wonder what hypocritical message we are sending to the public, especially to the younger and more impressionable of our population. While we have decades-long campaigns to end illicit drug use (witness the stupendously ineffective, harmful, and costly "war on drugs"), we nonetheless seem to be spring loaded to resort to chemical solutions as the first choice in solving most any problem, whether real illnesses like high blood pressure and diabetes, or the fake ones like "depression" and "anxiety." And keep in mind while the chemicals for real illnesses actually correct the very bodily defects causing them, psychiatric chemicals are not corrective because there is no neurochemical defect to correct.

You might be surprised to know that psychiatric drugs first came on the scene quite by accident. It was discovered that when people were exposed to particular chemicals, such as dyes used in the textile industry[16] and surplus rocket fuel from World War II,[17] they reacted in sedating or stimulating ways. This gave medical doctors the idea to synthesize these toxic chemicals into different compounds, call them "medications," and prescribe them for the problems labeled "mental illnesses." But the term "medication" is just part of early drug company marketing efforts to sell psychiatric chemicals to the public as cures. It wouldn't have worked well to honestly call them what they were: toxic chemicals from dyes and rocket fuel. But does it really make a substantive difference when we call these chemicals "medications"?

So, "medication" is not a true descriptor of the substance because there is no medicinal property of the chemicals any more than there is for recreational and illicit chemicals. The only difference is they are distributed to the public under the legal authority of physicians, not the illegal authority of drug dealers. Plus, they do not medicate in a curing sense. They merely affect central nervous system activity similar to how alcohol and cocaine do. We don't refer to those recreational chemicals as medications (at least not yet), so why would we do so with psychiatric chemicals unless it is to create the illusion that they are legitimate forms of medical treatment? Psychiatric drugs are toxic to body functioning, even though they have the ability to produce desired effects such as sedation and stimulation. This is similar to how alcohol and cocaine can have desired effects while still being toxic and potentially quite harmful.

Psychiatric chemicals are talked about using another marketing campaign term, "side effects." A quick Google search will reveal hundreds associated with psychiatric drugs.[18] These dangerous chemical effects are discovered by the drug companies' own pre-marketing research trials that test the drugs' safety and effectiveness. You're already familiar with this if you've paid attention to drug company ads. They take a few seconds to explain the alleged benefits of the drug, but then far more time to rattle off all the dangers. And this is if you can decipher the muffled speed-speech they use. Also, note the video portion of the ads only portray the benefits and none of the dangers, while the audio portion is used to present the dangers as soft "background noise." This is because we pay attention to and remember visual stimuli better than audio stimuli.[19] It probably wouldn't be effective in selling the drug if the ad also depicted the little cartoon characters gradually gaining weight, throwing up, and drooling as they pranced through the flowers under the smiling sun!

But in truth, even though the term "side effects" implies they aren't important, they are arguably more important than the desired effects. Why are diabetes, sexual dysfunction, and weight gain, which are common reactions to some psychiatric drugs, any less important than the desired sedation? How about tardive dyskinesia? This is an ailment caused by the prolonged use of some psychiatric drugs. It is characterized by involuntary and sometimes irreversible muscle movements.

But of course, drug companies are quick to offer additional drugs to suppress these harmful effects. For instance, insulin is prescribed for those who develop diabetes, antiemetics are given to those who get nauseous, and Viagra is suggested for sexual dysfunction. When Seroquel causes tardive dyskinesia, Ingrezza is proposed as the remedy. But what about the harmful effects of Ingrezza? Do we use Ritalin to treat the sleepiness caused by Ingrezza? And what of Ritalin's harmful effects? Do we use a benzodiazepine such as Xanax to settle the agitation from Ritalin? Where do we stop? Or do we? This is why we frequently see prescribed cocktails of multiple drugs at a time. It is somewhat like suggesting the person drink alcohol, smoke marijuana, snort cocaine, and drop acid each day. And it is especially harmful given that, just as with alcohol, marijuana, cocaine, and LSD, none of the psychiatric drugs medicate or cure anything. They are merely attempts to stop the person from complaining about real-life problems, yet they can create far more problems in the process, which become additional complaints to be further "medicated."

The guardians of the Myth use the concept of *risk-benefit ratio* to gloss over these harmful effects of psychiatric chemicals. I can imagine the psychiatrists in the 19th century claiming this same risk-benefit ratio when administering rotational therapy or insulin shock. The risk-benefit ratio idea suggests that despite the risk of being harmed by these chemicals, their benefits far outweigh that risk. So, if a person drools and can't think straight, it is claimed these negative reactions are worth it because the person does not suffer from "schizophrenia." If the person flies into a violent rage because of *akathisia* (an inner sense of intense agitation) and emotional numbing known to occur with the typical antidepressants, it is said to be worth it because the person's "depressive symptoms" are reduced. But what exactly is happening here? The chemicals prevent the person from functioning naturally, to include the ability to feel emotional fluctuations, to complain, and to take action to resolve meaningful difficulties in life. They don't correct faulty brain chemistry so where is the "benefit" in the risk-benefit ratio? It appears there is only risk.

With regard to other prescribed drugs for real medical purposes, there are side effects too, but there is also a potential benefit – the disease process is being corrected. So, for instance, an antibiotic has risks associated with its use, including digestive problems and the development of fungal infections and fever. Yet it also kills harmful bacteria that can ultimately be fatal. Other prescribed drugs for real diseases (e.g., insulin for diabetes, Synthroid for hypothyroidism, chemotherapy for cancer, etc.) have negative effects as well. But the difference between them and psychiatric drugs is that they are curative. There is a clear benefit that can be worth the risk. On the other hand, psychiatric drugs are not curative. They are only harmful, unless we want to use them just like we do alcohol and cocaine to deaden or enhance emotions. But those emotions are not diseased or caused by any kind of defect.

Using drugs that have little benefit and mostly harm is bad enough for adults being prescribed these chemicals. But it borders on criminal that they are being routinely prescribed to unsuspecting children, even to infants. Keep in mind that optimal childhood development depends on children being able to experience emotions, to understand their meaning, and to learn socially useful ways of tolerating and dealing with those feelings. Psychiatric drugs interfere with that ability because they unnaturally alter the child's emotional processing. Further, there is nothing in their brains to cure or correct with these chemicals in the first place. Using them with children is exclusively based on their parents', teachers', and Industry professionals' desire to stop unwanted or troublesome behaviors.[20]

In 2014, the Director of the National Institute of Mental Health (NIMH) reported[21] that as many as 10,000 toddlers were prescribed stimulants such as Ritalin. This is just for children 2-3 years old and just for one type of psychiatric drug. He also said the prescription rate for these stimulant drugs to children increased five-fold between the 1988-1994 and 2007-2010 periods. I remember in the 1960s my parents being very careful to keep coffee out of our reach because it contains the stimulant drug caffeine, which was said to stunt our growth. Every once in a while, they gave in to our curiosity, yet avoided this perceived danger, by allowing us to taste decaffeinated coffee (of course, with as much sugar – an inflammatory substance – as we wanted). But nowadays we liberally give children daily doses of stimulants such as Ritalin and Adderall, and we call them "medicines" and "treatment," even though their chemical structures are nearly indistinguishable from caffeine and cocaine.

The NIMH Director also noted that 7.5% of all children between six and 17 years old were taking psychiatric drugs during the 2011-2012 timeframe. Given there were about 42 million children living in the United States at that time,[22] this would mean there were over 3 million children (not counting <6-year-olds) on psychiatric drugs for emotional or behavioral problems. Other statistics reported by the NIMH Director are: 1.3% of children are prescribed antidepressants (nearly 1 million); the rate of antipsychotic drug prescription for children increased six-fold between 1988-1994 and 2007-2010; and 1.45% of children under 5 years old were prescribed psychiatric drugs (around 348,000).[23] These figures demonstrate that a huge number of children are being subjected to the dangerous effects of toxic chemicals falsely peddled as "medications."

Such widespread use of these drugs and their potentially harmful effects understandably trouble a great many people. Several of them can increase the chances of very serious behavioral, emotional, and physiological reactions and some of these reactions are far worse than the alleged "mental illness" for which they are prescribed. This is why the United States and other governments demand black box warnings for several of the psychiatric drugs (there are black box warnings for non-psychiatric drugs as well). As of 2018, the Food and Drug Administration (FDA) had issued the following black box warnings (bold font) for psychiatric drugs that can cause serious injury or death, as well as warnings for other adverse reactions (regular font):[24]

Abilify	**Increased mortality in the elderly**, CNS, Endocrine
Adderall	GI, Respiratory
Atarax	CNS, GI
Ativan	CNS, CV
Buspar	CNS, CV
Celexa	**Suicidal thoughts**, GI, CNS
Cymbalta	**Suicidal thoughts**, GI, CNS
Dexedrine	**High abuse potential**, CNS, CV
Effexor	**Suicidal thoughts**, CNS, Dermatological
Elavil	**Suicidal thoughts**, CNS, CV

Inderal	CV, CNS
Ionamin	CV, CNS
Keppra	CV, GI
Klonopin	**Increase risk of overdose with opioids**, CNS
Lexapro	**Suicidal thoughts**, GI, CNS
Lithium	**Toxicity**, CV, Dermatological
Lyrica	CNS, CV
Neurontin	CNS, Viral infection
Paxil	**Suicidal thoughts**, CNS, Endocrine
Prozac	**Suicidal thoughts**, GI, CNS
Remeron	**Suicidal thoughts**, GI, CNS
Restoril	**Increase risk of overdose with opioids**, CNS, GI
Risperdal	**Increased mortality in the elderly**, CNS, GI
Ritalin	GI, CNS
Seroquel	**Suicidal thoughts**, CNS, CV
Strattera	**Suicidal thoughts**, GI, CNS
Topamax	CNS, Endocrine
Trazodone	**Suicidal thoughts**, GI, CNS
Trileptal	GI, CNS
Valium	CNS, CV
Vyvanse	**Abuse and dependence**, CNS, GI
Wellbutrin	**Suicidal thoughts**, CNS, CV
Xanax	**Increase risk of overdose with opioids**, CNS
Zoloft	**Suicidal thoughts**, GI, CNS
CNS=	Dizziness, headache, anxiety, agitation, depression, fatigue, confusion, drowsiness, malaise
CV=	Hyper/hypotension, chest pain, bradycardia, tachycardia, edema, arrhythmias, thrombosis, flushing
GI=	Diarrhea, constipation, nausea/vomiting, abdominal pain, xerostomia, dyspepsia

Even though these reactions only occur in a minority of people taking the drug, this still means thousands of people are affected. Keep in mind around 41 million adults in the United States are prescribed psychiatric drugs. Just with a low .1% risk for a particular reaction, that would equate to 41,000 being affected by just that one problem and one drug alone. And this is just with adults. Imagine how many children and adolescents suffer a similar fate. And remember, these drugs are prescribed routinely, frequently in combination with other psychiatric as well as non-psychiatric drugs, and for long periods of time, despite the fact that nothing is ill, diseased, or malfunctioning in the person's brain.

Furthermore, the risk for many harmful drug reactions is far greater than .1%. For example, the following show the percentages of people who experience negative reactions when taking just one of the drugs, Prozac:

> **More than 10% (as high as 33% for insomnia):** headache, somnolence, drowsiness, dizziness, tremor, insomnia, anxiety, nausea, weakness, anorexia, loss of libido, flu symptoms.
>
> **Between 1 – 10%:** amnesia, hyperkinesia, paresthesia, difficulty concentrating, sensory disturbance, abnormal dreams, agitation, emotional instability, hostility, restlessness, abnormal thinking, personality disorder, sleep disturbance, accidental injury, erectile dysfunction, infection, chest pain, hypertension, edema.
>
> **Between .1 – 1%:** loss of control of body movements, depression, memory impairment, akathisia, apathy, depersonalization, intentional overdose, mania, neurosis, paranoia, psychosis, suicidal attempts, suicide, malaise, heart attack.[25]

One would wonder how drugs, that are not curative but that have these kinds of harmful effects, are legally brought to the market. The Food and Drug Administration (FDA) is responsible for the oversight of drug company marketing efforts in the United States, but the process is fraught with potential corruption. There are two main problems: (1) there are many conflicts of interests due to political and financial relationships between the drug company executives and FDA officials; and (2) the standard for approving a drug for market is merely two studies that show the drug is better than placebo. The benefit over placebo can be trivial. Also, studies can be designed, and the data interpreted, in such a way as to maximize the chances of positive results. Further, studies that fail to show effectiveness, and that might show negative effects, are frequently discarded. The drug companies just conduct studies until they find two that support their drug.

Is It Rocket Science?

Within the last few decades, there have been turf battles in the Industry between psychology and psychiatry about who is qualified to prescribe these chemicals to people. Psychiatrists are physicians who completed medical school with all the training about anatomy, gastroenterology, cardiology, immunology, and all the other subfields of medicine. They are also trained on the molecular composition of psychiatric chemicals and how those chemicals might affect human functioning, both positively and negatively, and how different chemicals might react when prescribed together, although this knowledge of "polypharmacy" is quite limited.[26] On the other hand, psychologists, even those trained in clinical psychology like me, are social scientists. Other than brief overviews, we have no medical training. Still, many of my psychology colleagues believe they would be able to help people better if they were allowed to prescribe chemicals to them.

Whereas many of them sincerely think they can help people in a better way by prescribing toxic chemicals, and they truly believe the chemicals correct brain imbalances, I think this move is mostly driven by two other factors: (1) financial incentives; and (2) self-esteem. First, a prescriber can see far more people in one hour than a psychotherapist can, potentially increasing the amount of income for that hour. Second, many psychologists with prescription privileges boost their self-esteem by feeling like psychiatrists, who have historically been placed in a higher social status than the other professionals of the Industry.

In states where psychologists can prescribe psychiatric drugs (I wonder if they will soon be called psychological drugs) they are required to obtain additional training, usually a master's degree in a field related to psychopharmacology. With this additional training, there is no reason they wouldn't be as equally qualified as psychiatrists at prescribing because, as I said before, there are limited scientific guidelines about which chemicals work best with which problems. Still, psychiatrists don't like the competition.

I think this push by psychologists to get prescription privileges is a huge mistake, except in cases where they want prescription authority for the purpose of helping people wean off those psychiatric drugs. If they do obtain privileges to prescribe the drugs, it will likely drive them out of the psychotherapy business and make them akin to junior psychiatrists rather than psychologists, inundating society with even more potentially dangerous chemical solutions to what are meaningful life challenges.

Because the problems labeled "mental illness" are not about bodily defects, there is nothing to cure or correct with psychiatric drugs. These toxic chemicals merely alter natural brain activity, which in the process might result in desired effects. And even though each are created to affect a particular neurochemical, such as serotonin, they also affect numerous other neurochemicals, but we just don't know exactly which ones or how.[27] Look at any description of a psychiatric drug's "mechanism of action" listed at websites such as www.drugs.com, or for you old-timers, the weighty *Physicians' Desk Reference*,[28] and you'll see most mechanisms of action are listed as "unknown."

Furthermore, all of the psychiatric drugs combined are designed to address only a few neurochemicals in the brain – serotonin, norepinephrine, gamma-amino butyric acid, dopamine, glutamate, and acetylcholine. But there are a multitude of neurochemicals and hormones that affect brain functioning, not just these six. Imagine the complex disruption of brain chemistry, especially when multiple psychiatric drugs are prescribed at the same time. Additionally, in some situations there is more of a particular neurotransmitter in the rest of the body than in the brain. For instance, about 95% of all serotonin is in the gut, not the brain.[29] It is no wonder there are so many unwanted harmful effects of these chemicals, especially gastrointestinal problems.

So, it must be remembered that psychiatric drugs work as chemical slaps in the face just like how lobotomies and electroshock are surgical and electrical slaps in the face, respectively. They are not much different than the early barbaric forms of coma- and seizure-inducing procedures, along with other assaults on the human body. The whole point of prescribing them is to get the person to stop having the so-called "symptoms of mental illness." Since those "symptoms" consist of legitimate complaints about life, a successful psychiatric "treatment" is that which stops people from noticing and complaining about their real-world problems, which makes them more submissive and in line with moral norms of thought and conduct dictated by the Industry's authorities.

To make matters worse, in the instances when people claim benefits of psychiatric drugs, a large part of this observed benefit is due to the *placebo effect*.[30] This means a person can feel better just because they know they are taking a drug, they think the drug is a medication, they feel the psychoactive effects of it, and they believe it will help. This is a self-fulfilling prophecy they experience in a positive way, and so they report feeling better. The placebo effect is powerful, but its effects are mistaken as the medicinal property of the drug itself.

The fact that psychiatric drugs can alleviate distress for some people does not mean the distress was a symptom of illness. At best, the drugs are better understood as chemical means of stabilizing a situation like a life preserver does for a person who is drowning in deep water. They can be useful as temporary measures in limited situations of extreme distress. When that person is struggling to stay afloat, it is not the time to teach her how to swim. Neither is it the time to scold her for not planning well or for making bad choices. People in severe circumstances may desire the immediate help of a life preserver to keep them afloat, and then later they can consider better ways to swim in the depths of life's waters. Or, they just might decide to stay out of the deep end. But one thing is for sure; wearing a life preserver all the time is not the same as learning how to swim.

Despite my negative view of psychiatric drugs, I am not anti-drug. I am actually an advocate of the legalization of illicit drugs and the relaxation of prescription privileges. Other than the benefit of a physician advising about the effectiveness and safety of a drug for particular problems, I don't understand the justification for giving that physician (or psychologist) the moral authority to approve its use by adults. If a person is inclined to use a drug, don't you think they are going to find a way to do it? How does prescription authority prevent this? Remember, around twice as many people use prescribed psychiatric drugs than who use mind-altering illegal drugs. Which is the epidemic?

Instead of being anti-drug, my position is better described as pro-informed consent. My concern is these chemicals are peddled as cures for illnesses when that is a clear falsehood. The human problems for which they are prescribed are not illnesses and the chemicals are not medicines. So, I am not critical of people who decide to take psychiatric drugs, if they find relief that way, and if they have been fully informed about how the drugs work, what they do, what they don't do, and any potentially dangerous effects. But this is not happening in today's Industry. Instead, people are being fooled. In nearly three decades of working with people who have been prescribed psychiatric drugs, I have yet to meet even one who has been told the truth by the person who prescribed them.

Some prescribers intentionally misinform people about these chemicals just to persuade them to start or continue taking the drug. Others merely repeat the conventional wisdom taught in medical schools and what they hear from drug company representatives who visit their offices from time to time. Either way, whether outright lies or honest mistakes, prescribers are peddling the falsehood that psychiatric chemicals are cures for real illnesses. In truth, they and all other forms of psychiatric treatment within a medical model are merely different ways of slapping people in the face in order to silence their complaints; in other words, to reduce their "symptoms."

Chapter 10

How Psychiatric Drugs Affect the Brain

Creating the Chemical Imbalance

Psychiatric drugs are not medications. Instead, they are chemicals that are toxic to the human body. They don't cure anything, and they don't balance brain chemistry. They aren't smart bombs that target defective brain systems even though they clearly have effects on the brain. Yet, the Industry works very hard to create the illusion that they are medicines that treat illnesses so consumers will feel more comfortable consuming them. On the other hand, and in stark contrast to this, medications for real illnesses like diabetes and hypertension are prescribed to correct disease processes in the body.

When traumatic and upsetting things happen to us, our brains naturally react as they do, and we experience this reaction in a variety of ways. We become sad, frightened, ashamed, and a whole host of other painful emotions. However, neither these brain reactions nor our negative experiences of them have anything to do with malfunctioning brain chemistry. In fact, they are our experiences of proper brain functioning. There is nothing to be cured because there is no disease. No disease; no illness.

When you look behind the medical disguise, it is quite evident that psychiatric drugs *create chemical imbalances* in the proper functioning of the human brain. They are also indiscriminate. Using them is like using a sledgehammer to swat a fly on a window. Whereas you might hit the fly, you'll do a lot of extra damage in the process. This is a grand irony. In the attempt to balance allegedly out-of-balance brain chemicals and cure the problems called "mental illness," psychiatric drugs create those imbalances, and they have very harmful consequences. Here is a simplified explanation of how they do it.

Our brains function by sending signals[1] along very complicated networks of nerve cells called neurons. Neurons have a central cell body (the soma) and a long "arm" with multiple "fingers" at the end (the axon) reaching out to "touch" particular receptor sites (the dendrites) of other neurons. Where two neurons meet, they don't actually touch each other. Instead, there is a very small gap between them (the synapse). Neurons are able to stimulate each other through this gap with the help of brain chemicals called neurotransmitters. When one neuron activates, it releases neurotransmitters into the gap, and this stimulates the next neuron. That second neuron then releases neurotransmitters into the next gap, stimulating the next neuron, and so on. This is how the "signal" passes from one neuron to the other. After each neuron activates, its neurotransmitters are removed from the gap. They are either destroyed or reabsorbed back into the neuron. Neurotransmitters are either *excitatory* (activates the next neuron) or *inhibitory* (deactivates the next neuron).

There are about 100 billion neurons in your brain. This is about the same as the number of stars in the Milky Way galaxy. Each neuron has about 1,000 connections to other neurons. That equates to around 100 trillion connections where signals cross from one neuron to another. To further amplify this, each neuron can send multiple signals a second. If you counted each neuronal connection, one per second, it would take you more than 3 million years to finish. Imagine the vast complexity! It makes one wonder if we humans will ever be able to understand the workings of this incredible organ. And we use that very organ in our attempt to understand it.

As signals spread through this nearly limitless network of brain cells, a kind of domino effect is created. For example, when you are tapping your foot to music, neurons fire like a line of dominoes falling from the auditory center of your brain to your motor cortex to your foot and back to your sensory cortex to tell you your foot moved, and to trigger the desire to either continue or stop tapping your foot. When you watch a movie, the same kind of domino wave goes from your eyes to the vision center of your brain, and back to your eye muscles to keep focus on the movie. The wave also goes to a multitude of other parts of your brain involved in various thoughts, emotions, and memories related to the movie content, and then to yet other parts of your brain involved in the motivation to continue watching the movie or to yet other brain areas involved in pushing the button on the remote to change the channel. Astoundingly, this massive amount of neuronal signaling (dominoes falling) can happen in just milliseconds!

The domino action does not have a beginning or an ending like with a real domino display when they are all set up and then the first one is knocked over, triggering a cascade of elaborate designs of falling dominoes. Your brain dominoes do not start falling when the movie starts, or when you have the initial urge to tap your foot, or when any human action or experience begins. In other words, there is never a time when all your neurons are quiet, and then you decide to do something which causes the first neuron to fire, which then causes the next one to fire, and so on, ending with all of them having fired and returned to a resting state. The truth is that your neuronal dominoes have been firing and re-firing in simultaneously countless directions and through complicated networks of connections ever since they first formed when you were a fetus in your mother's womb. The only time they stop is when you die.

When you take a psychiatric drug such as Paxil, it gets into your bloodstream and bathes your whole body. When it gets to the brain, it prevents a neurotransmitter called serotonin from being reabsorbed back into the neuron, resulting in a surplus of serotonin remaining in the gaps between the neurons. You would feel this psychoactive effect and it is the "evidence" the Industry uses to claim "depression" is caused by a deficit of serotonin (chemical imbalance) and it is why drugs like Paxil are called *selective serotonin reuptake inhibitors* (SSRIs). See Chapter 2 for a detailed explanation of the bogus chemical imbalance theory.

But notice the chemical effect of Paxil creates an unnatural elevation of serotonin in the gap. Another drug, Seroquel, desensitizes neurons to a chemical called dopamine. But, similar to Paxil, it creates an unnatural chemical state in the brain. The stimulants (e.g., Ritalin) and benzodiazepines (e.g., Valium) also artificially change neuronal functioning. These drugs create unnatural changes in the concentration of, or sensitivity to, certain neurotransmitters in the brain. Similar kinds of chemical disruptions of normal brain functioning occur when ingesting any psychoactive substance such as alcohol, nicotine, caffeine, and marijuana.

Grace Jackson, M.D. and Joanna Moncrieff, M.D., are two psychiatrists who have courageously, and in opposition to the orthodox view, detailed the way psychiatric drugs negatively affect brain functioning in their books: *Rethinking Psychiatric Drugs: A Guide For Informed Consent*; *Drug-Induced Dementia: A Perfect Crime*; and *The Myth of the Chemical Cure: A Critique of Psychiatric Drug Treatment*.[2] They explain that because these drugs alter the natural chemical reactions of the brain, the brain responds to compensate for that unnatural change in chemistry. This oppositional reaction of the brain continues as long as the person is taking the drug. And this is how it goes for all drugs that affect the signaling process among neurons in the brain. This is why the drug loses its effect over time and the dosage has to be increased to maintain the same effect. Eventually a different drug in the same chemical class might be prescribed in order to counteract the brain's compensation (e.g., Zoloft instead of Paxil). But once a new drug is prescribed, the brain's compensatory reaction starts all over again.

This chemical disruption and all the harmful effects of psychiatric drugs are just the start of the problem. The biggest problem is the same we find when people are addicted to illicit drugs like heroin or cocaine. Over time, the brain is thrown into such an unnatural state of dependency on the drug that if the person stops taking it, especially abruptly, they will go into withdrawal and be at risk of suffering from horrible symptoms – real symptoms. Withdrawal is a real disease process caused by the introduction of toxic chemicals into the body. The symptoms are sometimes very severe and dangerous, not only because of how terribly they are experienced, and thus how they can affect a person's behavior, but also because of how the abrupt removal of the drug can negatively affect physiological functioning, to include the possibility of seizures, coma, and even death. Withdrawal from the benzodiazepine class of drugs, such as Xanax and Klonopin, is particularly life threatening.[3]

When people experience withdrawal symptoms, prescribers frequently and falsely say these are the symptoms of the "mental illness" for which they were being treated. They claim those "symptoms" returned when the drug was stopped. It is also common to hear prescribing doctors tell people they must take the drug indefinitely just to manage those "symptoms." But in these cases, they are essentially using the psychiatric drug to manage the real symptoms of withdrawal from that very drug. It is not unlike how a heroin addict continues to use heroin in order to avoid withdrawal. Thinking about psychiatric drugs just like we do illegal and recreational drugs makes things clearer. The body knows nothing about whether the drug is prescribed or not, legal or not, or recreational or not. It only responds to the chemical properties of the drug.

Prescribing or Drug Trafficking?

There are many examples of illicit and recreational drugs once prescribed as medicines. In the 19th century, for instance, heroin was used for cough, chest, and lung problems. Cocaine was prescribed for toothache pain. The list goes on: ergot fungus (which contains a precursor to LSD) for irregular menstruation; Quaaludes for insomnia; smoking tobacco for asthma; opium for gastrointestinal distress and convulsions; and methamphetamine for "depression."[4]

Furthermore, there are illicit drugs currently being prescribed as psychiatric "medications," or researched for approved use in the future. Examples are: LSD, ecstasy, marijuana,[5] ketamine,[6] and psilocybin mushrooms.[7] Just recently, the Food and Drug Administration (FDA) approved a ketamine-like nasal spray for "depression."[8] This, and the fact that there are no disease processes of the brain associated with so-called "mental illness," demonstrates the non-medicinal nature of psychiatric drugs. Their value lies in the way they disrupt brain functioning in order to produce certain desired, but many times undesired and harmful, effects.

If the chemical effects of these otherwise illegal or recreational drugs are pleasant and relieve the emotional pain or behavioral urges troubling a person, they can be useful. But it must be remembered they don't cure faulty brain systems. Neither do they address the meaningful core of the person's problems. That takes a lot more work than popping a pill. At best, they just provide a temporary reprieve for the suffering person. Relying on them as a permanent solution is dangerous.

Recognizing how these illicit chemicals have been rebranded as "medications" helps us better understand all prescribed psychiatric drugs. They don't cure; they just have chemical effects that are experienced in various ways. Sometimes the person desires those effects and sometimes they don't. There is ample research verifying that psychiatric drugs can have very unpleasant effects, just as when people using illicit drugs have bad reactions to them.[9] What's worse is that while the use of otherwise illicit chemicals as "medications" signals the gradual legalization of those drugs, the legalization only applies to the professionals with prescription authority. They are being given the moral authority to decide who is allowed to get high.

I had the unfortunate opportunity to experience the negative effects of psychiatric drugs myself. Toward the end of my military career in the late 1990s, I was anticipating the difficult transition into civilian life as a psychologist in independent private practice. I realized I would be giving up the very regimented and predictable life of the military, as well as a consistent salary. Although the anticipation of a freer lifestyle was very appealing to me, I would be on my own and faced with creating a new structure, coping with an uncertain future, and adjusting to erratic income. In addition, I was losing much of my social support network and trying to establish a new one. This was particularly difficult as I was part of a sensitive agency socially cut off in many ways from the rest of the Air Force and civilian population.

By coincidence, I was also going through a marital breakup, which caused a lot of feelings of uncertainty about my future as well as that of my four children, who were between 15 and 22 years old at the time. This was quite frightening, and I reacted with considerable angst. In an attempt to deal with the problem, I sought out professional help and was prescribed Paxil after only a few minutes of explaining my situation to the doctor.

Although I was already skeptical about psychiatric drugs at that time, I thought it might help me, at least temporarily. However, once I started taking the daily dose, I quickly noticed a rising sense of apathy. I felt like a zombie and I didn't care much about anything, including my transition into civilian life, my crumbling marriage, or my kids. Note that this is the very "therapeutic effect" desired by the Industry – the drug deadens the "problem" of emotional pain and, thus, the ability to care. Paradoxically and painfully, I was troubled by those numb feelings at the same time I didn't care about them. After a week or so, I decided to stop taking the drug. Looking back, it was the best thing I could have done. It allowed me to feel the natural emotional reactions to this challenging time of my life, to know what was meaningful to me, and to take actions in order to maximize my success in the process. I can only imagine how things would have gone if I had heeded the conventional advice to ignore these "side effects," stay on the drug, increase the dosage, or even add other drugs in order to counteract these harmful effects and to "assist" the Paxil.

These negative feelings associated with psychiatric drugs and the chemical imbalance they create can also increase a person's risk of being violent and suicidal.[10] This makes sense when one considers the numbing effects of the drugs. If a person taking them feels apathy and indifference as I did, he is more likely to ignore the lawfulness and consequences of his actions and, thus, be at higher risk of impulsivity. The drug companies' own research reflects this risk (see the previous chapter). Just like with alcohol, methamphetamine, and cocaine, prescribed psychiatric drugs can increase the risk of violent and impulsive behavior.[11] In fact, of the top 31 prescribed drugs in 2010 associated with violence, 26 of them were psychiatric drugs. The number one drug was Chantix, the smoking cessation drug.[12] As a result of this problem, the FDA demanded a black box warning for Chantix. But in 2016, at the urging of the drug's maker, Pfizer, whose annual revenue from Chantix fell $175 million from 2008 to 2015, the FDA narrowly *voted* to remove the black box warning. Pfizer claimed newer studies failed to show any link to violence,[13] although they did not provide any reasonable explanation countering the earlier studies' results.

Even though there is very robust research[14] about the psychological and social factors that increase one's risk of violence, governmental and Industry authorities continue to peddle the falsehood that "mental illness" is one of the factors. This is despite the fact that research conducted to construct a particular violence risk assessment guide demonstrated a diagnosis of "schizophrenia," one of the most severe diagnostic categories, was shown to *reduce* the risk of committing a violent act.[15]

In fact, there are aspects of the problems labeled "mental illness" that are associated with an increased risk of violent behavior. These are: poor social support; current feelings of persecution and paranoia; and alcohol and drug use (which would include psychiatric drugs). However, one or more of these factors can easily apply to people who do not fit a *DSM* category completely. Therefore, while they would be at increased risk of committing violence, they would not be identified in any kind of effort to detect the "mentally ill" because such an effort would necessarily be based on identifying people who have already been given a *DSM* label. Furthermore, most *DSM* labels do not describe these problems.

If someone is suspected of being at risk of violent behavior, and court-ordered to be evaluated by an Industry professional, he would likely be given a *DSM* label, and remember how ambiguous and all-inclusive those diagnostic guidelines are. The professional conducting the evaluation would also be aware of the authorities' concern, so she might very well use one of the more serious *DSM* categories, especially if she is fearful of legal repercussions later if that person does commit a violent act. And, even though this person might not be violent, he will still be branded for life as a violence risk and "mentally ill."

By using the empirical, non-*DSM*, factors known to increase violence risk, we can identify people who are at relatively higher probability of being violent and attempt to *manage* that risk in order to reduce it. However, we are not able to *predict* who will commit violent acts and even when we can reduce the risk, we cannot prevent violence with certainty in any one case. It is easy to *postdict*; in other words, to look at these factors after a person has already committed a mass shooting and to say to ourselves "we should have known." This gives a false sense of predictability. But any prediction of violence, even with accurate prediction methods, will necessarily result in very high false alarms where the great majority of people (probably in the neighborhood of 80% to 90%) who are identified as potentially violent will never be violent.[16] Yet, they would very likely be subjected to the onslaught of forced psychiatric interventions and loss of freedom.

These interventions would include the prescription of psychiatric drugs, which ironically is one of the risk factors for violent behavior, probably because of how they can negatively affect one's thought processes (see the previous chapter). Those subjected to Industry intervention would also feel persecuted and mistreated in the process (another violence risk factor) especially if they are committed to a hospital against their will and forced to take psychiatric drugs. They would also likely become paranoid due to how they are being treated (another violence risk factor). All these things together are likely to increase the chances they become socially disconnected from others (another violence risk factor). Therefore, the orthodox attempt to prevent violence will have the opposite effect of actually *increasing* the risk of violence!

Psychiatric drugs, in particular the antidepressants, can also increase the risk of suicide. The conventional wisdom is the opposite: psychiatric drugs reduce suicidal risk. That is why they are prescribed to people who complain of the problems labeled "depression." However, much of the orthodox research on this matter downplays this risk, likely in response to the influence of drug industry financial interests. The use of psychiatric drugs to reduce suicide is without merit as it is based on a biased selection and interpretation of the evidence.[17] It fails to take into account the corruption in drug research, and it ignores the deleterious effects of the drugs as mentioned earlier.

One particular analysis showed how the rise in psychiatric drug prescriptions paralleled the rise in suicides from the 1980s on, which was the decade the SSRIs (e.g., Prozac) came onto the market.[18] This does not support the orthodox narrative. Instead, it shows psychiatric drug use is correlated with suicides – as drug prescriptions go up, suicides go up. Population growth is a third variable that can account for this correlation – as the population increases, we would expect both the number of suicides and the number of people prescribed psychiatric drugs to also increase. Those advocating this interpretation of the data might say without the drugs, the number of suicides would be even higher.

However, since around the turn of the century, the *suicide rate* has been increasing.[19] This increase cannot be due to population growth as rates take into account the effect of total population. One possible explanation for the correlation between this increasing suicide rate and psychiatric drug use is that suicides were climbing during those years, indicating an increase in the incidence of "depression," and that necessitated an increase in prescriptions. However, two things argue against this interpretation. First, black box warnings have been issued about these drugs causing suicidal thoughts, as shown in the previous chapter. Those black box warnings are based on the drug companies' own research about the drugs' harmful effects. Second, an effective drug would be expected to weaken any rise in suicide rates, but that isn't shown in the data. Therefore, a more reasonable interpretation of the data would be that psychiatric drug use increased the rate of suicide, which is consistent with the drug companies' black box warnings.

There is another theory that could explain the rise in a widespread sense of malaise and suicide rates across our country.[20] It is an apparent social condition seen in working class communities of increasing poverty, despair, illicit drug use, and suicides. More research would be needed to disentangle the extent to which psychiatric drugs and these socioeconomic conditions interact to increase suicides. One would think, though, that if psychiatric drugs are effective in reducing suicides, they would be a solution for this condition. But they don't appear to be.

Despite the orthodox claim that psychiatric drugs correct chemical imbalances in the brain, they do the exact opposite – they create a chemical imbalance. But this reality is hidden behind the language used in describing and marketing those drugs. They are said to be "medications" that treat "mental illnesses" by balancing brain chemistry. But in truth, they place the brain into an unnatural neurochemical state that, despite some possible temporarily positive effects, puts the person at risk of dependency, withdrawal, violence, suicide, and other dangerous outcomes. Despite the relatively low risk of these harmful effects, the fact that millions of people are taking these psychiatric drugs can result in hundreds of thousands of them being negatively affected, and this is without any true curative benefits.

This is the same as with illicit drugs. And all the while, they do nothing to address the problem for which the person sought out help in the first place.

Chapter 11
Psychotherapy

A Kinder, Gentler Way

At this point you might be thinking that despite the widespread use and harmful effects of psychiatric chemicals, the Industry can still safely help people in emotional distress with psychotherapy. You would be right, but just as with the other forms of "face slapping," psychotherapy comes with its own potential problems. Whereas it can be extremely helpful, depending on how it is done, it can be just as inhumane and harmful as using chemical, surgical, and electrical procedures to silence complaints about meaningful life challenges. Further, it can be a huge waste of time and money.

All psychotherapy is "talk therapy." In other words, it is an ongoing series of conversations with a therapist, counselor, or analyst focused on exploring problems in living and identifying possible solutions to those problems, if there are solutions. Not all significant problems we encounter in life can be solved, leaving us with the necessity of accepting, tolerating, and struggling with them. There are many varieties of this conversations-to-help-solve-problems assistance and in my view, they differ only in terms of whether they are directive or explorative, clinical or humanistic, and short- or long-term.

Directive forms are clinically or medically focused and short-term in duration. The goal is to efficiently "diagnose" the problem and then to identify "symptoms" in order to eliminate or reduce them through "treatment." These forms are largely instructional in nature and agenda driven. On the other hand, explorative forms view people more in humanistic terms, rather than clinical or medical ones, and they tend to take longer. The goal is to gradually uncover deeper and more significant themes of personal problems and then to encourage painstaking changes to improve life satisfaction. This latter form of psychotherapy is a wandering and flowing process, not a step-by-step prescriptive path from illness to cure. It focuses on meaningful adjustments to life rather than on efficient "symptom" reduction.

There is also the more recent development of the *coaching* profession. Coaching is seen especially in the corporate world and other non-clinical settings where people want help with life problems. This was an attempt in the late 20th century by professionals who wanted to help people in times of trouble, but without having to be a state-licensed psychotherapist or to conform to the clinical rules or medical model of the Industry. So, coaches don't concern themselves with things like "diagnoses," "symptoms," "personalities," and "defense mechanisms," but they still do what they can to help guide people in living a more satisfactory life, similar to how a football coach helps people become better players.

There have been many attempts to precisely delineate the substantive differences between psychotherapy and coaching, but all appear to have failed.[1] These attempts to make the distinction between the two are more or less exercises in language gymnastics intended to give the appearance of a difference when the essential nature of coaching and psychotherapy are very much the same. While extreme examples of the two might be easier to differentiate (e.g., patient on a couch and analyst sitting behind; two people in suits talking at a conference table), it is difficult to distinguish them in most cases just by watching the interaction without knowing ahead of time which kind of session it is. Therefore, most of my comments about psychotherapy in this chapter apply to coaching as well.

It is important to point out that any kind of coercive psychotherapeutic intervention is unethical and likely to fail. There are many situations when this happens. The courts order people into psychotherapy to avoid jail time, spouses demand their partners enter psychotherapy to avoid divorce, parents force their children into psychotherapy to avoid punishment at home, and employers mandate employees engage in psychotherapy to avoid being reprimanded or fired.

Unless the person is genuinely desirous of help, these are nothing more than strong-arm practices. They are as much a slap in the face as psychiatric drugs and the other harmful interventions because the person is being extorted. At best, he will learn how to make it look like he has benefited – how his "symptoms" have resolved, meaning how he is no longer complaining about life struggles. He'll tell the psychotherapist what she wants to hear just to appease the person who demanded he seek out help.

All too often, psychotherapy is thought to be something that is *done to a person* – applying a technique that makes the person change. This is due to the false but common belief that it is similar to chemical and surgical medical procedures, where you are basically a passive participant in the process. This false belief is reinforced by what seems to be a growing popular demand in our culture for quick and easy solutions to difficult life problems. It is easier to take diabetes medications than to alter one's eating and exercise habits for life. Likewise, the idea of applying a clever technique to eliminate the problems labeled "depression" or "addictions" seems easier than taking on the arduous task of examining one's meaningful expectations about life and possibilities about how to react differently to life's ordeals.

The essential purpose and process of psychotherapy depends on the nature of the problems being addressed. Since those problems are not true illnesses that can be diagnosed and treated, psychotherapy cannot be a medical model procedure. Instead of true illnesses, the problems are a combination of emotional distress and how people react to that distress. They have nothing to do with the treatment of illnesses.

So, effective psychotherapy cannot be the simple application of a technique and it does not work with a passive participant. It requires persistent emotional investment, active participation, and a driving concern by the person being helped. This applies even to the most basic forms of psychotherapeutic types, such as "exposure therapy," in which a person is progressively exposed to a feared object (e.g., spiders, closed spaces, etc.). This can be fairly effective in reducing one's fear; however, it is not a passive process, as the person must invest the time and effort.

Because of the emotional discomfort involved, many choose to stop the process and just live with the fear.

In my private practice, when psychotherapy starts getting stale, I bring the person back to this point by asking him, "Why are you here and what do you want?" This ensures his driving concern, and not mine, is at the forefront of the process. Further, the commitment to change doesn't end when the sessions are over. You can't just attend a few psychotherapy sessions, "get fixed," and then go back to how you were living your life. In order to have lasting effects, the changes it encourages must continue. Therefore, the person must have a genuine desire and willingness to struggle, often painfully so, and to indefinitely work toward something meaningful.

A Smorgasbord of Options

There are hundreds of different types of psychotherapy for hundreds of different types of problems. This is far different than it is with conventional medical treatment. If you have a cough and fever, it really doesn't matter which doctor you see, you'll get roughly the same treatment. If you happen to be in Canada when this happens, the doctors there will treat you basically the same as doctors would in Nigeria, China, or France. But, if you fall into deep despair in northern California and seek out psychotherapy, you can get very different kinds depending on whom you approach just within that limited geographical region.

There are many "theoretical orientations" of psychotherapy. These are the general theories that underlie and inform a psychotherapist's approach. They grew from the early works of historical figures in the field such as Sigmund Freud, B. F. Skinner, Abraham Maslow, Aaron Beck, Carl Rogers, and Rollo May. Each of these orientations emphasizes different aspects of human living and the meaning behind people's behaviors and experiences. In contrast, there is no meaningful variation of theoretical orientations with medical treatment. Physicians' approaches to treating defects in the human body are basically the same internationally. But there is a huge difference between how a physician treats the body and how a psychotherapist deals with a person's unique experiences of living.

The human body is at the heart of medical health issues and all bodies react similarly to each other regarding basic mechanistic and chemical changes triggered by environmental conditions. On the other hand, the sources and meaning of emotional distress vary greatly among people and not all people experience them the same. I think this is why there are so many theoretical orientations and techniques of psychotherapy. They reflect the incredible variation of different kinds of individualized human experiences and meaning, not just of the people seeking assistance, but also of the psychotherapists who work with them.

There is an overabundance of theoretical orientations: psychodynamic, existential, humanistic, behavioral, cognitive, cognitive-behavioral, eclectic, psychoanalytic, person-centered, interpersonal, family systems, object relations, rational-emotive, self psychology, Jungian, feminist, Gestalt, narrative, constructivist, social constructionist, and probably several others I'm overlooking. The American Psychological Association (APA) boils all these down to five broad types: psychodynamic and psychoanalytic, behavioral, cognitive, humanistic, and integrative.[2] And these are just the theoretical orientations. When looking at the number of specific psychotherapy techniques, it can get overwhelming. One website lists 160 different techniques, and these are just the "more common [psycho]therapy types."[3]

But don't be fooled by all the different types of psychotherapy theoretical orientations and techniques. They substantially overlap with each other because each evolved from a previous one and they all address the same basic human phenomena. New orientations spring from adjustments made to address perceived weaknesses in the original one. Specific techniques are also developed this way. Out of dissatisfaction, a practitioner develops a new psychotherapy technique based on an existing one, but with a twist. It is given a catchy name and, presto, a new technique is born.

Many psychotherapists use particular theoretical orientations and techniques without realizing it. This is because most named forms are just different ways to mix, emphasize, and implement the same basic principles. They are best understood as different languages describing essentially the same things. I remember reading a study[4] early in my career demonstrating that psychotherapists tend to see their own orientation in other psychotherapists' recorded sessions, even when the sessions they were watching were of another orientation. For instance, when not knowing they're watching the session of a humanistic psychotherapist, a cognitive-behavioral psychotherapist might tend to interpret the work as cognitive-behavioral. The same biased interpretation can occur when observing specific techniques.

I think this happens because there is enough commonality and overlap among the different types of orientations and techniques that we emphasize the elements similar to our own when observing them. As an example, a cognitive-behavioral psychotherapist might refer to a person's adoption of an authority figure's behaviors as having to do with "modeling"; whereas, a psychodynamic psychotherapist might interpret the same issue in terms of an "internalized object." As another example, a person-centered psychotherapist who shows interest and acceptance of another's perspective can be seen as offering "unconditional positive regard"; whereas a behavioral psychotherapist can see the same actions as "operant conditioning reinforcement."

In fact, if one looks historically at the development of all forms of psychotherapy from the 19th century on, it is apparent that their main purpose has been to "make the unconscious conscious."[5] In other words, each of these different orientations have the same goal of helping people develop insight into motivations, thoughts, feelings, and actions, all of which are mostly out of our awareness. And so, when we make them more conscious, we are able to see their effects and how we can make changes for long-term benefit.

Notwithstanding the essential similarity of different forms of theoretical orientations and techniques, the sheer number of them can intimidate people who are looking for help. But there's good news. Research tells us it isn't necessarily the particular theoretical orientation or technique, or even the academic degree or training of the psychotherapist, that makes for good outcomes. Instead, it is the "chemistry" that forms between you and your psychotherapist. We call this the *common factors* of psychotherapy.[6] They account for a large portion of psychotherapy success and they are more important than those other things (e.g., technique, training, etc.). These common factors include psychotherapist empathy and respect, the expectations of the person seeking help, and a strong therapeutic bond between the two. When they are present, they tend to result in good outcomes, regardless of the theoretical orientation or techniques being used.

This brings us to the phenomenon of the placebo effect. As a reminder, placebo is when a person's expectations create a self-fulfilling prophecy of good outcomes. As with the prescription of psychiatric chemicals explained in Chapter 9, a large part of the benefit in psychotherapy can also be considered placebo. Placebo is a negative thing when it comes to psychiatric drugs, since in those cases any benefit seen isn't really due to the claimed chemical or medicinal properties of the drug. Instead, a large part of the benefit is due to the expectations and hope of getting better. But in psychotherapy, placebo can be a positive thing. When it comes to psychotherapy, a positive expectation and faith in the process is one of the common factors that lead to good outcomes. Reliance on technique is secondary.

Psychotherapy isn't a process of introducing a chemical or mechanical manipulation of the person with the claim it will be curative. Neither is it some mysterious hypnotizing-like process that *makes the person change* how they think, feel, or act. In other words, psychotherapy can't be about clinically or medically administering a treatment. Instead, it is an ongoing process of interpersonal engagement and encouragement to see the world in different ways and to make experimental changes that can provide relief in the long run, even though those changes might result in discomfort in the short run. It includes the nurturing of *faith in the process.*

Therefore, placebo is intentional in psychotherapy. All this means is one of our goals in psychotherapy is to help the person develop a sense of trust and hope for a positive outcome. In the case of psychiatric drugs, the placebo effect is tantamount to a lie because the drug is claimed as the healing element. During psychotherapy, however, placebo is admittedly the heart of the process.

Standard of Care

In practice, the Industry mostly ignores these issues. It downplays the primacy of common factors, the idea that different theoretical orientations and techniques of psychotherapy are different perspectives of the same basic phenomena, and how placebo is essential for psychotherapy effectiveness. Instead, the Industry continues to nitpick from a medical model and clinical perspective in search of the theoretical orientations and techniques that are "proven," and therefore, should be the only forms of psychotherapy allowed within the Industry's *standard of care.*

In medicine, standard of care is important because there are chemical and mechanical things that help alleviate real disease processes in the body, and the wrong treatment can be harmful. But in using this model, human problems in living are wrongly viewed as illnesses affecting people in uniform fashion and caused by defects that can be corrected by applying a stepwise procedure. This is a misapplication of a medical model standard of care to emotional distress and problematic behaviors because those things aren't caused by diseases that can be chemically or mechanically fixed.

Instead, they consist of individualized problems in living, not bodily defects causing those problems. Given this, and the overlapping nature of orientations and techniques, there is little scientific basis for agreeing on a specific standard of care for any one person's problem, especially considering the unreliable and invalid nature of the categories in the *DSM* that the Industry uses to describe those problems. Due to this lack of specificity, there can only be broad and general guidelines for how to help people in distress.

Still, those who have relied on the medical model of human distress over the years commonly use terms like "empirically validated treatments," "empirically supported treatments," "research-based psychological treatments," and "evidence-based practice" to describe the different forms of psychotherapy. They battle with each other over which forms are the best and demand psychotherapists use only the forms supported by research.[7]

However, it has been suggested, I think rightly so, that the criteria for standard of care in psychotherapy remain non-specific and broadened in order to accommodate the great diversity of the human condition, not just of the people being helped, but also of the professionals who try to help.[8] This emphasizes the basic idea that we are unique, culturally immersed, and sentient; we are not like rocks, stars, livers, and brains. Instead, we are meaning making, self-creating, and always in process, not stagnant objects that can be accurately diagnosed and treated as can happen with an inflamed appendix.

Notwithstanding the medical model's longing for precise diagnoses and treatment of different forms of emotional distress, the very guidelines proposed by the Industry contradict this by admitting the standard of care "is the integration of the best available research with *clinical expertise in the context of patient characteristics, culture, and preferences*"[9] [italics added for emphasis]. What this means is even though research might be important in identifying forms of psychotherapy that appear to be helpful to some people, those forms might not, in fact, be helpful, depending on clinician expertise (i.e., lessons from life experiences and training) and the characteristics, cultural background, and preferences of the person being helped. Can these elements be the common factors mentioned earlier? If this is so, then what is the justification for identifying specific forms of authorized psychotherapy techniques to be administered to all people as a prescribed treatment?

Despite these problems of applying the medical model concept of standard of care to psychotherapy, the American Psychological Association's (APA) division on clinical psychology has officially endorsed 79 different psychotherapy forms.[10] This is in furtherance of the goal of developing approved "how to" manuals that lay out the steps in administering psychotherapy to people, as if the psychotherapy process were similar to taking out an appendix. In the case of appendectomies, it is important to get the steps in the right order, to not miss any, and to not ad lib. In psychotherapy, however, this is not the case. Still, the Industry tries to make it look that way.

Randomized Controlled Trial

There is an even more serious problem when applying a medically minded standard of care to psychotherapy. It is the research method used in assessing and arriving at that standard of care. In its efforts to stay within a medical model of real health and illness, the Industry has adopted the *randomized controlled trial* (RCT) type of research method, which is the gold standard of medical research. But remember, human distress and conduct are not medical matters to be addressed with medical interventions. In other words, there is nothing wrong with the person that can be fixed like there is with a person suffering from a defective kidney or high blood pressure. Therefore, applying this research method to psychotherapy is forcing a square peg into a round hole.

The basic layout of the RCT research method compares people who are randomly assigned to one of two groups: a psychotherapy group and a control group (group receiving no intervention). Sometimes additional groups are included in the study in order to simultaneously compare several different forms of psychotherapy against each other. For instance, a study might have the goal of determining the most effective among four groups: psychotherapy alone, psychiatric drugs alone, a combination of psychotherapy and psychiatric drugs, and a control group.

Randomly assigning people to the groups ensures they are similar prior to the experiment. In other words, it ensures there is nothing regarding group assignment that biases one group over the other in terms of their average level of the problem being studied, such as the despair and passivity of the problem called "depression." The people in the psychotherapy group are subjected to some form of intervention and those in the control group are not.

Random assignment enables the researchers to have confidence that any benefit seen afterwards in the psychotherapy group and not in the control group is actually due to the psychotherapy and not the result of other factors that originally biased the groups. For instance, if the people in the psychotherapy group started off with a higher economic standing than the control group, that might result in a better outcome for them, but it would have nothing to do with the particular psychotherapy being studied. Random assignment ensures there would be similarity in economic standing for each group at the outset of the experiment.

This approach makes it look like the Industry has a clear scientific way of identifying the "proven" forms of psychotherapy. But looks can be deceiving. The RCT design is a marvelous tool and it is essential for research into medical treatment. But remember, psychotherapy is not medical treatment and emotional distress does not uniformly affect all people the same. Thus, it is a mistake to apply this research design to determine how best to help a particular person with his unique problems.

The RCT method is a *nomothetic* form of research. This means its purpose is to come up with general laws of human behavior that apply to *all people*. It is in contrast to *ideographic* research, which is when one individual is studied over time and the results only apply to that one person. For our purposes in discussing psychotherapy effectiveness, a nomothetic general law would be a statement about how people respond to a certain form of psychotherapy. Notice, though, the statement refers to *people*, not *a person*, and that's why it is called nomothetic.

But its nomothetic feature is also a weakness. This is because the results of nomothetic research are entirely based on the *average* of each group studied. Remember an average is a way to use one number to best describe an entire group of people, not each person in the group. We calculate the average by adding everyone's score in a group and dividing by the number of people in the group. There is no other way to study the differences between groups of people, in an attempt to seek out general laws of human behavior, than by relying on a measure of central tendency like the average. Correlations are also used, but they are merely another kind of average – the average standard deviation of an entire group.

But as we've seen in Chapter 4, the average rarely represents any one person in a group. Therefore, using an average to describe everyone in a group washes out all individuality and this is evident when looking into the nuts and bolts of these studies. This reliance on averages is the same as stereotyping. With stereotyping, we erroneously judge people from a particular group because of the experiences we've had with one or a few members from the group. With an RCT study, we erroneously judge people from one group because of the experiences we have with the average.

So nomothetic research does not allow an understanding of individual uniqueness. It stereotypes everyone in a group based on the average of the group and it doesn't consider the amazing variation among people within the group in terms of their values, expectations, preferences, and their life's meaning (the important common factors mentioned earlier). In essence, nomothetic research relies on the *myth of the average person.* It assumes all people will react similarly to how the average person reacts to the particular form of psychotherapy being studied. But there is no such thing as the average person. It is a construct, not a person.

In nomothetic research there is another statistic of key importance called the *effect size.*[11] It shows us how much the psychotherapy group differs from the control group. So, it tells us whether the particular form of psychotherapy being studied has an impact and how much of an impact. We would not want to invest the time and money in psychotherapy having only trivial effects. For instance, a psychotherapy technique that increases life satisfaction by an insignificantly small amount would not be worth the person's investment and commitment.

Look at the following figure.[12] It shows a psychotherapy group and control group of a typical RCT. Each group is shown with the same kind of bell curve I presented earlier in Chapter 4. Let's assume the horizontal axis reflects scores on a scale that purports to measure the problems labeled "depression," less problematic to the left and more problematic to the right. The height of the curve shows the number of people who had that particular score. The vertical line at the center of each distribution is the score representing the average person for the group. Prior to going through psychotherapy, these two groups would have overlapped almost completely. This is because all people were randomly assigned to the two groups; therefore, each group's curve would be nearly identical at the outset.

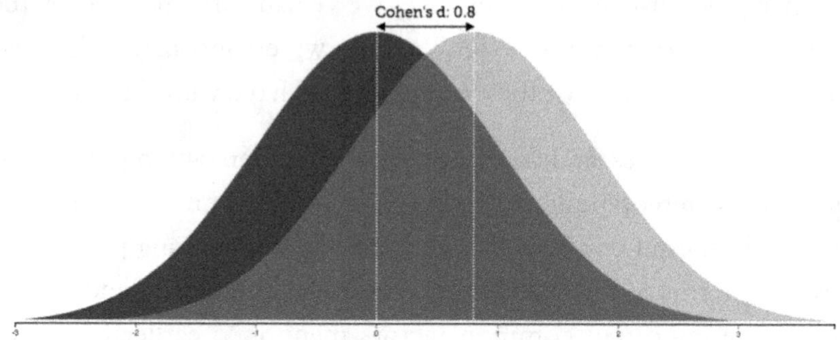

The figure shows the situation of the groups after the study. The distribution on the left (darker shaded) is the group of people who went through psychotherapy and the one on the right (lighter shaded) is the control group who waited throughout the study without any intervention. In this example, it would be concluded that the particular form of psychotherapy was effective, since the psychotherapy group's average score is less than the control group's average score.

The "Cohen's d: 0.8" shown at the top is the effect size I mentioned earlier. You can see it is measuring the difference between the groups' averages. An effect size of .8 like this is considered a large magnitude in the social sciences. Effect sizes of .2 and .5 are considered small and medium magnitudes, respectively.[13] A result like the one shown would be deemed significant as validation for the type of psychotherapy. It had a practically important positive effect and, thus, was evidence-based. This effect size magnitude would be used to designate the particular form of psychotherapy as meeting the Industry's standard of care.

Do No Harm?

Because these RCT studies only give us information about the average person, we cannot tell how each individual fared unless we are able to examine the raw data, which typically is not reported in journal articles of research studies like this. We only know that the *average* score of the psychotherapy group improved when compared to the *average* score of the control group. And we've already noted it is a rarity for anyone to score the exact same as the statistical average. With this average information alone, we don't know the extent to which individuals in the psychotherapy group benefited, were harmed, or remained unaffected. We also don't know how many of the individuals in the control group got better, worse, or stayed the same during the study. And think about it, if you are emotionally suffering and had to wait during the course of a study, what is the likelihood you are going to feel worse while waiting?

Alarmingly, the results seen in the earlier figure could happen even if some of the people in the psychotherapy group became *worse* as a result of the particular form of psychotherapy, as long as the majority of them benefited. Further, if some people in the control group worsened during the study, it would increase the control group's average score relative to the psychotherapy group, thus increasing the magnitude of the effect size between the groups. For those of you who want to see the statistical details of how this might happen, look at the hypothetical example at Appendix D.

In this example, I created two groups of 30 people each. The people in each group were rated on a 9-point rating scale, with lower scores indicating less problems and higher scores indicating more problems. The psychotherapy group members were rated before and after. The control group members were also rated before and after but with no intervention in between. Both the groups started out with exactly the same scores.

I made it so 22 of the 30 people in the psychotherapy group were two points better at the end of the study. But eight of them were two points worse. I also made it so all but eight of the control group stayed the same while they waited during the study. The eight got worse by two points. After the study, the psychotherapy group's average score was lower than the control group's score, signifying the particular form of psychotherapy was effective. The effect size between the groups was .56, which is a medium effect size and it could be used to conclude the particular form of psychotherapy studied was evidence-based, and thus, standard of care.

But how can this be a basis for standard of care if 27% (more than 1 out of 4) of the people in the psychotherapy group scored *worse* after the study, suggesting the possibility that something about the particular form of psychotherapy harmed them, or at the least was ineffective in addressing their problems? I realize this is just a hypothetical example I concocted to make a point. But it still demonstrates a potential problem when unquestioningly using the results of nomothetic research to justify a psychotherapy standard of care that is applied to all people. Remember, these RCT studies are intended to discover general laws of human behavior and those general laws, by definition, are supposed to *apply to all people.*

How could we ever know which people we are about to subject to a particular form of psychotherapy will benefit, which will be harmed, and which will be unaffected? Do we switch to an unproven, non-standard of care, psychotherapy if the standard is ineffective or harmful? Within a medical model, wouldn't it constitute malpractice to abandon the standard of care like this? Or is it only malpractice to maintain compliance with standard of care when it is ineffective or harmful?

Do psychotherapists even pay attention to whether people are being harmed or do they interpret negative responses to psychotherapy as therapeutic resistance, "noncompliance with treatment," or a worsening condition? Do we ignore a person's complaints that psychotherapy is not working? What if they tell us they would rather do it a different way? Do we accommodate their request? How would we determine the point when harm is happening or when it is a waste of time, especially if the person has a negative experience of it but doesn't complain, just out of respect for our authority? And if we have to think on our feet and switch to a different form of psychotherapy midstream, wonder about which one to switch to, when to switch, and how many times to switch, then what is the value of having anointed techniques in the first place?

Moreover, even with the respectable effect size of .56, the practical importance of the results has less meaning than at first glance. While it is true the average score of my hypothetical psychotherapy group was better than the control group, indicating effectiveness, the relative difference between the averages of the groups is minimal and not impressive at all. The difference between an average score of 4.5 for the psychotherapy group and 5.8 for the control group on a 9-point scale seems only marginally important. Each is less than a point away from 5, which is the halfway point on the scale from 1 to 9.

A final problem that further accentuates the questionable value of RCTs in determining psychotherapy standard of care is seen in yet another statistic that gives us a different glimpse of the effect size and helps us quantify the practical importance of the psychotherapy being studied. This statistic is called the *percent of variance explained*. It tells us how much of the difference in scores pre and post-intervention is attributable to the psychotherapy technique itself. Obviously, we would want the percent of variance explained by the psychotherapy to be large. Ideally, the psychotherapy technique should be the critical element in the study, especially if it is considered the standard of care.

But in using accepted methods,[14] the effect size of .56 in my hypothetical study is about the same as a percent of variance explained of .073, or 7%. In other words, only 7% of the change seen in scores during my study was due to the psychotherapy technique. This would still be the case even if all the people in the psychotherapy group benefited. This means around 93% of the change in scores was not attributable to the psychotherapy, but to other variables not measured in the study. With a large effect size of .8, only about 14% of score changes are the result of the psychotherapy technique and 86% to factors not addressed in the study. Even with the unheard-of effect size of 1.5, the percent of variance explained would be .35, meaning only 35% of the change in scores would be the result of the psychotherapy technique and 65% attributable to other variables.

It is important to also note that standard of care studies must be *replicated* in order to have any confidence in their results. This applies to any kind of research. There must be a consistent series of studies conducted by different researchers and showing similar effect sizes. One or two studies are not enough because the results might be biased by a researcher's conflicts of interests, the results of poor research design and methodology, or just a fluke. When applying this replication standard to psychotherapy research, the results are poor as there are rarely any series of well-conducted studies showing consistent and respectable effect sizes.[15]

Another way to assess whether research results are stable over time is to conduct a meta-analysis. This is a protocol that combines the results of several studies in order to account for error that might be in the individual studies. Think of this as the average result of several studies – and remember the problem of relying on averages. But when doing this, we again find mediocre results. One such study examined 153 RCTs of the problem called "depression" and consisting of nearly 30,000 participants. The effect size of psychotherapy over control was only .35, meaning only 3% percent of the variance was explained by the psychotherapy techniques and 97% was due to factors not addressed in the studies.[16]

Of added concern, it is commonplace for psychotherapy studies to be designed and conducted in ways that contaminate the results. For example, a study of 115 RCTs of psychotherapy effectiveness for the problem called "depression" demonstrated that only 11 of them met quality criteria (e.g., independent raters, treatment manual used, trained therapists, blind ratings, etc.). Of the 104 studies not meeting the quality criteria, the effect size was .74. But of the 11 that did meet the criteria, the effect size was only .22, far less than in my hypothetical study.[17] This is only 1% of the variance explained!

When considering the results of my hypothetical study, it isn't an impressive performance when a standard of care psychotherapy harms one out of four people subjected to it and when 93% of the observed outcome is due to things other than the technique itself. Yet, a study with an effect size and percent of variance explained like my hypothetical example could be used within the Industry to demonstrate so-called evidence-based status, and thus, standard of care. Actually, even the RCT studies conducted to assess the value of psychiatric drugs show similarly problematic results. One review of 17 such RCTs showed the effect size ranged from .30 to .92 (2 - 18% of the variance explained).[18] Compare that with the effect size of .56 in my hypothetical study.

In essence, the Industry would be telling you that the anointed forms of standard of care psychotherapy techniques might harm you and won't help you much. This sounds suspiciously like the warnings you hear about the negative effects of psychiatric drugs; they won't help much and could in fact hurt you greatly.

This can be understood more clearly if we remember that RCTs are forms of nomothetic research and they are all about averages, not individuals. The results of these kinds of studies mean the *average person* does better with this psychotherapy and only minimally better. But who is the average person? The average is not a person; it is a statistic used to represent a whole group of people with one number. It washes out all individuality and, therefore, cannot be legitimately applied to any one person. In this sense, the typical standard of care in the Industry is unjustified.

Individual Lives Matter

Psychotherapy is not a medical form of treatment that can be prescribed the same to all people. Because of the great variation of individuals' values, desires, and hopes, each person responds to it differently. But instead of accounting for this individuality, the Industry treats people as if they were non-sentient, inanimate objects and that it is possible to administer the same medical model standard of care to each of them.

However, the only conclusion that can be drawn from standard of care research results is that something about the particular form of psychotherapy being studied had a *weak* and *general* effect. Yet, the standard of care does not necessarily help all people, those who are helped might not be helped much, and in fact, it can be harmful to some of them. More importantly, a very large portion of the effects seen during these standard of care studies is due to things other than the psychotherapy itself. Could these other things be the common factors mentioned earlier, or the clinical expertise, personal characteristics, preferences, and cultural background the American Psychological Association (APA) encourages us to take into account? Whatever they are, one thing is very clear. There is something far more important going on during psychotherapy sessions than the specific psychotherapy theoretical orientations or techniques. Thus, there is no justification in using RCT research to validate effective forms of psychotherapy and anointing them "evidence-based" standard of care.[19]

Still, this medical model of the RCT continues to be misapplied to the concept of individualized human emotional struggles and possibilities of personal change despite ongoing criticisms about it.[20] Because human distress and errant conduct is not about illness or disease, individual lives matter and, therefore, psychotherapy is more of an art form and not medical treatment.[21]

Psychologist Jan Smedslund, Ph.D., described this problem of applying nomothetic research to understanding psychotherapeutic change.[22] First, he pointed out there are an infinite number of things that determine any particular human reaction to life. This means people are not objects such as rocks, livers, and pancreases, which only react to the present time and location. On the contrary, people react to the "expected future, the remembered past, the logically inferred, the hypothetical, and the imaginary."[23] It also means "because theories can only include a small number of factors in order to be manageable, and because these factors, even jointly, tend to account for only a small part of the variance, psychological theories cannot be very useful in practice."[24] This is consistent with what I showed earlier about how even the most robust RCT study only accounts for a very small portion of people's responses to specific forms of psychotherapy.

Second, people are affected by their experiences and those experiences forever change them. The person can never return to the previous state of being. Each is a complexly flowing process and different at each moment in time. According to Smedslund, "the irreversibility of psychological processes...precludes the existence of absolute or general principles"[25] that can be applied to all people. This means each person is necessarily unique. There is no way to describe "people" with one generalization. Each one must be met and understood in her unique flowing journey of life, a journey that is always in flux. Treating everyone the same in psychotherapy would be like taking samples of 100 rivers, averaging their characteristics, and then describing all the rivers with the average. Not only would this reduce a river to a stagnant bucket of water, it would also ignore the vast diversity in flows, depths, life forms, minerals, and temperatures of the rivers.

In light of this problem, Smedslund suggested a flexible model of psychotherapy.[26] This means the psychotherapist must adjust to the flowing interaction with the person and her unique life, rather than applying an inflexible technique. However, with this, he does not suggest the abandonment of an empirical approach. Quite the contrary, he encourages a stronger reliance on empiricism, but an empiricism of one person at a time. This is the ideographic approach I mentioned earlier as an alternative to the nomothetic approach.

Effective psychotherapy is essentially what the person in psychotherapy decides it is. As long as psychotherapists have a broad theoretical framework that informs their choices, maintain a focus on the common factors, remain empirical, do not intentionally harm or deceive, respect the person's point of view, and have a sincere concern for helping, then psychotherapy can be effective regardless of the orientation or technique used. It is also important for psychotherapists to be honest about the process they are undertaking. It would be dishonest to claim they are applying a technique that will make the person change. That's not how the human change processes work.[27]

Further, psychotherapy doesn't lend itself to nomothetic analysis because the mythical average person does not exist. The average cannot represent each individual with his or her unique life circumstances and meaning. This is why idiographic research is far better when trying to learn about effective ways to help people in the throes of emotional pain. And idiographic research is exactly what can happen when psychotherapy is underway. Each person's psychotherapy is a research study in constant process.

To be effective, psychotherapy must be a personalized process at every moment that applies to the one person being helped. Clearly, psychotherapists must use a theoretical orientation that informs the process. This framework must provide flexibility that allows for individual adjustments while maintaining a foundation. After all, psychotherapy isn't a random conversation with the person in the form of chit-chat. Instead, the psychotherapist works together with the person, but the work is tailored to what seems to be the most helpful to the person along the way. It cannot be prescribed like insulin can be for diabetics. It has to be a work in process that evolves with one person at a time in each moment of that process.

Part II

The Unveiling

> I try to encourage people to think for themselves, to question standard assumptions.... Begin by taking a skeptical attitude toward anything that is conventional wisdom. Make it justify itself. It usually can't. Be willing to ask questions about what is taken for granted. Try to think things through for yourself.
>
> Noam Chomsky (2010)[1]

In Part II, I want to show you what is revealed when we remove the medico-moral disguise of the Industry. I recognize that what I am saying is at odds with the conventional wisdom shared by thousands of Industry authorities. They will probably react to my words with dictatorial condemnation. They are likely to make patronizing claims that I "just don't understand." They might say I am just like the climate deniers, anti-vaxxers, or other conspiracy theorists. They might even try to turn the system against me and suggest I am "mentally ill" to explain my rebellion against the status quo, as has happened to some of my like-minded colleagues who speak up about the Industry's abuses.[2] My guess would be a toss-up among "oppositional defiant disorder," "paranoid schizophrenia," or maybe even "autism" (see my screening results in Chapter 3). They frequently resort to these ad hominem tactics because they have no sound scientific evidence or critical reasoning to counter my primary assertion that the problems called "mental illness" are not truly illnesses, and so a medical model response to them is unwarranted.

These orthodox defenders of the Myth are also fond of falsely accusing critics like me of being Scientologists or members of its Citizens' Commission on Human Rights (CCHR), in an attempt to use the poor reputation of Scientology to vilify us and discourage people from taking us seriously.[3]

But I am neither a Scientologist nor a member of CCHR. I never have been, never will be, and I am not speaking on their behalf. I do not support Scientology, as I am very disturbed about the allegations of emotional and financial exploitation of their members and how they are reported to retaliate against critics and ex-members.[4] In my view, if these allegations are true, it would make them just as inhumane as the Industry.

Despite the potential for these kinds of simpleminded attacks against me, I continue to present a logical, empirical, critically reasoned, and scientifically honest portrayal of the human phenomenon I study and with which I have worked for many years. When the language and layers of deception are peeled away, we can see a clearer picture of what is going on behind the disguise. Just as in the scene in *The Wizard of Oz* when Toto pulls back the curtain to reveal the true nature of the Wizard, we can plainly see what all the medical smoke and mirrors are hiding. When we do this, we don't see illnesses and we don't see medical problems. Instead, we see very natural, understandable, and meaningful human phenomena.

For more than two centuries, the story has been told by the guardians of the Myth about internal disease entities that somehow invade us, grow from within, or that people develop, making them feel and act in annoying, inconvenient, or socially inappropriate ways. This story has been perpetuated by tricks of language and pseudoscience that deceive and paint the picture of real illness and medical treatment when, in fact, there is a different reality hiding behind this disguise.

As Noam Chomsky suggested in the epigraph, it doesn't matter how many expert authorities agree about something. Instead, what fundamentally matters is whether critical thinking is used to support a certain proposition. There is no room for "strength in numbers" or conventional wisdom in any scientific field, especially when the authorities of that field have financial and guild interests in defending their flawed position. In science, those who propose a theory are obligated to present the evidence and reasoning that supports the theory. The defenders of the Myth have not done so.

The Industry is widely considered scientific, but time-honored scientific standards are not applied to its basic foundation. Some critics have gone so far as to use the analogy: psychiatry is to neurology, as astrology is to astronomy. The point of this analogy is the Industry is more like astrology than astronomy in the sense that it has adopted a belief system, not a science. Yet, it still retains a large following of devotees and official recognition by governmental and professional bodies. But when its claims are tested scientifically and subjected to critical thinking, they fall apart.

In this second part of the book, I will first examine the notion of brain-mind dualism and how its traditional use within the Industry has created the illusion that the mind can be diseased. I'll then present an alternative model of understanding mental suffering and problematic behaviors within the theoretical framework of human emotion and existential psychology. I'll propose that emotional distress is not the problem. Instead, *the problem* is when we try to escape those feelings of distress. Specific examples from *DSM* categories will be explained in this way. Then will follow an exploration of the ideas of human desire and willingness, which are at the heart of our struggles and our choices. I'll conclude Part II with some thoughts on the future of the Industry.

Chapter 12

The Difference Between Brain and Mind

Mind Doctors

It is very important to remember the title of Benjamin Rush's textbook that sparked the birth of psychiatry over two hundred years ago. It was *Medical Inquiries and Observations Upon the Diseases of the Mind.*[1] This title, as well as the etymological origin of the term "psychiatry" (the Greek *psykhē*: mind; and *iatreia*: healing), shows that the mind, and not the body, was psychiatry's original focus of inquiry and claimed expertise, leaving actual bodily diseases to other medical specialists such as neurologists. This is similar to how astrology claims the constellations are its area of expertise, leaving the astrophysics of the stars and planets to the astronomers. In his thinking about these diseases of the mind, Rush said:

> They have been divided, 1, into such as act, *directly* upon the body; and, 2, such as act *indirectly* upon the body, through the medium of the mind." [2] [Italics in the original]

He gave examples of the first type as brain lesions, tumors, epilepsy, exposure to toxic substances, and excessive consumption of alcohol. Some examples of the second type were intense study, rapid shifting of attention from one topic to another, extensive and constant imagination, excessive memorization, and intense emotions. Even though Rush considered the first category to be diseases of the *mind*, they are clearly true medical matters, in other words, diseases of the *body*. On the other hand, Rush's second category includes those problems that would today be considered within the realm of "mental illness."

Rush's second type of mind disease consists of problems not caused by bodily pathology or defective physiology. In fact, he proposed it was the other way around – the mind negatively affected the brain. While orthodox psychiatry will sometimes admit this lack of evidence for a pathological brain origin of emotional distress and problematic behaviors, they still maintain faith that proof is just around the corner, despite decades of failed attempts to find that proof. In the meantime, they just assume these problems are real illnesses and deal with them accordingly by applying a medical model of diagnosing and treating them. But this is inconsistent with science. When a scientific theory is not supported by the data, the theory is adjusted to fit the data, or it is eventually discarded altogether. In opposition to this scientific approach, the Industry faithfully defends the theory in the face of contradictory data and continues looking for "proof."

However, if that long-awaited proof of bodily pathology were ever discovered and shown to account for Rush's second type of "mind diseases," they no longer would be called "mind diseases" or "mental illnesses." Instead, they would be genuine illnesses. In other words, they would become part of his first type, "...such as act, *directly* upon the body." Ironically, this means the discovery of evidence of a real bodily disease basis for "mental illness" would threaten the very existence of the Industry as it would no longer have a purpose as a separate medical specialty. This is because those illnesses would fall within the scope of neurology and the other disciplines of medicine, such as nutritional science and immunology, that treat the defective bodily systems involved.

So, given this conundrum, and notwithstanding their continuing focus on "mind diseases," the Industry has desperately held on to the body over the years, more specifically the brain, as its professed organ of interest. This is because in order to maintain a façade of legitimate medicine, it must have some kind of focus on the body. Because mind appears to emanate from the brain in some way, these defenders of the Myth continue to look for mind diseases in that three-pound mass of squishy matter encased in our skulls. Again, using the comparison to astrology, this is similar to how astrologists continue to look for the meaning of earthly affairs, but by examining the heavens. The Industry and astrology are both looking in the wrong place. More precisely, there is nothing to look for.

Disease of the mind has always been the Industry's forte and its rationale for existing. This has been the case ever since those early days when medical science took over the jurisdiction of troublesome people from religious authorities, and it continues on into the modern era of the medical model of human suffering. Despite much effort in searching for "mental illness" in the brain since then, there has always been the tacit belief that the disease was *in the mind* and that the mind somehow inhabits the brain, making it necessary to look there for "mental illness." This is like Russian nesting dolls. "Mental illness" is not in the outer doll – the brain. Instead, it resides in the mind, which is one of the inner dolls.

But this doesn't make sense. The mind is vastly different from the brain and it doesn't reside within it. The brain is located in three-dimensional space and has mass. At an autopsy, you could cut into the brain and see its internal components. With the proper technology, you could examine the microscopic workings of its blood, neurochemistry, and metabolism. The brain is organic and has parts that can grow tumors, be damaged, and get infected. It can become afflicted with illness and disease.

In glaring contrast, "mind" refers to subjective experiences; it is not an object. It has no location and it is not on the public stage. The "contents" of mind, such as memories, sounds, thoughts, intentions, perceptions, images, decisions, and feelings, are objectified sensations and they aren't found in the brain alongside the amygdala, hypothalamus, and cerebellum. These mind things do not exist in nature like neurons and blood vessels. Most importantly, the meaningful nature of mind can't be understood by examining the brain.

There are no parts of the mind that can break or become inflicted with disease. Therefore, the mind cannot become literally ill. The mind can't be seen, heard, touched, tasted, or smelled. There are as many minds as there are people living in the world (perhaps animals too?), but no one can know the mind of another. We can only know what they say and do and then make inferences about their minds. Other than an abstract model, there is no mind to study except that each of us can study our own. This makes the mind quite elusive and yet it is very real and powerful. Mind is strictly a phenomenon of individualized consciousness, or awareness, or experience, and it is arguably the most mysterious thing about human life.

Human behavior is also the focus of the Industry. But just as with mind, behavior is not an object located in the brain, it cannot be literally ill, and we cannot understand the meaningful nature of it by studying the brain. The only way to fully understand someone's behavior is to get a sense of that person's values, desires, and goals, in other words, her mind. Trying to understand mind or behavior by studying the brain's amygdala, neurotransmitters, and hippocampus would be like trying to understand justice by studying the contents of a courtroom. You will not find it there alongside the judge's bench, witness stand, and court reporter's desk.

You might object to my reasoning that mind cannot be literally diseased by pointing out the example of physical pain. For instance, the experience of pain from arthritis is an element that belongs to mind, not brain. The pain itself has no location and it is not an object in nature. It is purely an experience and, as an element of mind, no one can experience the pain of another. Yet physicians treat it, right?

Wrong. It is important to understand the experience of arthritis pain is a symptom of a disease, not the disease itself. The disease is joint deterioration and inflammation. If the disease can be successfully treated, the associated experience of pain can be lessened or eliminated. Ideally, the primary focus of medical treatment is the disease and not just the symptomatic pain. The root of the problem, and what makes it a true illness, is the disease.

On the other hand, that which the Industry dubs "mental illness" is about emotional pain and problem behaviors that are not caused by disease processes of the brain, but by meaningful life experiences – Rush's second type of "mind disease." That's why they're still called "*mental* illness" and not simply illness, as they would be if they were caused by faulty brains. It is true that brain chemicals change in signature ways during any experience or behavior including those called "mental illness." But, as explained in detail in Chapter 2, those physiological events are not the same as disease or any other type of dysfunction. They are the ordinary biological happenings that undergird all experiences and behaviors.

Prescribing a psychiatric drug to calm a person's extreme distress or to prevent problem behaviors is not medical treatment of a disease. It merely masks the emotional pain for the person's comfort or thwarts that person's behaviors for society's comfort. The use of psychiatric drugs is limited to this kind of anesthetizing purpose (the psychiatric stimulants are used for the opposite purpose of artificially stimulating brain activity) because there is no psychiatric disease to treat and alleviate as there is with arthritis.

Using the chemical properties of any drug to prevent physical pain, emotional pain, troublesome thoughts, or unwanted behaviors is fundamentally indistinguishable from prescribing a shot of vodka three times a day in order to help a person deal with a life of tedium, or to recommend students use crystal meth on a daily basis in order to stay alert and attentive at school. This is precisely what Valium – "Mother's Little Helper"[3] – did for neglected and subjugated housewives in the 1960s. It was not treating a disease. Rather, it artificially and unnaturally altered their experiences and behaviors, making them more compliant with their subordinate social status of the time. *Experiences and behaviors* cannot be literally diseased or ill. They can be symptoms of a disease, but that is only if a bodily malfunction or defect, such as arthritis, can be demonstrated or reasonably theorized. Other examples would be the lethargy associated with hypothyroidism and the confused thoughts associated with a urinary tract infection. Neither of them is a "mental illness," instead, they are both genuine illnesses.

If we opened up the definitional gates to the extent that any painful human experience or troublesome conduct were considered an illness or symptom of a diseased mind or behavior, not only would it be nonsensical, as mind and behavior cannot be literally diseased, it would also lead to inhumane results. The Industry would become dictatorial and any problematic or unwanted human experience or behavior could then be dragged into its paternalistic clutches in order to be controlled. But wait, isn't this already happening?

The remainder of this chapter explores some basic philosophical issues stemming from my assertion that brain and mind are profoundly different. The discussion might seem esoteric and pedantic to some, but I think it is necessary in order to fully understand how you are being fooled about "mental illness" – why it is not literal illness but instead a matter of moral judgments about the appropriateness of experiences and behaviors.

The Dualism Trap

Suggesting a difference between brain and mind, as I have done, is sometimes criticized as falling into a *dualism* trap. This is the trap we find ourselves in when we propose that brain and mind are fundamentally different (one is material and the other mental) but they can still interact in a causal way. It is called Cartesian dualism, after the 17th century philosopher René Descartes (1596-1650)[4] who was famous for declaring, "I think, therefore I am."

In pondering reality, Descartes noticed the only thing he could know for sure was that he was thinking ("I think…"). He concluded from this fact that he existed ("…therefore I am."). Incidentally, it is ironic that he was dualism's namesake, as his own declaration demonstrates there was only one fundamental reality available to him, not two. That was his thinking, or mind. His conclusion necessarily negates a material reality that can be known.

Despite his recognition that mind was the essential nature of reality to him, Descartes still considered the brain and body to be material things, along with all other material things in nature, that existed separately from mind, a mental thing. He pondered the difficult question of how they could possibly interact, and eventually came up with the proposition that they connected somehow inside a small organ deep in the center of the brain. It was here, in the pineal gland,[5] where he suggested there was a gateway between the brain and the mind, or the material and the mental.

Still, he was left with the very same question he started with. That is, exactly how does this interaction occur between the brain and the mind inside the pineal gland, given the fact that he assumed they were fundamentally different natures? Steeped in the religious teachings and authority of the Church of his time, he just pushed the question into the religious realm, implying that it happened in some supernatural way. He left the question unanswered from a natural or empirical perspective.

The question is: how is it possible for material things in the brain, such as neurons and neurochemicals, to cause nonmaterial things, such as the experiences of despair and traumatic memories? If we follow the chain of causation from brain component to brain component, we will never see this chain directly connect to mind components such as despair or memories. Remember, mind things are not objects located in the brain.

Further, if we assumed there was a causal connection between brain and mind, which is the cause, and which is the effect? Do mental experiences, such as traumatic memories, cause brain chemistry to change? Or, do changes in brain chemistry, such as elevations in neurotransmitters and electrochemical signals, cause the memories to happen? When I decide to think about my childhood memories, am I causing brain changes to occur or are those brain changes causing me to decide to think about my childhood memories? The inability to answer these questions over the centuries from a dualism perspective has been called the *hard problem of consciousness*.[6] In other words, how does a material thing directly connect with and cause a mental thing to happen, similar to how the cue ball on a pool table connects with and causes the eight ball to fall into the corner pocket?

However, by emphasizing the distinction between brain and mind, I am not proposing a dualism as Descartes did. This is because I am proposing instead that we understand brain and mind, not as two fundamentally different kinds of things that interact in nature, but as two different ways we use language to describe our experiences of someone. Such a focus on how we use language to describe experiences, and not objects in nature, is more in line with *monism*, not dualism. More specifically, I am suggesting there is only one kind of stuff in nature, and that is mind. This is ironically the same thing that Descartes concluded when he noted he could only know his thinking.

This perspective is consistent with philosopher, psychologist, and often considered the father of American psychology, William James's (1842-1910) ideas about "radical empiricism" or "pure experience."[7] Regarding this, James said:

> "Thoughts" [mind] and "things" [brain] are *names* for two sorts....My thesis is that if we start with the supposition that there is only one primal stuff or material in the

> world, a stuff of which everything is composed, and if we call that stuff 'pure experience,' ...one of its '*terms*' becomes the subject or bearer of the knowledge, the knower [mind], the other becomes the object known [brain][8] [italics added for emphasis].

This is also consistent with the broad philosophical concept of *idealism*, which is the proposition that all reality is composed exclusively of mind, or experience.[9] Although, I am suggesting a somewhat agnostic version of idealism and monism since I am not denying the existence of something else "out there" separate from our experiences. But if it is there, we can never access it directly, so we can never verify its existence or whether it is material, non-material, or yet some other type of stuff. If it exists, it is forever beyond our grasp. Moreover, when we try to study it, we are studying our individual experiences, not the thing "out there," so any conclusions based on that study apply only to our experiences – our mind.

This philosophical approach asserts the counterintuitive idea that reality is composed of only one fundamental type of thing, and it is experience, or mind. There are no material things that we can know. It is an inescapable observation that we experience the five traditional senses of sight, sound, touch, smell, and taste, of our "outer world." We also experience our thoughts, feelings, desires, and memories of our private "inner world." In actuality, though, our "outer world" is just as inner as our "inner world." Think about it, both worlds are exclusively "inner" experiences or sensations. Whether I am looking at the trees out my window, or I am noticing a sense of sadness, I am having an "inner" experience. All I know is the experience.

From these mind experiences, we make inferences about our world (both "outer" and "inner") and we communicate with each other about these inferences. From this perspective, then, brain and mind do not interact in a causal fashion because they are not two bits of stuff. Neither do they coexist in parallel fashion but without a causal relationship.[10] Instead, they are words we use to communicate with each other about our experiences of a person. Each comes from a different category of description.

See this graphically portrayed on the next page. The large oval represents our reality – our total mind experiences. Anything outside that oval forever remains beyond our knowledge. The two small ovals represent our objectified experiences of mind and our objectified experiences of brain. Additional small ovals could be inserted into the large one to represent other "objects" in nature, alongside the brain. Examples would be "cars," "trees," "dogs," and "stars." Further, the objectified experience of mind could be subdivided into "memories," "thoughts," and "feelings," while the objectified experience of brain could be subdivided into "motor cortex," "brain stem," and "temporal lobe."

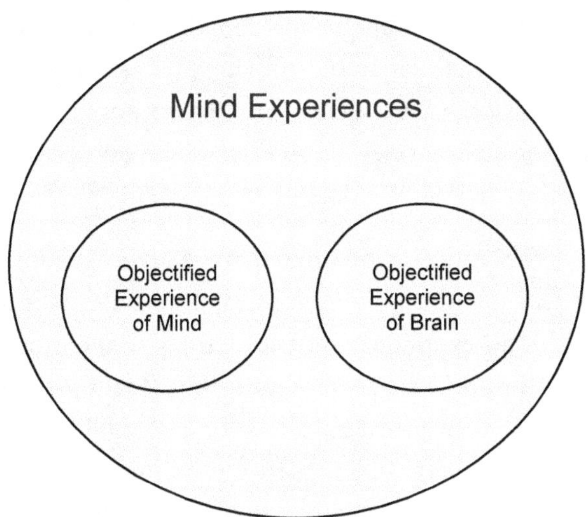

In this sense, we are stuck "inside" our experiential mind-world and that world is the extent of our reality. We cannot get "outside" of it in order to know something independent of the experience of it or even if that something exists at all, and then return inside to see if our experience matches that independently observed reality. We only know the experience. This means it is futile to attempt to understand the fundamental nature of things independent of our experiences of them because we are forever limited to knowing only those experiences. All else is fantasy.

Still, if we want to function effectively in our social context, we must objectify and reify those experiences by describing them in language and thinking about them "as if" they were interacting objects in nature. This provides us with "facts" to understand the world and it allows us to coordinate with each other for mutual and practical benefit. This "as if" approach has worked very well for us in achieving a variety of significant things, such as space travel, computer technology, and medical advances.

When objectifying brain and behavior, it feels natural, as those things seem to be located "outside" of us and publicly observable to all. However, I'll reiterate, they aren't "outside." The experiences themselves are just as private and "inside" as any other mind element. Objectifying mind is far more difficult and confusing than objectifying brain and behavior. This is because there seems to be a unique and separate mind hidden within each of us, it can't be publicly shared, and the process of objectifying it is recursive. In other words, we use mind in the very act of trying to objectify it. This is like trying to bite one's own teeth or see one's own eyes without the benefit of a mirror.

Incidentally, this monism of mind perspective explains why when a tree falls in the forest and no one is around, it doesn't make a sound. This is because sound is an experience, not something that exists outside a person's subjectivity. Sounds aren't like butterflies floating around in the air waiting for someone to hear them. The sound of a falling tree only exists when the compression waves generated by the impact of the tree hitting the forest floor eventually come in contact with our eardrums, which trigger a cascade of actions of the inner ear, auditory nerve, and so on. While these "facts" are happening, we experience sound. But these "facts" are not the same thing as the sound.

So, someone, or a deer, or a squirrel, or some other hearing organism, must be in the area of the falling tree in order for a sound to even exist. As an aside, it is important to note that the "facts" regarding the falling tree and auditory system reactions do not *cause* sound. That would be a dualism account of the event. Instead, we experience sound at the very same time we experience those happenings. The sound and the happenings are different categories of description for the same event, and they are both experiences. The first is in mental terms and the second is in material terms. As with sound, it is the case with all other mental sensations. They are experiences and in order to exist at all they require an experiencing agent.

Further, each person's experience of them is a private happening that can't be directly shared with others.

Along this same line of thinking, sugar doesn't taste sweet until someone tastes it. Sweetness is not a property of the sugar, as is conventionally thought. It is a product of the experiencing agent. The same goes for a hard surface, a vivid color, or a pungent odor. Likewise, a memory doesn't exist until someone remembers it, and when the person stops remembering it, it ceases to exist. The memory isn't stored in the brain and it isn't located there when it is being remembered. There are ongoing neural activation patterns in the brain when we are remembering, but those activations are not the same as the memory. This goes for a thought, an emotion, and a desire. Experiences are the only things that exist to us and they don't exist independently of us. So, for instance, when no one is in the forest, the sight of the tree doesn't exist either.

But does the tree still exist when no one is present? Unfortunately, we cannot answer that question because in order to attempt an answer, we would have to look at the tree, which creates the sight of the tree. We could also close our eyes and feel for the tree to see if it is there. But, just as with looking, touching it to see if it exists creates the tactile sensation of the tree. We would have the same problem if we ventured to taste or smell the tree. Something appears to exist there when we aren't listening, looking, touching, tasting or smelling it, in other words, experiencing it. But we can never confirm if it is so, or what its essential nature is. We can only confirm *our* essential nature in operation. This demonstrates our experiences are as much a reflection of us as they are of anything "out there."[11]

A way to solve the hard problem of consciousness is to understand the problem as an illusion. Brain and mind are not two substances that interact in a mechanistically causal way in nature and so we aren't obligated to explain how one causes the other or to demonstrate which is the cause and which is the effect. Instead, they are different ways we can describe our experiences of a person so that we can communicate with each other about those experiences.

When describing a person in brain terms, we say things like neurons fire, brain circuits activate, and genes get expressed. That is one way to describe the person. When describing that person at the exact same time in mind terms, we would say they are sad, have memories of abuse, and ponder the meaning of life. That is another way to describe the person. One doesn't cause the other. Instead, brain and mind are very much like two different languages we can use in describing someone, similar to how we can use the Spanish and English languages to simultaneously describe someone. When we do so, we are not describing two separate things that can interact in a causal fashion. Instead, we are describing one person in two different ways. Just as Carlos doesn't cause Charles, brain doesn't cause mind, or vice versa.

Another analogy that can help in understanding this monism idea is how we can describe our experiences of other things. For instance, we can describe apples in terms of their taste and color. Each is a different category of description for the apple, not two elements of an apple that interact. Apples can taste sweet and sour, and they can be red and green. But it is clear to us that an apple's taste doesn't cause its color and its color doesn't cause its taste. They aren't connected in a causal fashion even though they exist simultaneously, just like brain and mind. They are merely two different, but simultaneous, ways we can describe our experience of an apple.

We are particularly fooled about brain and mind interacting because we can experience both at the same time. This creates the illusion that certain brain things cause mind things and certain mind things cause brain things. For instance, when we drink alcohol and it enters the bloodstream and eventually into the brain, we simultaneously experience inebriation. This makes it appear to us that the alcohol and our brain's reaction to it cause our inebriation. In other words, it gives the dualism illusion that the changes in the brain cause the changes in the mind. But with a monism perspective, there is no causal relationship between these two things. Instead, they are merely two different ways we can describe the same human happening.

Similarly, it is tempting to think that calming thoughts can cause brain activity to slow down. But each is just a different way to describe the same human happening. They are occurring simultaneously. The first is in mind language. The second is in brain language. Calming thoughts do not cause brain activity to slow and reduced brain activity does not cause calming thoughts. That would be a dualism account of the event.

The illusion that mind causes brain or brain causes mind only happens because we "inhabit" our bodies and we use mind to "observe" both the brain and mind experiences at the same time. That's why we don't ponder about whether an apple's taste causes its color. We don't "inhabit" the thing being described, and we don't use one element of it to describe both itself and the other element, as we do with brain and mind. If an apple's color was its mind, the apple might struggle with the same hard problem of consciousness that we do and forever wonder whether its taste causes its color, or vice versa.

Understanding the brain-mind difference this way dissolves the hard problem of consciousness because it portrays the problem as an illusion caused by a dualism perspective and misunderstanding of how language is used to describe the different categories of things we experience. Wondering how mind activity causes brain activity or vice versa is just as illogical as wondering how Carlos causes Charles or how an apple's taste causes its color. By the way, this would also mean that with real diseases like arthritis, the disease doesn't cause the symptom of pain. Instead, we can experience X-ray images of joint deterioration and inflammation simultaneously while we experience pain. Still, in this case, we're talking about a real illness, not a bogus one.

Of course, in a colloquial sense and for practical benefit, we can say things like "drinking alcohol *causes* inebriation," "arthritis *causes* joint pain," and "calming thoughts *cause* brain activity to slow down." These are the "facts." But we shouldn't misunderstand these everyday routine comments as reflections of literal causal connections in a dualistic sense. They are "as if" comments. This is similar to how it is practical to say, "the sun rises in the East and sets in the West," when from a more accurate perspective, the sun's apparent movement is an illusion created by the earth spinning on its axis. Its rising and setting is accepted as a "fact," even though it is not literally true.

Furthermore, we can combine these two kinds of descriptive language categories for the purpose of emphasizing a point. As an example, we use the terms "mental disease," "mental illness," and "mental health" to describe different qualities of human living. Because they are a mixture of these two descriptive categories, it makes them figurative expressions or metaphors, not literal. It would be acceptable to use these terms if their figurative essence remained clear. But this hasn't happened, and they are popularly understood as literal. This is a serious problem since it is ineffective and harmful to treat metaphorical illnesses as literal ones.

We can also combine other descriptive categories for figurative purposes such as when using the phrase "fiery red" to describe the intensity of an apple's color. But we realize we wouldn't burn our mouths by eating the apple. We likewise combine different descriptive categories when we use phrases such as "diseased economy" in order to emphasize the instability of the financial markets, or "social ills" to highlight systemic problems in our society. But we would never think the economy or society were literally diseased or ill, and we definitely wouldn't rely on a medical doctor to fix them.

Our use of figurative language like this is seen in common Industry phrases such as "pathological personalities," "unhealthy relationships," and "sick behaviors." These expressions are just as metaphorical and figurative as a diseased economy, social ills, or a fiery red apple, so why would we call in a doctor to fix them or use a medical approach to think of them as matters of literal health and illness?

Typically, fiery red apples and diseased economies do not fool people. However, many do get fooled when it comes to pathological personalities, unhealthy relationships, and sick behaviors. This is because the Industry has long ago abandoned the metaphorical origin of these phrases, whether inadvertently or intentionally, and instead treats them as literal when, in fact, they are no more literal than "spring fever" and "heartbreak." They are not true illnesses.

So why do these philosophical issues matter? They matter because it means studying the brain in order to understand human distress and troublesome behaviors is a relic of the dualism perspective. It is a waste of time, just like it would be foolish to study the mind in order to understand the essentials of how brain components work and how they become diseased. In order to understand how the human brain functions and fails to function, we have to examine its macro and microscopic causal connections. While a patient's report of mind experiences can be useful in pinpointing certain brain disease processes (e.g., when a person feels pain in the front of the head instead of the back of the neck), the essential target of medicine is the brain, not the mind. This is in opposition to what the Industry currently focuses on – the mind within the brain.

It is also a waste of time to approach human struggles and emotional suffering as if they were literal illnesses of the mind, as the mind is not something that can be literally diseased and, thus, ill. It is "pure experience." This is why there are no laboratory tests for "mental illness" – there is no defect to find. Instead, in order to fully understand those problems labeled with the *DSM* categories, we must get a sense of the person's meaningful experiences in life, not what her genes or neurons are doing. And it would be folly to go about searching for defects in her mind, as mind is not something that has a chemical or mechanical mode of operation. To fully understand her struggles and distress, we must undertake the nearly impossible challenge of grasping what the world is like through her mind, not ours.

Accuracy Is Irrelevant

The monism of mind perspective presents us with a significant challenge. This is the recognition that reality is our experience "in here" and we can never know if anything is actually "out there" or what it truly is. Still, each of us must make inferences about our experiential world and we decide what to do on the basis of those inferences. As mentioned earlier, for practical benefit we function in society "as if" there are causal connections between brain and mind and our experiences accurately reflect the "facts." Sometimes the decisions we make with these facts work for us and sometimes they don't. Sometimes others agree with us and sometimes they differ passionately about what is real and true. But is it necessary for us to accurately know a universal reality independent of our experiences? I think not.

Some examples of the inferences we might make about the world are the best political candidate, the proper wine to pair with lobster linguine, and what constitutes the most advantageous chess move. The answers to questions like these do not reflect a universal reality. It is easy for most people to agree with this, as these things are commonly considered subjective opinions and expected to differ among people without posing much of a threat to each person's sense of reality.

But the monism perspective dictates the same thing also applies to what are typically thought to be objective facts and this does present a significant challenge to our sense of being tethered to reality. Some of these facts would include whether there are ghosts in my house, whether my neighbor is plotting to harm me, and whether I am an alien from another planet living here on Earth. Although it might sound alarming, there is no way to determine a universal reality about these things either. The key point is that no one can make a claim of accuracy about the truth (with a capital "T") because there is no way to access the world except through the limitations of one's own experiential lenses. We cannot see reality "as it is." We can only see it "as we see it," and all we "see" are private experiences that can never be verified or directly shared with another. This is why conflicts between us about important things can be so heated and frustrating.

When hearing about someone who claims to have ghosts in his house, a malicious neighbor, or an alien identity, it might be easy to discount her as being detached from reality. This is only because not many people hold these beliefs. Remember the definition of abnormality in Chapter 4? The less frequent something happens the more abnormal it is and, thus, at risk of being designated "mentally ill." But it is not possible to verify that these assertions depart from an independent and universal reality because one cannot gain access to such a reality. We must rely on personal and private realities. What we collectively consider real is based on a consensus among us about our experiences, not verification of the absolute truth.

In the everyday process of attempting to build this consensus, navigate through life, and negotiate with each other about important things (what is "true" or "real") we use two standards. The choice in using one over the other in any particular situation is based on our assumption about which one can lead to the most useful kind of knowledge. What makes one better than the other is how it has worked for us in the past and whether we have confidence it will work in the future. One of these standards can be described as *critical* and the other *dogmatic*. It must be remembered that neither of these standards can give us complete certainty about anything – we can't accurately predict the future; we can only speculate about it. Therefore, after the application of either of these two standards in a particular situation, there will always be an element of uncertainty and, given that uncertainty, we must take a "leap of faith" in deciding how to act, regardless of which standard we choose. Some situations require a larger leap of faith than others.

The critical standard consists of empiricism (observation), logic, and the scientific method. With this standard, we skeptically demand evidence and the reasoning used in making any assertion. So, if I am going to use this standard to claim that ghosts really do reside in my house, I am obligated to share with you my critical reasoning for claiming it. Only then can you decide if that evidence convinces you to agree with me, so we have consensus on the matter. This is the standard I am using as I write this book in my attempt to convince you the Industry is harmful. Therefore, nothing I say is a reflection of a universal truth (capital "T"), as it is not possible for me to access such a truth. Neither is it possible for you to access it. Instead, my ideas are based on my personal experience-limited truth and reality (the "facts"), and they are presented to you for consideration.

The other standard commonly used in arriving at a personal reality is one based on dogma. This is the trust placed in what an authority says, such as a charismatic leader, religious scripture, belief system, or other set of unquestioned doctrine, including the doctrine proposed by a scientific authority. This standard relies on faith in a predetermined worldview, not on skepticism about that worldview. With this dogmatic standard, evidence and logic are not to be trusted; the dogma is. In using this standard, I can claim that ghosts are in my house, even though I don't have any evidence. This is because I adopt a particular belief system's dogma that claims people have a spirit that survives death, it can have consciousness and intention, it sometimes remains behind for a purpose, and it can be observed by the living. I can accept this belief exclusively on trust in the dogma and despite any evidence to the contrary.

This is the same standard the Industry uses to base its beliefs. Their foundational claim that distressing experiences and behaviors are matters of illness and disease is not based on critical thought. It is based on dogma. From that point forward, however, the Industry does sometimes use the critical standard, but this is only to create a smokescreen that hides the dogmatic foundation of its doctrine. It doesn't justify it; it just conceals it. This is part of the medical disguise I explored in Part I. Other dogmatic systems also employ this kind of mixing of dogma with critical thought as a disguise. Creation science is one example. It starts out with dogma about life, and then cherry picks scientific findings to support that dogma, which creates the illusion of science. But it doesn't fully use the critical standard since it does not allow unlimited questioning and testing of the basic doctrine or its corollary ideas, just as the Industry does not welcome unlimited questioning and demands for evidence of its basic doctrine and associated ideas.

Once the dogma is accepted that "depression" is an illness "just like diabetes," that a person's understandable complaints about life are "symptoms," and that stopping those complaints is the same as "effective treatment," a very well designed and controlled study can be conducted to give the illusion of sound scientific results. But there is no scientific merit to the foundational claim that "depression" is a real illness or that a person's meaningful complaints about life are "symptoms" of that illness that, when reduced, equate to "effective treatment."

Our personal realities, based either on the critical or dogmatic standard, are our working theories about life, not the final word about a topic. They are always tentative and typically adjusted as we learn novel things or become exposed to different perspectives. Interestingly, this adjustment process happens regardless of the standard being used. With the critical standard, adjustment is its key feature. In other words, evidence and dogged reasoning are continually compared to the working theory. When the theory is inconsistent with the results, it is adjusted to fit the observed evidence and critical reasoning.

However, adjustment is officially discouraged when it comes to using dogma as the standard for gaining knowledge. Nonetheless, people still make adjustments to their chosen dogma because they don't interpret or adopt every tenet of the official dogma exactly the same as authority instructs or as their peers do. This is why there are so many different types and subtypes of religions and other belief systems. When enough people significantly deviate from a particular group's dogma, they band together to form the membership of a newer group. Still, even within the most fine-tuned dogmatic group, the members don't all agree on the full details of the dogma. This means each person is ultimately his or her own dogma sub-group and that person's intuition becomes the dogma. In fact, intuition is the basis of all dogma, religious or secular. Dogmatic systems start with someone's beliefs – intuition – about something, then followers join in the belief system. More and more details about the dogma get incorporated until it reaches the status of orthodoxy.

To reiterate, regardless of which of these two standards one uses, neither accesses a universal truth or reality independent of the experience of it. But I argue that knowing such a Truth or Reality is not only impossible to attain, it is also unnecessary. The important issue is whether we have consensus about our versions of truth and reality, and whether they are *practically useful* for the people involved as they interact and coexist in society. This is a significant challenge for us in terms of getting along with each other, given the fact that, while we can agree about the reality of many things, we can also differ greatly on subjective opinions as well as on the so-called objective facts. Yet, the key is to coexist, given our disagreements about these things when there is no consensus. In the final analysis, it is not important to authoritatively determine which of us is accurate or correct in our experiences.

If I think my house is haunted, the important thing isn't whether ghosts really reside there. Instead, the important thing is what I do about it and how that works for me and others. If I exhaust myself in constant surveillance of my house in order to find the ghosts, this could interfere with my other obligations such as sleep, eating, and going to work. It isn't practical and it can eventually harm me. On the other hand, if I decide to live in harmony with the ghosts that I believe are there, what is the problem?

If I think my neighbor plans to harm me, I might accuse him and hound him with my suspicions. That would likely ruin any relationship between us. Further, my attacks on him are likely to result in counterattacks against me. This increasing exchange of accusations and retaliations will create chronic tension between us and highlight any injustices we perceive brought on by the other. It is also likely to convince me I'm correct in my original suspicions. But if I continue in my belief that my neighbor intends to harm me, but I take no action, what is the problem?

If I start killing people at the direction of my alien superiors, it would obviously be a problem for those who I threaten, as well as for me. But if I do nothing to harm people, and still maintain the belief I'm an alien living peacefully among you, what is the problem?

Accurate correspondence to a universal truth or reality doesn't matter in these situations, especially since no one can possibly access it. What matters is how we respond to our personal versions and how they work out for us, and others, in mutual living, regardless of whether we use the critical or dogmatic standard to arrive at that personal truth or reality.

Let's consider a less bizarre situation. If you believe there is a God, but your neighbor doesn't, which of you is correct? Is it a matter of consensus? If so, what level of consensus among people is needed in order to verify something is real – 50%, 90%, 100%? Why isn't a belief in God considered a delusion? Is it a "fact" in our "as if" world that God doesn't exist?

Now, just replace a belief in God with my belief that I'm an alien. Is this a "fact"? Am I really an alien or am I delusional? If one of our friends also believes I'm an alien, does that mean you are delusional? What if two more friends agree with you? How could we ever verify the truth about things like this?

All experiences and beliefs can work, depending upon the willingness of people to cooperate and coexist with others who believe in different things and who have different perspectives. This applies to all matters of diversity among human beings. There are times when we do this, and there are times when we choose not to, given the significance of the differences. I have decided that I will not accept the orthodox Industry's belief system and so I work to expose its weaknesses and dangers. Other times of refusal to cooperate and coexist can span the range from avoidance and interpersonal detachment, to harbored animosity between groups of people, to international wars.

Other important questions we commonly have about the Truth are: Is life really worth it? Are people really trustworthy? Do I really have the ability to change things? Am I really likable? Do I really deserve a good life? These are the kinds of questions we typically encounter when working with people in psychotherapy. But universally accurate answers to these questions don't matter. This is because, first, there is no way to access those answers and, second, the important issue is not accuracy. The important issue is whether one's answers are helpful or harmful – whether they work in social living. Each person is a separate reality and no reality is superior to others in terms of corresponding to "the way it really is."

The problems that get called "mental illness" are fundamentally about mind, not brain, and that is why they cannot be considered real illnesses or medical matters. Specifically, they are about the meaningful problems of personal realities and interpersonal relationships, not problems of malfunctioning brains or bodies. Neither can they be about malfunctioning minds since mind can't malfunction. It is not a mechanistically structured thing with interconnecting parts that function like a clock and that give us accurate access to Truth or Reality. It is a flowing and purely individualized and experiential domain that has no naturally proper or accurate manner of functioning like the body does. There are only competing moral standards regarding what kind of mind is appropriate.

Since the Industry is founded upon this profoundly impactful error of language – "diseases of the mind" and "mental illnesses" – how can we better understand that very real problem of troublesome behaviors and emotional turmoil? In the next few chapters, I will describe such an alternative that retains the elements of scientific honesty, human dignity, and self-determination.

Chapter 13

Emotions and Meaning

Attempting to Escape Emotions

It is undeniable that people suffer from emotional distress and problematic behaviors. But other than in cases of demonstrable or reasonably theorized bodily defects, those problems are not illnesses or diseases. Instead, they are natural and expected responses to the obstacles we encounter in our life's journey. In order to understand this better, it is crucial to emphasize the distinction between (1) those obstacles (e.g., interpersonal conflict, economic problems, trauma, discrimination, etc.), (2) the emotions we experience as a result of those obstacles (e.g., sadness, fear, shame, etc.), and (3) how we respond to that emotional distress (e.g., hypervigilance, passivity, drug use, etc.).

We live in a social context that presents us with obstacles. We have no choice but to play the cards we are dealt at birth. Just as in a poker game, how we play them depends on what resources are available to us at the beginning of the game, how we are treated by the other players and whether they cheat, and the chance events that might happen along the way. These things will affect how we can parlay our resources into "winnings." Of course, our success also depends on how social institutions account for the inherent inequities regarding each person's ongoing access to essential services, such as healthcare, education, protection, and political patronage.

When presented with these contextual factors, we experience a variety of emotions, ranging from agony to ecstasy. These emotions are natural human reactions to the meaningful nature of the context. Even though they can be very painful at times, they are not signs of illness unless something in the brain is defective. Nevertheless, the Industry frequently labels people "mentally ill" merely because they experience these painful emotions and it demands they make changes in order to become "healthy." While it is quite reasonable to voluntarily seek out professional help in coping with these troublesome feelings, it is unjustified for the Industry to declare emotional distress an illness and to coerce people into "treatment" in order to reduce that angst.

We naturally feel emotions when we notice contextual problems, and those feelings form the rationale for our subsequent choices. However, I suggest they aren't the principle problems in our lives. In fact, they are essential elements of a meaningful life and, therefore, it would be important to tolerate and listen to them as much as possible. *The principal problem* lies in our attempts to avoid or make those emotions go away.

So, many of us react to emotional sensations by trying to escape them. Even though this is an understandable reaction – we naturally recoil from pain of any kind – trying to escape them indefinitely can be very problematic. This is because, given its ubiquitous nature, we can only get brief moments of relief from emotional pain. It will come back. If we continuously try to escape these emotions, it will trigger a spiraling effect of more problems that worsen the pain, which lead to more urges to escape even further from the increasing pain, which trigger more problems, and so on. This kind of escape strategy will not be successful.

We seem to be hardwired to respond strongly to both the immediate consequences of our actions and the immediate environmental conditions. But we are not affected as much by longer-term considerations, even when we are clearly aware of them. In fact, this seems to be how all organisms function, not just human beings. This general principle of behavioral learning has been around for quite some time in the concepts of *operant and classical conditioning*. Simply put, we tend to repeat actions that are immediately followed by some type of good feeling or that we associate with a good feeling. This general principle is what perpetuates our attempts to escape emotions.

It is also why gambling is a successful multibillion-dollar industry, despite the fact that most people realize they will lose money in the long run when they gamble. They gamble because there is an immediately good feeling of excitement about the possibility of winning big, even if the chance is minuscule. The chance of winning either the Mega Millions or Powerball lottery is roughly 1 in 300 million[1] and around 97 million people played the lottery in the United States in 2017.[2] That was about a third of the population then. Yet, it means more than three times that many would need to play in order to have the chance of just one winner.

Our tendency to focus on the immediate consequences of our behaviors and not the long-term ones is also why 40 million people a year continue to smoke cigarettes even though half a million will die each year from smoking related illnesses.[3] The immediately positive sensation of lighting up is so great that it overshadows the recognition of the highly probable, but delayed, harmful effects of smoking.

As another common example, when people drink alcohol, they experience a sense of soothing inebriation, at least initially. That immediately good feeling reinforces the behavior of drinking alcohol. In this sense, alcohol helps us to escape what would otherwise be boredom, fear, meaninglessness, or any other kind of undesirable feeling state, in other words, some type of emotional pain. So, drinking alcohol is likely to continue despite knowing that longer-term social and physical harm can result from drinking too much.

Even when those delayed problems do occur, such as health issues, marital conflicts, and legal problems, the person's drinking behavior is frequently unaffected. This is because those negative effects occur far too long after the drinking behavior itself, and so drinking continues based on the immediately positive sensations. Those sensations can include the inebriation itself, the avoidance of alcohol withdrawal symptoms, or just the generally positive sense of communing with others at the local tavern.

However, when a person takes the drug Antabuse, which reacts to the ingestion of alcohol to cause nausea and a host of other very negative symptoms, the consequences of drinking become immediately negative, not positive. Just as soothing consequences increase the likelihood of a behavior, immediately punishing consequences decrease the likelihood of that behavior. Antabuse causes the "morning after" feelings, but immediately upon drinking. And so, Antabuse is very effective in most cases to stop the person from drinking alcohol. However, the person has to agree to take the drug each day, and what happens in real life is he quickly stops taking it because of its punishing effects. Then, he continues to drink.

Viewing problematic behaviors and emotions this way turns the sterile and clinical ideas of internal defects or "diseases of the mind" into meaningful and individualized reactions to quite common challenges of human living. Dare I say it is normal? Well, at least it is natural, rational, and expectable. But before continuing on with a detailed examination of these emotional challenges and attempts to escape them, let's first address the emotional pain that prompts one to engage in strategies of escape in the first place.

Affects and Emotions

One theory I find very helpful in understanding human emotions is that outlined by psychologist Silvan Tomkins, Ph.D.[4] Tomkins described several innate human emotional settings that are present at birth as biological responses to increasing or decreasing neural stimulation of any kind. Tomkins's model incorporates the two descriptive language categories of brain and mind I detailed in the previous chapter. Specifically, it addresses both *affects* and *emotions.* Affects are the different biological activations in response to environmental stimulation. Emotions are the person's experiences while those biological activations are underway. Affects are from the descriptive category of brain. Emotions are from the descriptive category of mind. The two are describing the same human condition or happening from different perspectives. They do not have a causal relationship.

Each affect corresponds to a distinct set of meaningful environmental circumstances. According to Tomkins, affects and emotions serve the purpose of amplifying those circumstances so we can orient ourselves toward them in order to further assess their meaning. Affects also prepare us for certain actions concerning the particular environmental triggers. This feature of our affects and emotions has been described elsewhere as "body postures and hormonal settings that form the necessary support system for our actions."[5] This means affects and emotions are not problems, per se. On the contrary, they are the sources of our life's meaning.

Tomkins differentiated the affects as punishing, rewarding, or neutral. The cascading emotional sensations during each affect is accompanied by nonverbal reactions, especially signature facial expressions, which are the primary nonverbal means of interpersonal communication and sharing, particularly between the infant and caretaker. Being face-to-face and witnessing another person's nonverbal affective reactions stimulates a similar affective reaction in ourselves, thus, it gives us a "mirror" emotional reaction and an optimal, but not exact, understanding of the other person's experiences.[6] This is the basis of empathy.

For instance, when in anguish, the mouth is turned down, tears start to flow, the face becomes red, and the brow is furrowed. When a person is afraid, the eyes and mouth open wide, the face becomes pale, and the eyebrows are raised. With shame, the eyes look down and away, the head falls, and the hands come up to cover the face. With the positive feeling affects, like excitement, there is an intensity of stare and the eyebrows fall. With joy, physical relaxation and the smile are the main expressions.

Below is a synopsis of this model's more important elements. There are nine main affects. All but two of them are on a continuum reflecting the intensity of the neural activation as well as the person's sensations.

Punishing	**Neutral**	**Rewarding**
Distress — Anguish Fear — Terror Shame — Humiliation Anger — Rage Dismell Disgust	Surprise — Startle	Interest — Excitement Enjoyment — Joy

For example, there is the punishing affect called *distress-anguish*. It is an expression of emotional pain, signifying something is amiss in one's environment and comfort is desired. Distress-anguish is triggered by persistent and intense stimulation of any kind. Some examples of the emotions we experience during this affective reaction are sadness, boredom, and despair. This might happen when we are lonely and starved for human contact or when we suffer the death of a loved one.

There is also the punishing affect of *fear-terror*, or what we would commonly consider the emotional experiences of fright, trepidation, and dread. Fear-terror is important in emergency life and death situations. It occurs when environmental stimulation indicates something is threatening and it enhances that threat to orient the person so full attention can be focused on survival. Imagine how this works when you are sleeping soundly in your bed at night, but then you awaken to a creaking noise easing up the staircase. The noise is the stimulation triggering the fear-terror affect. It helps you survive.

Another punishing affect is *shame-humiliation*. In common emotional terms this would be embarrassment, guilt, and remorse. It reflects an interruption of any rewarding affect (see the next page for the rewarding affects). In other words, it occurs when we are in the midst of joy or excitement, but then that positive affect is abruptly terminated by something. An example would be if you thought you were alone and started singing gleefully, without concern for an audience, only to abruptly realize someone was watching and listening the whole time. The purpose of shame-humiliation according to Tomkins is to accentuate that which stopped the positive affect in order to avoid the interruption in the future.

Next, there is the affect called *anger-rage*. But as will be explained in far more detail later, I depart from Tomkins's views on anger as I think this particular affect can be seen as unique among all the other affects and in its own special category. It is triggered by exceedingly high-density and persistent stimulation of any other negative affect. This is why anger surfaces only when a person hurts too much, far too much. When we are overloaded with misery, embarrassment, or fright, we react with anger. Anger is one way we escape from those kinds of emotional pain, although only temporarily. It also gives us a sense of power to confront the source of the problem. The anger-rage affect is the only "bad" affect that feels good, and in that sense, it can be rewarding, as in a protective feeling, even though it is formally considered inherently punishing by Tomkins's theory.

There are two other punishing affects not on a continuum of intensity. From an evolutionary standpoint, they are related to the hunger drive. They are called *dismell* and *disgust*. Although these affects were originally related to the feeding process, they have developed also as reactions to interpersonal contact. While dismell refers to an impulse to pull away from a noxious item of food, it is also our reaction to someone for whom we have disdain and desperately try to avoid. Disgust is the expelling reaction after having eaten something noxious. But it is also our response to "rotten" people, like those whom we despise but nonetheless encounter and unexpectedly experience their foulness. Dismell and disgust can also arise when confronted with circumstances that "stink," such as doing our taxes or shopping on Black Friday.

There is one neutral affect dimension: *surprise-startle*. It is triggered by a sudden and brief stimulus and it functions to stop us in our tracks. Tomkins considered it a "reset button" for our affects. It takes whatever affective posture we happen to be in and resets us to a neutral state so we can reactivate whatever affect is appropriate for that novel and sudden trigger. An example is when I am intently and quietly working on this book and my Maltipoo suddenly and sharply barks at something she hears outside. Regardless of what I was doing, my reaction is reflexive, and it would reset my attentional awareness so I can respond to the abrupt demand.

On the rewarding side of affects, there are two: *interest-excitement* and *enjoyment-joy*. The first, interest-excitement, is triggered by a slow increase in neural firing, focusing you on something novel and of possible benefit. This is like when you are quietly reading on a Sunday afternoon and hear a faint and pleasant birdsong coming from outside the house. Interest-excitement orients you to put down the book and seek out the bird.

This brings us to the second rewarding affect, enjoyment-joy, which is triggered by the opposite: a reduction in stimulation, such as after you find the colorful bird and settle down to watch and listen. Enjoyment-joy also happens when we alleviate a situation of distress-anguish. Examples are when we drink water when thirsty, eat food when hungry, or find warmth when cold. When enjoyment-joy is experienced in others' presence, it is the foundation of social bonding.

You may have noticed interest-excitement and enjoyment-joy can be sequential. Whenever we experience the reducing stimulation of enjoyment-joy we were first experiencing the increasing stimulation of interest-excitement, and vice versa, leading us to a repeated loop of increasing and decreasing stimulation of a rewarding nature. This is because even though they are rewarding, interest-excitement and enjoyment-joy can lead to the punishing affect of distress-anguish if they persist too long. We switch to the other when one of them becomes too intense or enduring. Just like the punishing feelings of thirst, hunger, and cold, too much stimulation of a rewarding nature (interest-excitement) leads to agitation and too little (enjoyment-joy) leads to monotony. Both agitation and monotony are distressing. I think this is the basis of our apparent demand for contrast in life. For instance, in the dead of winter we yearn for summer days, and at the height of summer's sweltering heat we long for cooler weather.

Tomkins's theory makes it clear the problems labeled "anxiety" and "depression" (as well as most other diagnostic categories in the *DSM*) are not emotions, even though we commonly converse about them that way. For instance, we frequently hear people say they feel "anxious" or "depressed." To be more precise, though, we do not feel "depressed" or "anxious." Those are diagnostic category terms. Instead, we feel despair, fear, and shame. As will be pointed out in more detail in the next chapter, it would be more accurate to say we "do depression" and "do anxiety," as they are our reactions in an attempt to escape the pain of those emotions. Actually, it would be far better to just discard those diagnostic terms since they are neither reliable nor valid descriptions of the problems, they conflate emotions with escape attempts, and they have no useful purpose.

Whereas Tomkins's affects are presented as distinct from each other, in reality we experience them as blends. For instance, we can be afraid of future distress. Likewise, we can feel shame for openly exhibiting sadness. Emotional sensations such as jealousy can be composed of sadness and shame. Love can be seen as a combination of excitement and joy. So, it must be remembered that even though each emotion can be informative, that information can be quite complex, subtle, and blended.

Above all, affective and emotional responses are not random or meaningless. When we feel them, even though painful, they are reflecting something important going on in our lives. That's why it is crucial we pay attention and not attempt to escape them excessively. Now, with this understanding of affects and emotions, the following section explains the unavoidable givens of life that trigger them.

The Sources of Emotional Pain and Meaning

The previous ideas about emotional pain dovetail with the thinking of psychiatrist Irvin Yalom, M.D., who described four unavoidable givens of life. Since they are unavoidable, they affect *all people*, not just the mythical average person as critiqued in Chapter 11. In other words, this is truly a general law of human behavior. Yalom refers to these givens as *existential ultimate concerns.*[7] They form the foundation of the emotional discomfort from which we try to escape. But they also form the foundation of meaning in our lives.

The ultimate concerns are *existential* in the sense that they are the givens of existence and we can neither change nor eliminate them. For this reason, neither can we permanently escape them, despite our attempts, and despite the intense distress they can present to us. The only permanent escape is death, and that is debatable, depending on your religious views. All other attempts to permanently escape them are futile and trying to do so can significantly worsen the emotional pain. The interesting thing is when we give up the struggle against these existential ultimate concerns, the emotional pain seems to subside some because at least the futility of trying to escape them goes away.

I think this is because the person who is struggling and the thing being struggled with are the same. In line with the monism perspective I explained in the last chapter, our emotions aren't separate entities floating around in our heads. Instead, they are our experiences of ourselves in reaction to meaningful things, and thus, trying to escape them is the same as trying to escape ourselves, which we can't literally do. Also, any persistent attempt to escape from those experiences only serves to emphasize them.

This occurs when we maintain constant and intense attention to anything we deem problematic. Doing so emphasizes its existence. On the other hand, to the extent we are willing to allow emotional pain to be, it fades into the background and becomes the "noise," not the "signal." It is similar to my tinnitus. When I pay attention to it, it gets worse (like what happened just now when I typed those words). But if I allow it to be, notice it, but don't try to escape it, it eventually blends into the background. I'll repeat, emotional pain is not *the principal problem*. Instead, emotional pain is a natural and inevitable human experience and it is laden with meaning. Therefore, it is essential and if we allow it to be and notice it, but not try to escape it, it can help us ultimately find satisfaction in life. *The principal problem* lies in the futility of our attempts to escape the pain.

Emotions are indispensable because they are the only sources of meaning. The core meaning in our world, our values, and what sets the stage for our actions, comes from our emotional bedrock – what seems right to us in the gut. This even applies to the two standards we use in determining our personal realities as mentioned in the last chapter. Choosing one over the other is an emotional decision (an assumption) as much as an intellectual or rational one. We can consider the pros and cons of each standard. But when it comes to finally choosing one, we must ultimately make that leap of faith about which is the best way to know and predict our worlds at that moment. Neither gives us complete certainty about the outcome, only probabilities. The leap of faith choice is what feels right, given the information we know. It is not a decision based on some type of algorithm that has a finite series of instructions leading to the best outcome.

Therefore, trying to escape those emotional sensations is not only problematic because we are trying to escape ourselves. It is also a problem since in trying to escape them, we are ignoring the sources of meaning in our lives. Viewing emotions as problems is part of the problem. They tell us what is important for survival, what is getting in the way, and how we can enhance our lives. We blind ourselves by trying to escape them. Parenthetically, remember that psychiatric drugs are also escape attempts. That is one reason they are dangerous – they prevent us from fully experiencing the emotional significance of life.

With this emotional significance as a backdrop, let's consider Yalom's four existential ultimate concerns. They are called: (1) death; (2) freedom; (3) isolation, and (4) meaninglessness. You'll notice that as you read along, some of the ultimate concerns blend into the others. There is overlap among them just like there is with anything we try to distinguish from other things. This is similar to how we saw that emotions are not distinct sensations and *DSM* labels refer to greatly overlapping and wide-ranging problems.

The first ultimate concern is *death*. The recognition of our eventual and certain death can be terrifying. But this death concern can also include other kinds of deaths or endings: death of loved ones, death of opportunities, death of relationships (goodbyes), death of the day (nightfall), and the idea that even the most wonderful moments are transitory and must end in order to retain their value – remember how interest and enjoyment become distressing if they last too long? The proverbial example of this last kind of death concern is "you can't have your cake and eat it too." In other words, in order to enjoy the cake, you must eat it, and the act of eating it makes it end. If you are more interested in keeping the cake available indefinitely, you don't eat it and, therefore, you can't enjoy it. Moreover, if you had an unlimited amount of cake and ate it constantly, it would quickly lose its value. To repeat, in order to have value, things must end.

The recognition that we must face these forms of death presents us with a terrible challenge. It challenges our willingness to move forward in life despite the reality of death. A common thought for some in the face of this death concern is, "Why struggle to live or bother to enjoy anything if it is all going to end anyway?" This is a great and important question. It forces us into finding a reason to continue on…or not.

Some people invoke the idea of a God or gods that provide the answer. There will be an afterlife, and how one lives life now determines whether she will be rewarded with the eventual bliss of that other world. Others see purpose in the act of living itself. To them the realization that death occurs doesn't negate the motivation to live in the moment. Quite the contrary, it can heighten every moment as a wondrous and precious opportunity, providing a reason to live quite well and enjoyably, despite knowing it will all eventually end. This is the recognition that there is no other place or time to live except here and now.

Even the simple experience of drinking cool water when very thirsty accentuates how marvelous the apparently mundane moments of life can be, despite the fact that the feeling fades quickly after the glass is empty. The same goes for all the things we do for entertainment and recreation. Their value lies in the fact that they end. If they didn't, they would become wearisome. So, for some, life's purpose can simply be to live and enjoy each moment fully, while it is possible, taking advantage of this exquisite gift. But it also includes allowing death to occur and giving up any of the futile attempts to hold on to life, as well as trying to escape the natural emotional pain accompanying death. Whatever the solution, each of us is stuck with having to face this death concern.

Next, there is the ultimate concern of *freedom*. This means we are stuck with choice. Try as we might, we cannot escape the fact that we must choose. In describing this ultimate concern, Yalom paradoxically says we are "doomed to freedom."[8] We choose in every moment of our lives and we will suffer or benefit from the consequences of those choices. Further, life does not provide us with a given structure or design that informs us about the "right" choices. Don't confuse the existential ultimate concern of freedom with the concept of *free will* or the *political idea of freedom*. Those are more complicated philosophical issues and well beyond the scope of this book. For our purposes here, it is obvious we can't avoid making choices in life and those choices affect us as well as other people.

Recognizing the fact that we must choose is frightening since it places the burden of our world squarely on our own shoulders and no one else can take that burden from us. Even when we allow others to make decisions for us, or when we ask for their advice and suggestions about something, we are still choosing. We choose to ask them and then whether or not to follow their lead. The same thing goes for moral codes of conduct and religious beliefs. We follow them because that is what we choose to do based on the benefits we anticipate they will bring.

In these situations (following someone's advice, a moral code, or religious beliefs) there is a false sense the choice isn't ours. But that is an illusion as we cannot escape the reality that we must choose the action, and we retain the existential responsibility of the choice and its consequences. It is important to understand my use of the term "responsibility" in this context has nothing to do with the ideas of fault or blame. It is merely pointing out an existential given that we must choose action and reap the consequences of our choices. It is not to disparage people for what they choose.

We frequently react with indecisiveness in the face of choice because we have no certainty about what choice is best or how it will work out. In those situations, it is frightening to choose even though we are overlooking the fact that our stagnation of indecision is still a choice. In the face of indecisiveness, it helps to remember that thinking in terms of good and bad choices is fictional. We can't compare one choice against another in order to see which one works out the best and then choose the "best" one. This is because once a choice is made, it kills off all other potential choices at that moment in time. All we can do is entertain possibilities, their potential risks and benefits, and then take that leap of faith in choosing one of them.

It is only with the benefit of hindsight that we say things like, "I knew that was a bad idea" or "Of course that was the best thing to do." Our choices reflect our best guess estimates about how something will turn out. They do not reflect certainty about the outcome. It is impossible to obtain such certainty, thus, the difficulty in choosing. The point of the freedom ultimate concern is that, absent real physiological defects such as paralysis or the effects of intoxicating chemicals, nothing stands in the way of our choices except for ourselves. The fears, desires, and urges "in" us might make things difficult, but they aren't things that battle against us. They are us.

Related to freedom, there is the third ultimate concern of *isolation*. We are all stuck "inside" ourselves and can never get "outside" to see how the world really is, and then go back "inside" to compare the two in order to assess the accuracy of our version of reality. This idea was explored in great detail in Chapter 12. It is like we are each a submariner living within our own submarine, alone, but we don't realize we are in a submarine. We cannot leave the submarine and we cannot see outside it – the periscope is broken, and it has no windshield like the fictional Seaview in the 1960s series *Voyage to the Bottom of the Sea.* No one can join us in the submarine. All we have are the gauges on the instrument panel and we infer what is "out there" from the readings on those gauges "in here."[9]

In fact, we think those readings are the outside reality because, remember, we don't realize we're in a submarine. When I see the red and green plant in my office, I am looking at my instrument panel. I am not looking at an object that exists outside of me. Similarly, when I am greeted at the end of the day by my excited and adoring dogs, and I feel their comfort, I am noticing my instrument panel. Even though some of you who also have pets might understand the incredible joy this brings, you cannot directly share my joy because you cannot get into my submarine with me.

We cannot directly compare our instrument readings with those of our friends, family, and acquaintances. My experience of blue, for instance, may not be the same as your experience of blue, even though you and I agree the sky is blue. If I could get inside your submarine, I might see what you are pointing at when you say blue, I see as another color. We don't necessarily have the same experiences. It only seems like we do because we have linguistic consensus about those experiences.

The impossibility of truly sharing the reality of the color blue is just a small predicament created by the ultimate concern of isolation. Imagine the serious differences we may have when trying to share more significant things like justice, love, loyalty, and beauty. It is incredibly frustrating at times when trying to precisely explain our isolated sense of these realities to another person. Despite the most intense of efforts, we still frequently get the sense that others don't understand us, leaving us with a terrible loneliness and disconnection.

This also presents us with dilemmas about self-esteem. What is wrong with me if I think okra tastes terrible when another person can relish the flavor? What if I feel delightful when I hug my friend, but he feels intensely awkward in my embrace? How about if I react with horror at a politician's comments, while others gleefully encourage his cruel words?

Even though we seek out contact with others and yearn for that connection, we can't truly know them. We are locked inside our own submarine prison and cannot directly see what life is like for them, and they can't see what life is like for us. Notice how this might negatively affect bonding with others. We might react with disapproval when they act in ways we don't understand. As a result, we might fear them or consider them "mentally ill." If we're not careful, this can lead to great interpersonal and societal conflict, as will be explained in the next chapter.

This leads us to the last ultimate concern called *meaninglessness*. It is the idea that life doesn't give us a ready-made purpose. All aspirations, rules, and claimed purpose in life are individual human creations. As such, all religious beliefs and atheistic guidelines are frequently tailored to meet individual desires. This is why there are as many forms of these guidelines as there are individuals to interpret them, as no one interprets all of them exactly the same as another.

In our search for meaning, we create that meaning and it can change over time. This presents us with no authoritative foundation upon which to anchor ourselves (other than "because I said so"), resulting in a sense of insecurity about the meaning and purpose of life. Such a groundless feeling can be terrifying. To think each of us is the author of our life's meaning and we narrate that meaning as we go along is a lonely and awful burden we cannot escape. What if we are wrong?

These four existential concerns are the wellsprings of emotional sensations during the act of living and every emotional reaction can be traced back to one or more of these ultimate concerns. They are always there, and they will never go away while we are alive. They present us with distress, fear, shame, and disgust, along with a thousand other tonalities and blends of emotions in our moment-to-moment awareness of life.

Our challenge is to tolerate the uncomfortable emotions and "listen" to them in order to understand what is significant to us, rather than trying to escape them. Success in doing so is the basis for knowing what is important and, thus, what course to take in our life's journey. This is a very hard thing to do because, as I said, we appear to be hardwired to recoil from pain of any kind, both physical pain and emotional pain, and to seek out a more soothing state. Our challenge is to inhibit the urges to escape those feelings and instead weather the storm with some sense of protection from the elements. This challenge is what makes us human. In the next chapter I'll examine some common *DSM* categories and explain them in terms of emotional distress and attempts to escape that distress.

Chapter 14

Strategies of Escaping Emotional Pain

Being Human, Not Ill

Let's examine some of the Industry's diagnostic classifications in light of the preceding ideas of escape strategies, emotional experiences, and existential ultimate concerns. To reiterate, I am proposing that emotional pain is not the principal problem. Instead, the principal problems are our reactions to the pain in an effort to escape it indefinitely.

This is like how running away from a snake is an action to escape the fear of it. The fear isn't the problem; the fear is meaningful, as some snakes can be dangerous. If we can successfully get away from the snake, the fear subsides. This reduction in fear feels good and reinforces the action of running away, and so we are likely to run away again when we see another snake. Remember, any action immediately followed by a good feeling tends to be repeated. In this example, the fear of snakes is an analogy for any emotionally painful state. Whereas it is possible to permanently avoid snakes, if you desire to do so and if you don't live in their habitat, it isn't always possible to permanently avoid the other painful emotions encountered in life.

These escape reactions are more than behaviors like running away from snakes. They also include cognitive "doings" such as directing our attention and thinking intensely about a particular topic, entertaining different ideas about getting revenge against someone, and "putting on different hats" in order to feel more comfortable in different social contexts. Even though it might sound awkward, it would be more accurate to say we *do* the things that get called "depression," "anxiety," and "bipolar disorder." We don't have them or get them, and they don't happen to us.

Although, as I said in the last chapter, it would be far better to just abandon *DSM* labels altogether, as they aren't reliable or valid and they falsely imply disease where none exists. Still, when someone is said to be "depressed," or "anxious," or "bipolar," they can be experiencing significant problems. However, the problems are not illnesses or in any other way medical matters. They are one's reactions to emotional pain and this is inherent in being human.

The escape model I am proposing is in stark contrast to popular and widespread ideas of "mental illness" as being either true illness on one hand, or a type of character flaw on the other. But this is a false dichotomy and does not accurately portray the problems. They are neither signs of pathology nor moral weaknesses, although the Industry portrays them as a fusion of both (see Chapter 4). But when these problems are viewed as *strategies of escaping emotional pain*, it is clear they are natural human reactions that make sense. They just aren't effective in reducing the emotional pain indefinitely and they can worsen the pain in the long run.

Given the fact that many people are faced with ongoing traumatic circumstances (e.g., terrors of combat; prolonged emotional, physical, and sexual abuse; discrimination; dire economic situations, etc.), these escape strategies can be quite reasonable and useful in order to survive and function while those circumstances are present. There may not be viable alternatives other than the attempted escape. This is a sad state of affairs as substantial change in those adverse social conditions is warranted. But such change is very difficult to achieve because many of these systemic and harmful conditions, and their potential solutions, are politically driven.

It is important to understand that we do not always engage in these escape strategies consciously. They are habitual and chronic responses to the meaning we place in life and each person's meaning is different. We "grow into" different escape strategies just like we grow into the languages we speak, the religious views we have, and the political ideologies we adopt. But with awareness and effort it is possible to inhibit these urges to escape and, instead, continue to engage with emotionally charged moments of life, even when they are painful. In doing so, we can reap longer-term benefits at the cost of the shorter-term pain. However, this is extremely difficult to do.

For someone whose alcohol use is causing problems, this means resisting the urge to reach for a drink and struggling through the feelings encountered when living life without alcohol. "Alcoholism" isn't a disease that makes someone drink excessively. It is how we label the problem when someone drinks excessively. In the case of the problems labeled "depression," resisting the urge to escape means tolerating a sense of meaninglessness and despair yet getting out of bed and getting on with life anyway. "Depression" doesn't make people stay in bed. It is the label we slap on them when they try to escape through perpetual inaction. With the difficulties the Industry calls "anxiety," resisting escape means accepting the reality that one cannot achieve certainty about potential threats in life, and to be willing to stop paying attention to this reality. "Anxiety" doesn't make people worry. It is the label that gets assigned to people who try to escape by seeking maximum certainty in life.

I want to repeat that the following conventional categories as contained in the Industry's diagnostic guidelines are unreliable and invalid from a scientific perspective (see Chapter 5). They neither describe true illnesses nor distinct problems. I am using them only to point out general and loosely described problems many people experience, not to reify them as diagnoses of illnesses.

"Depression"

When faced with what seems to be a very painful, dreary, and directionless life, you will naturally experience emotional distress. The emotional distress is meaningful. It tells you something about your life is off track or missing. You might feel sadness, disappointment, despair, and a variety of other painful feelings. Given this, you might be tempted to gradually recoil into a mode of inaction, shutting down, staying in bed, refusing social invitations, and rejecting the meaning in activities you had once enjoyed.

In other words, this is an attempt to disconnect from the painful reality you experience. To do otherwise would be to face that reality head on and experience the full force of its discomfort and challenges. Shutting down like this can also occur with a variety of other emotionally charged situations. These would include when you are distressed over a friend's death, when you fear an upcoming test, or when you anticipate owning up to an embarrassing mistake.

Such an escape attempt is characterized by intense passivity in the face of emotional pain. This escape strategy's value lies in the immediate, but fleeting, relief it provides by the blanket attempt to shut out the world. It can feel comforting to pull the covers over your head and go back to sleep. But it unfortunately can quickly lead to negative consequences such as lethargy, guilt, self-loathing, and more despair. Plus, it does nothing to resolve the things that generated the original emotional angst in the first place.

This is like an extensive and intensive procrastination of life. But remember, meaning resides in emotion. Attempting to escape from those emotions through passivity leads to an increasing sense of meaninglessness. These spin off negative feelings then feedback to increase the "pile" of the emotional distress you face, which can lead to the temptation to withdraw even more, given this increasing sense of distress.

It proceeds like this in a downward spiral of pain, escape, more pain, more escape, more pain, and so on. Each attempt to shut down and withdraw provides an immediate sense of relief. While that relief is only momentary, it still reinforces the turn toward passivity. Remember, any immediately pleasant consequence of an action tends to reinforce the continuation of that action. The immediate sense of comfort through passivity is a relief, even though it doesn't last long at all, and it has to be indefinitely repeated to retain its value.

Suicide can be seen as the ultimate escape strategy through passivity. In fact, it is the only way to truly shut down and permanently escape the inherent emotional turmoil of living, and in that sense, it appeals to people in the throes of intense pain they believe will never end while they are alive. However, it is important to remember that the primary motivator of suicide is to escape the pain, not necessarily to die.

"Anxiety"

When we are afraid of something, whether it is an upcoming speech, the possibility of shame, the dangers of combat, or just a general sense of uncertainty in life, we naturally take on a hypervigilant posture, both mentally and physiologically. The purpose in doing this is to maximize the sense of preparedness, to seek more certainty, and to detect and avoid any threats that might be lurking.

This is like juggling numerous "thought balls." You might be good at three or four, but 15 are far too many, even for the most skilled juggler. Research tells us we are quite limited in the number of things we can "juggle" or pay attention to at any one time,[1] so juggling too many increases the chance we'll exceed our attentional capacity and drop some. When that happens, we become more fearful that the ones we dropped were significant. So, we try to maintain awareness of them through increasing hypervigilance, even though they're rolling around on the floor. But in doing so we have a hard time staying focused enough on the ones we're still juggling, causing us to drop more, losing our balance by tripping on those we dropped, which leads to more hypervigilance focused on this increasingly blurry sense of uncertainty and threat. The balls in this analogy don't represent the fear. Instead, they represent the feared object and our ideas about defending against it, what happens if we can't defend ourselves, and whether we're overlooking something important.

This is the same kind of spiral of escape that happens with shutting down in passivity, but it goes in the opposite direction. It spirals upward with hypervigilance in an attempt to escape the painful feelings associated with life's uncertainties. The problem is the hypervigilance, not the fear. If not checked, it can lead to panic and cognitive confusion. It can also lead to a host of bodily ailments because of the physiological tension accompanying it.

As with passivity, attempting to escape through hypervigilance only works to provide momentary relief. That relief is the feeling that we're preparing, or figuring out, or defending in the face of the perceived threat. But because we can never gain complete certainty about that threat or what exactly it is, we have to keep up a frantic pace just to maintain a minimal sense of readiness, similar to how someone in deep water must desperately tread water just to breathe. Resorting to intense hypervigilance in order to escape fear is like treading water in order to reach the safety of the shore. The only way to get to the shore is to swim there. The only way to reduce the fear of uncertainty is to encounter it.

This is very similar to superstitious actions. They must be enacted continually, not just once. In other words, a single hypervigilant thought is not sufficient to ward off the sense of uncertainty and fear. It has to be repeatedly enacted, over and over again, in order to get just the minimal sense of protection. When a superstitious person hopes something bad doesn't happen, he might "knock on wood." This gives him a brief sense of relief. But, one knock isn't enough to cover all situations. He feels the urge to knock on wood every time he hopes for something. With a hypervigilant strategy, as with superstitions, the feared thing rarely occurs and so there is a false sense that doing it is protective.

Those who take on this kind of strategy in life are afraid to drop all the thought balls except for a few and adopt a "what will happen, will happen" attitude. To them, doing so would be tempting fate and terrible things might come as "punishment." But even though this attitude might be frightening to them, it is likely to be a far better strategy in the long run than maintaining the ever-increasing cycle of attempted escape through hypervigilance.

Alan Watts explored this concept in his book, *The Wisdom of Insecurity: A Message for An Age of Anxiety.*[2] In it, he suggested the key to life satisfaction was to allow, even to embrace, uncertainty and give up the attempt to corral and predict life. He noted that uncertainty is an inherent part of living. So excessive attempts at being secure by seeking out certainty are futile and counterproductive, and they enhance the ongoing sense of fear, angst, and dissatisfaction.

It is commonly thought one can control the course and outcome of life. Unfortunately for those who think this, all we can do is *influence* our course and outcome, not control it in the sense of ensuring it takes a straight path to a specific endpoint. It is more like navigating a sailboat than driving a car. With a sailboat, one cannot go from point A to point B in a direct, straight line. Instead, one must account for the wind, tide, and current, in addition to unforeseen circumstances that happen along the way, and then *trust* that the boat arrives close enough to the desired point. The sailboat's captain is no more in control of the boat any more than are these other factors. They all have an influence on the boat's journey. This lack of control prevents us from precisely knowing or guaranteeing what will happen to us in our life's course.

There is another harmful consequence of this hypervigilant strategy. Psychosomatic problems can develop, such as headaches, muscular pain, and a variety of gastric problems like ulcers, acid reflux, and diarrhea. This is because with mental hypervigilance comes overall physiological tension. At the same time that one is mentally preparing for a threat, the body is also reacting for the same threat. We operate as a whole. When we take on a hypervigilant posture to escape threat, we also do things like squeezing our hands into fists, clenching our teeth, furrowing our brows, tightening our shoulders, and becoming fidgety. These are just some indicators of overall bodily tension in preparation for threat.

In addition to these things, internal bodily reactions are occurring. Cortisol level surges, blood pressure increases, digestion slows, blood flows to the major muscles and organs, and our hearts beat harder and faster. If these bodily responses become chronic throughout life, we are at risk of developing things like irritable bowel syndrome, chronic headaches, and metabolic syndrome problems. It might also be the source of common and elusive problems that sometimes get diagnosed as fibromyalgia and restless leg syndrome (the consequences of attempted escape through passivity can sometimes get diagnosed as chronic fatigue syndrome).

Also, if we aren't aware of our in-the-moment thoughts and emotions, the first things we might notice are these physical indicators of bodily tension. That is why many people have "panic attacks" that seem to come out of the blue. What is happening in those situations is the person's mental world is on autopilot (remember, these escape attempts are not necessarily conscious reactions) and a lot is going on out of present awareness. This autopilot state has been called various things such as the unconscious, subconscious, preconscious, and supraconscious.

Much of our mental world, as well as our actions, work this way. Think about the act of speaking. We seem to do it with ease and without much thought even though it requires an incredible amount of fine motor movements of the mouth and tongue, particular breath patterns, and the formulation of ideas, syntax, and grammar. But when we are first learning a new language, all these things become quite noticeable. So, despite the autopilot state when these things are happening, they are nonetheless voluntary actions – we do them – and so they can be started, stopped, and altered at will.

This also happens with other cognitive and behavioral actions. Meaningful ideas that are out of one's awareness (out of awareness but the person is still thinking them) can trigger a cascade of bodily tension. The bodily sensations might be noticed without being fully aware of the meaningful ideas that triggered them. The meaning and implications of the bodily sensations are absent, making the experience even more frightening and a spiraling effect occurs with the person becoming more hypervigilant and wondering if she is having a heart attack, stroke, or some other threatening crisis. This leads to more and more hypervigilance and disorientation, which serve to worsen the problem.

This fear of bodily threat is also why some physical ailments can seem never-ending. Our hypervigilance directs our attention to common aches and pains as potentially dangerous conditions. Then our bodily tension accompanying the hypervigilance can exacerbate those very aches and pains, which become the focus of increasing hypervigilance. The result is a cycle of exaggerated focus on and increasing sensations of bodily ailments, and the fear those ailments could be life threatening.

"Schizophrenia"

When faced with overwhelming emotional agony, especially related to traumatic experiences, no-win situations, feeling out of control, questioning others' motives, or trying to verify reality, we sometimes abandon the conventional order of things in an attempt to lessen the pressure. It can be frightening to trust and to perceive one's life with what had been a conventional world shared with others, especially if harmed by those very people. In describing this problem, counterculture psychiatrist R. D. Laing, M.D., said:

> …without exception the experience and behaviour that gets labelled schizophrenic is a special strategy that a person invents in order to live in an unlivable situation. In his life situation the person has come to feel he is in an untenable position. He cannot make a move, or make no move, without being beset by contradictory and paradoxical pressures and demands, pushes and pulls, both internally, from himself, and externally, from those around him. He is, as it were, in a position of checkmate.[3]

As explained earlier, we usually operate in an ongoing manner with an "as if" approach. Additionally, basic social psychology research tells us our view of reality is strongly affected by what others think.[4] In this sense, reality is mostly consensus based, not based on an accurate correspondence to what is "really out there." Remember the submarine analogy, the existential ultimate concern of isolation, and the monism of mind perspective. Sometimes we can feel quite alone with the dilemma of determining what's real and the best course of action to take, given that reality, especially if we demand maximum certainty about it.

Optimally, we trust things are what they appear to be, and we have faith in others and in our actions despite the inherent uncertainties and insecurities in life. But in the face of these intensely painful emotions we might demand complete certainty, throw off conventionality, withdraw from the apparent reality we experience, and think outside the box, and sometimes far outside it, in an attempt to get a better sense of things.

I am currently working with a person who is entertaining the possibility she is being tested in life because of having experienced an unusual series of negative events. While she is unclear as to who or what is testing her, she is wondering if it is some kind of all-powerful entity. Is this a "symptom" of "schizophrenia"? Is it a delusion? Does it matter what entity she thinks is testing her? Does it make a difference if she thinks God is testing her? Would it matter if she believed her future self is testing her through some kind of time travel? Either way, breaking free of conventionality and coming up with this "theory" helps her make better sense of what otherwise seem to be nonsensical. Perhaps this is the same reason why human beings have come up with religion in order to explain otherwise unexplainable happenings in the world.

Having a renewed sense of reality like this can provide immediate relief from the context and emotional distress of our lives, but only temporarily. Without eventually trusting or having faith in the face of uncertainties, the person is likely to turn toward increasing questioning, fear, and suspiciousness, which can lead to the development of disorientation, dissociation, cognitive confusion, and experiences that would be considered hallucinations and delusions. These worsen the original distress, especially if the person is socially isolated. A colleague of mine put it this way:

> The "schizophrenic process" is simply the mind's ability to dissociate, or split from full awareness, from violating and/or overwhelming feelings and experiences. Schizophrenia is the description of a pattern or set of behaviors and thoughts that a particular person consistently uses to dissociate or stay dissociated from the felt violations to one's selfhood or sense of self (i.e., purposeful behavior). Consequently, each person who has been diagnosed with schizophrenia will have his or her unique set of symptoms or behaviors that if examined carefully, are related to violating experiences in his or her life.[5]

But this is not an illness that attacks us or grows from within. Instead, it is an unwitting strategy of attempting to escape the emotional discomfort that precedes it. It is clear what happens when this particular kind of escape attempt is made. Notwithstanding the sense of immediate but fleeting relief it might provide, the person becomes increasingly isolated, ridiculed, persecuted, and misunderstood – the trauma continues. This leads to more distrust and uncertainty about the world, more emotional angst, and more attempts to escape outside the conventional box even further.

"Bulimia, Anorexia, Binge Eating"

Eating provides the immediate relief of satiating hunger. But overeating is a common problem in our culture, and it leads to weight gain and increasing shame over time. In an attempt to escape this sense of shame, we try to limit our food intake by dieting. The problem, though, lies in the fact that weight loss through moderate means takes a long time. Therefore, feedback is neither immediate nor significant. One or two pounds every month might not be fast enough to escape the ongoing sense of shame of being overweight.

One solution is to resort to more extreme food restriction, vomiting, laxatives, intense exercise, or skimping during a meal in order to compensate for overindulging at others. But while these measures might provide quicker and more significant feedback about losing weight, thus relief, they can also be physiologically harmful, especially if lacking in critical minerals and nutrients.

Further, a person who is restricting food, whether in moderate or extreme form, is presented with a dilemma. That is, at what point does she stop restricting? If the desired weight goal is reached, what does she then do in terms of her eating habits? If she continues restricting, because there is still a sense of shame and it isn't enough weight loss or change in body shape, she might get into physiologically dangerous underweight territory.

If, on the other hand, she goes off the particular diet she was on, what does she do instead? The tendency is to resort to earlier patterns of eating that had been familiar, especially if there is a sense of accomplishment at having lost the weight, which frequently reduces shame and creates a relaxation of eating rules and a sense of permission to splurge. But this eventually leads to increasing weight and the cycle starts all over again.

The other typical answer is that a "maintenance diet" takes over so she can stabilize at her new, more attractive, weight. But if such a maintenance diet is of a caloric amount that keeps her at that weight, why doesn't she just start the whole process of weight loss with the more moderate maintenance diet? Besides this, how many of you have ever heard of someone successfully transitioning to a maintenance diet and remaining on it for life?

The usual reason for not starting out with a maintenance diet is it takes too long to reach the goal that way. She would have to tolerate the feelings of shame longer until the goal is achieved. More extreme restriction of food provides faster and more immediate relief from shame. Quite frequently, people find themselves alternating between eating too much and eating too little. This results in the back and forth periods of the shame and pride experienced in "yo-yo" dieting.

The key to effective weight management (other than when quickly losing significant weight for a specific purpose, such as surgery) is to eat in a way feasible for life that provides the necessary calories and nutrients to sustain healthy body functioning, while simultaneously accounting for the person's interests and values. This means any diet too costly, of insufficient calories, laborious, disruptive, or boring is destined to fail.

"Bipolar Disorder"

Inherent biological and social limitations in life are emotionally painful. When something exciting and self-enhancing is happening, it obviously feels great. There is an urge to keep the excitement going in an attempt to escape the reality that we have limits and all good things must end. Remember the death ultimate concern.

Given this, a person may begin to think sleep is a waste of time. After all, it takes up about a third of the time he has to live, and he could be doing "more important" things during that time. He also might purchase excessive amounts of items in order to prolong the excitement of obtaining new "toys." He might excessively engage in anything that is exhilarating, such as alcohol and drug use, gambling, sexual pursuits, and binge eating. He may entertain ideas of self-importance because of how extraordinary his achievements appear to be and how rewarding and intensely exciting it feels. Sometimes people do not reach a level that would be considered extreme excitement. Instead, their outlook just becomes exceptionally positive. This is formally called "hypomania," to distinguish it from "mania."

But eventually, he will crash, whether through exhaustion, bankruptcy, arrest, sleep deprived psychosis, or shame. And then comes the plunge into despair. The limitations of life seem intensely punitive, agonizing, and unavoidable. The crash in this cycle reflects a shift in the attempted strategy to escape this new pain through passivity and inaction. The idea that all great things must end becomes painfully apparent and, moreover, the greater the feeling of excitement, the greater the crash when the excitement ends. Sometimes, people do not crash after recognizing the futility of perpetual excitement. Instead, they just give up the attempt and settle into a low-level sense of disappointment about life, not something reaching the depths of despair.

As with the other four examples that get labeled "mental illness," this attempt at escape is futile because those givens of life's limitations don't go away, and the escape attempts just serve to pile up more emotional pain, from which the person tries to escape even more. The problem with these escape attempts is their benefit is only short lived. There is an immediate sense of relief in escaping the original undesirable feeling state. But the strategy creates even more pain in the long run, from which further escape attempts are made, and the cycle of escape continues. See the figure below.

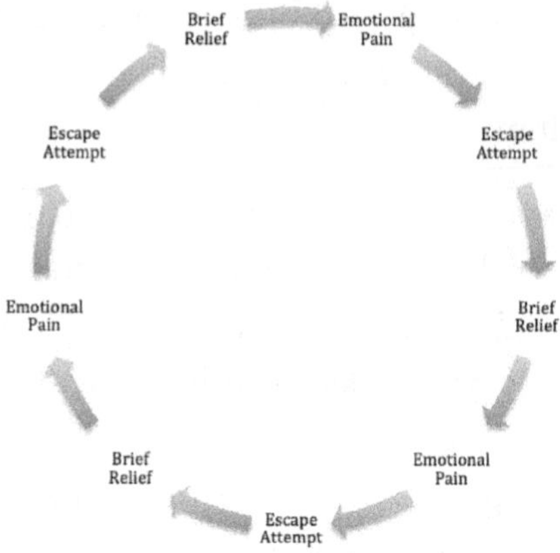

In addition to the previous examples, the escape model can be applied to all other forms of immediate soothing represented by the Industry's diagnostic classifications. For example, escaping through inebriation ("alcohol use disorder"), escaping through intrapersonal fragmentation ("dissociative disorders"), escaping through social isolation and rigid routine ("autism spectrum disorder"), escaping the effort to focus on otherwise disinteresting topics ("attention-deficit/hyperactivity disorder"), escaping the difficulty of following rules and delaying gratification ("oppositional defiant disorder"), and most of the other conventional diagnostic categories. All of these attempts at escape lead to more emotional pain in the long term and more escape attempts, which in turn lead to more pain. They are self-perpetuating.

Anger

As explained in the section on Tomkins's theory, anger is considered a punishing affect. However, it is quite different than the other punishing affects and is best understood as an escape attempt. This is more evident when we consider the fact that anger feels good while the other punishing affects feel bad – they are the reasons we engage in escape attempts in the first place. Anger arises when those other painful feelings become intolerable. It provides a sense of power with which to confront life's difficulties and it rescues us from pain. Anger takes over when we are faced with too much distress, fear, shame, or disgust. It helps us escape those forms of emotional pain through a sense of dominance and righteousness. Yet, as with the other escape attempts, this only works in the short term, as it has the potential to generate longer-term emotional pain and damage, and it threatens civil discourse and cooperation.

This seems reasonable from an evolutionary standpoint. Survival would be enhanced in times of immediate threat when intensely painful experiences are dissolved by anger. In threatening situations, anger provides the offensive posture and power to confront the threat. However, with some exceptions, such as in wartime, law enforcement activities, and living in high crime areas, the kinds of threats that beset our evolutionary ancestors are no longer of concern. In civil society, our threats are mostly emotional. The times of being threatened by predatory animals or rival tribes are mostly over. Yet, we are still burdened with this legacy of anger and it can lead to the cycle of attempted escape from the emotional pain, just like the previously mentioned examples of official *DSM* categories.

It is clear too much anger, especially if we do not harness it and inhibit the behaviors it drives, leads to counterattacks by those who are the targets of the anger. This retaliation serves as a further threat and triggers increasing mutual anger. It can create a never-ending cycle of interpersonal attack and counterattack, in addition to increasing animosity toward the targets of those attacks, and an ongoing urge to retaliate, vilify the other, and get revenge. We see this happening on a grand scale with examples like the Hatfields and McCoys in 19th century West Virginia and Kentucky, the Palestinians and Israelis in the present-day Middle East, and the Democrats and Republicans in the perennial world of political mischief in America. It even occurs with smaller scale conflicts such as between residents in neighborhoods, coworkers, friends, family members, and spouses.

Once this anger cycle gets going, it is next to impossible to stop it without considerable damage. Because of the layers of attack and counter-attack, it is very difficult to remember or even care about the original conflict. Even when the original dispute is recognized, the hostility that subsequently develops blinds and focuses us on justifying revenge instead of seeking resolution. It leads one to feeling validated in attacking and hurting other people because they are thought to be deserving of such harm.

Further, there is a related urge to assign blame and fault, rather than to cooperate in finding a solution to the conflict. But faultfinding is harmful when it comes to relationships because the purpose of assigning blame is to punish the other for a wrongdoing, even if the punishment is merely being forced to admit the wrongdoing. And so, the one to be punished has to be identified – this is the faulty or blameworthy one. This is what happens in criminal trials when an accused is found guilty and society exercises retaliation against the person through formal sentencing. However, it also applies to interpersonal punishment such as when a husband punishes his wife by giving her the cold shoulder or when a homeowner blows leaves onto his neighbor's lawn "by accident." Regardless of the type of situation, anger drives a desire to retaliate against someone for hurting us – it helps us escape that hurt.

We see this in how people react to horrific events like the apparent epidemic of mass shootings. We regularly hear calls to retaliate against these perpetrators of violence and give them a taste of their own medicine. But this overlooks the fact these shooters did the very same thing. They acted out of their own sense of revenge against those who they believed wrongly persecuted and harmed them. Punishing these shooters does nothing to address the problem of anger and violence in our society, any more than punishing a spouse would address marital problems or retaliating against a neighbor would bring harmony to the neighborhood. It merely gives one an immediately smug sense of justice about perceived wrongdoings but fuels the fire of continued conflict.

This retaliatory process also occurs in less tragic situations, especially in close relationships, and it can lock us into a perpetual cycle of violence. But in what kind of relationship is finding fault and punishing ever helpful, especially in relationships where our goal is to achieve a positive connection with the other? A far more effective approach in both small- and large-scale relationships would be to identify the things that lead to conflict and then to find ways to eliminate or reduce those things in order to resolve the conflict. Of course, when conflict cannot be resolved and it is significant enough, it might require dissolving a relationship or protecting society from dangerous people through law enforcement and legal measures.

It would be wise to discourage people from thinking in terms of seeking justice against wrongdoings or seeing the world in an unrealistic and simplistic dichotomy of "the good guys versus the bad guys." Besides, who gets to decide the identity of the bad guys; in other words, the ones who deserve punishment – the ones who are "in the wrong"?

The anger reaction to emotional pain is like pulling the hammer back on a pistol. Doing so increases tension in the system, and the tension can only be released by pulling the trigger or, as those of you who have fired a pistol might know, by easing the hammer down with your thumb as you pull the trigger so it doesn't strike the firing pin. This is difficult to do and takes a lot of practice and control. The same thing can be said of the tension from an escalation of interpersonal anger. It takes practice and control to release the anger without attacking the other. This is because anger and the aggression it stimulates is an escape attempt to reduce one's sense of the emotional pain of being wronged. Inhibiting anger necessarily leads to the continuation of emotional pain and the difficult challenge in tolerating it, listening to it, and resolving the conflict without anger.

Escaping with Psychiatric Drugs

The model of escape attempts I am proposing also applies to the use of psychiatric drugs. These prescribed chemicals have roughly sedating or stimulating effects on the central nervous system, which can provide either direct chemical relief, or the placebo relief found in believing they are "medicines" that will be curative. But they can cause the same cycle of pain, escape (through the drugs), relief, more pain, more escape, and so on, just like what happens with illicit and addictive drugs.

In fact, being dependent on psychiatric drugs ironically meets the clinical criteria contained in the *DSM* for a "substance use disorder" similar to how being dependent on illicit chemical substances meets those criteria. But the act of portraying them as prescribed "medications" obscures the reality they do nothing to address the meaningful problems a person is having in life. The drugs can't medicate a "mental illness" because there's no underlying disease process in the person that can be medicated. Their value is the same as the value of illicit and recreational drugs.

So, despite being called "medications," psychiatric drugs are just another way of attempting to escape emotional pain, but only in the immediate term. They must be consumed continually in order to maintain any ongoing short-term benefit. But this is at the expense of the longer-term harms of dependence, withdrawal, damaging physiological effects, and the drug's negative effects on one's work, home, and school obligations, for which additional drugs are typically prescribed. It is not uncommon for people to end up with multiple psychiatric drugs, creating an unpredictable and potentially dangerous chemical concoction.

Emotional and behavioral problems called "mental illness" are better understood as different types of natural escape strategies, not illnesses. The problem with them is the escape is focused on immediate emotional soothing, not lasting solutions to the real and meaningful problems from which the person is trying to escape. This causes an increase in emotional pain in the long run, from which the person tries in vain to escape, leading to a repeated cycle of futile escape attempts. But not all is lost. In the next chapter, I'll address how escape attempts can be useful if we are willing to manage them, so they square with natural and societal demands.

Chapter 15

The Willingness to Act

Are We Destined to Suffer?

Within the context of the existential ultimate concerns and the human emotions arising from those concerns, we can certainly understand the fuel that drives these flights into the escape attempts the Industry calls "mental illnesses." These attempts to escape reflect the desire to avoid discomfort and to seek out a more soothing state. However, as pointed out, they are counterproductive because they only provide temporary relief, and they fail to address the very real problems that lead to the emotional upheaval. Thus, they increase angst in the long run. This is consistent with the Second Noble Truth of Buddhist teachings. It warns that a single-minded desire to avoid pain and pursue pleasure can lead to great suffering.[1] But does this mean we can do nothing to alleviate the pain?

There is another Buddhist message that speaks to this problem.[2] It is called the parable of the "second arrow."[3] It goes something like this. If you are walking through the forest and a hidden archer shoots you with an arrow, it causes great pain. But the archer might be preparing for another shot, and you can do something so as not to get hit by the second arrow. In this parable, the second arrow is what you do in response to the first arrow's pain. The lesson of the parable is you can choose how to react (freedom existential ultimate concern) in the face of that pain so as not to cause further suffering. It is said, "pain is inevitable, but suffering is optional."[4]

I am tweaking this parable a bit in terms of the meaning of the second arrow. The parable usually emphasizes the second arrow as an analogy for how we emotionally react to the life circumstances represented by the first arrow. From my perspective, though, it is nearly impossible to control our emotions in response to environmental triggers for which we are not prepared. Yet, it is possible to choose much of what we *do* in response to the emotion, which will affect our follow-on emotional experiences. Unless we have resigned ourselves to a life of monastic living in perpetual meditation, we are very likely going to reflexively react with emotions when a life event (the first arrow) hits us. At the point when the first arrow hits, we are going to experience the stimulation brought on by it, as suggested by Tomkins's theory of affects. The first arrow includes the event, our biological reactions to the event, and our accompanying emotional experiences.

The key is how we act and think after the first arrow hits us, in other words what we *do*, in the face of those painful emotional experiences. That is the second arrow. By being aware of our behavioral and cognitive responses to the emotional pain, we can evade the second arrow. In other words, we still have a say in how we act and think in response to the emotional pain we will inevitably feel. The various escape strategies mentioned in the previous chapter, and others, are not the only types of actions available to us.

This model implies choice is at the heart of the solution and nothing, "mental illness" or any other mental entity, takes away our *ability* to choose our responses in order to avoid the second arrow. Instead, the first arrows are the understandable reasons for our choices. They don't dictate what we choose or how we subsequently react. Still, it is extremely difficult to inhibit these natural reactions (second arrows) to emotional turmoil (first arrows), partly because most of those reactions occur habitually and out of conscious awareness. Yet, we can become aware of those reactions and, with much effort and practice, we have the ability over time to inhibit them and to do otherwise.

The existential and emotional givens (the first arrows) aren't the principal problems in our lives and we cannot always avoid them. Instead, the problems lie in how we attempt to escape the first arrows, even though they have already hit us, therefore making the attempt to escape futile. Of course, it would be wise to identify and remove the archers when we can. This means addressing environmental triggers such as social inequities, discrimination, economic distress, interpersonal conflict, and traumatic conditions that can be the sources of the first arrows. However, in many instances, we will not have the ability to remove these harmful circumstances because of the political and financial incentives that keep them going, and so we are destined much of the time to experience those archers' first arrows.

This perspective asserts the various escape strategies are not about illnesses or dysfunctions within us. We don't *have* "depression," "anxiety," "schizophrenia," or "bipolar disorder" and they aren't things inside us that control or dictate our actions. Moreover, it would be quite limiting to take on the *identity* of those labels, as in "I'm a schizophrenic." Such common ways of talking are examples of how language can reify actions, which has a powerful effect on what we believe about ourselves and the possible solutions to our life challenges. Instead of believing we have, get, or are these things, it would be more accurate to say *we do these things.* They are the labels the Industry assigns to ways in which we choose to respond to the first arrows.

Useful Escape

Despite the potential dangers of these escape attempts, certain ones can be useful if we are conscious of and willing to manage the urges to escape. The key is what our purpose is, how long we keep up the escape, and whether we are aware it only provides temporary relief. Procrastination, for example, can be viewed as the same type of escape attempt as the problems that get diagnosed as "depression." It just isn't as severe, global, or chronic. But we are doing the same thing. We anticipate something will be difficult and so we shut down with passivity in the face of it, putting it off until later. Usually, though, we eventually reengage because of a deadline approaching or other negative consequence of remaining passive. The usefulness is we are given a temporary reprieve from emotionally painful circumstances. But if we do not give up the procrastination strategy at some point, it can worsen into what the Industry would call "depression."

Think of procrastination like driving a bulldozer with the blade down. We drive along and as we come upon tasks in our lives, the blade just pushes them ahead of us. Instead of dealing with them as we encounter them, we put them off and feel an immediate soothing effect of avoiding them. Then we encounter more and more life tasks. They pile up so much that we see them rising above the blade in front of us, making it very difficult to continue ignoring them. If we don't stop this at some point and reduce the pile it will continue to grow and might become so emotionally overwhelming as to seem insurmountable, putting us at risk of more global and permanent attempts at shutting down in the face of the escalating distress.

Another useful form of passivity is the weekend, which could be considered "authorized depression days." In order to avoid what would otherwise be a constant pace of stressful tasks in our ongoing lives, weekends are sanctioned times when we can escape the toils of work through passivity and detachment (of course, those who do not have 9 to 5, 5-days-a-week work schedules have other authorized time off). The same goes for holidays, vacations, and leave. They are socially sanctioned times of shutting down from the toils and the monotony of daily routine. Unfortunately, in our culture of apparently increasing desire for productivity, it seems all too often these free times are getting filled up with just more tasks.

There are even those times we've all experienced when we call in sick, but we aren't really sick. We just want a "mental health day." This is a useful and socially accepted way of shutting down for a while in order to recharge. But just as with the previous example of procrastination, this form of escape does not lead to the cycle of pain-escape-relief-pain-escape-relief. This is because we are willing to keep the passivity to a manageable level and eventually get back to the grind within a reasonable and socially expected amount of time.

There are also useful ways to escape through hypervigilance. Planning, organizing, and strategizing can be understood as types of increased vigilance about problems, but they are helpful. They are heightened states of awareness that increase our sense of certainty of the future. In other words, they can help us escape the discomfort of some of life's uncertainties. When we plan, organize, and strategize, we eventually come to a conclusion and set the plan into motion. It is like a sentence ending in a period.

But with the Industry's notion of "anxiety" there is no conclusion. Instead, it is a repeated series of unanswerable questions or exclamations that have no ending point. It is not focused on applying solutions to problems.

The so-called Yerkes-Dodson law[5] introduced over a century ago is consistent with this idea. It proposed that low levels of stress or vigilance will result in poor performance. This is because optimal performance requires a moderate level of stress. Think about it, if you are lackadaisical about a task, you probably won't do well. However, if the stress increases too far past an optimal point, your performance will suffer. The key is to notice when the optimal level of hypervigilance is reached, and at that point, to be willing to drop the matter with the sense that all reasonable planning and preparation are complete, despite the fact that the future will always be uncertain to a degree. This is why a sense of faith in the process is crucial. The difficulty is that the optimal level of hypervigilance is not a clear-cut point – it is ultimately a judgement call, thus the uncertainty.

The other forms of escape strategies described in the previous chapter can also be useful. For instance, "thinking outside the box" is a form of escape from conventionality that helps in creative endeavors as long as the person is willing to return to the consensual reality shared by those, or whose new reality is accepted by those, in his social network. If this doesn't happen, it is not a problem of seeing reality correctly. Instead, the problem is that living outside consensual reality too long can lead to social and interpersonal difficulties.

Brainstorming is another example of this. It is a process of breaking free of conventional thought without regard to previously existing guidelines or rules in order to identify otherwise overlooked solutions to problems. Other significant examples are the creative imagination needed to compose a poem, the melody and lyrics of a song, or other work of art. It can also be helpful in determining new approaches in engineering and science overlooked because of the restrictions of conventionality.

Likewise, surpassing our limitations can be excused for short bursts and can provide well-deserved splurges to enhance one's sense of excitement, enjoyment, and purpose in life. So, people might engage in drinking and eating too much on special occasions, at times staying up very late to enjoy some activity, spending too much, and enjoying special accomplishments with a narcissistic sense of self.

These forms of useful escape are not necessarily problematic if there is an eventual return to a socially acceptable baseline and the self-perpetuating escape cycle does not have a chance to set in. The point is that escape, in and of itself, is not necessarily a problem. What counts is whether it becomes futile in the attempt to keep it going indefinitely. In other words, it is important to recognize if we're doing it, how often we do it, why we do it, what are the consequences of doing it, and whether we are willing to remain within or return to socially accepted limits in the process.

Anger can also be useful. It exists on a continuum from low levels to high levels. As such, Tomkins called it anger-rage. At the very low end, we experience it as a sense of frustration and annoyance. At the high end, there is hostility and murderous fury. But if we are self-aware enough to notice the anger process starting and growing, which takes a lot of practice to do, we can harness some of the power and offensive posture it offers in order to escape the emotional pain of an obstacle. This power is essential for being assertive. It is a blend of passivity and aggression, either of which alone is not helpful. Assertiveness takes advantage of the civility of passivity and the candor of aggression. It is useful. But it requires we are willing to inhibit the urge to cross the line between speaking up to resolve conflict assertively on one hand, and resorting to righteousness, aggressive attacks, fault-finding, and seeking retaliation on the other.

Mental Disability

These escape attempts are what people do; they are not about *mental disability*. Therefore, they are what we choose to do in response to the emotional pain of living. While these choices are frequently enacted habitually, they are still things we choose to do. As an analogy for this kind of out-of-awareness choosing, consider the process of driving a car. We do so out of choice even though much of what we do and observe in the process is out of present awareness. We are not fully conscious of all the choices we make while driving, like the intricate and subtle movements and hand-eye coordination. Also, we are not typically aware of all the thoughts, sounds, and sights occurring along the way. This is because we drive so much it becomes a matter of routine and habit. It is only when something unexpected happens in the routine that we become aware. How many times have you driven a familiar route from point A to point B, knowing you must have passed a particular landmark, but you don't remember it?

Yet, being on "autopilot" like this doesn't mean your thoughts and actions during that time were not matters of choice. We certainly wouldn't say driving "happens to" us or we are not able to do otherwise while driving. The same goes for how we think and act much of the time. We do so habitually. Whereas we might not be consciously aware of our choices to think and act, we are doing so in a purposeful and meaningful way, nonetheless. The basic goal of many forms of psychotherapy is to help people become aware of these "out-of-awareness" thoughts and actions, and to change them in order to make them more beneficial.

In situations where someone is presented with abruptly overwhelming stimulation, like a loud and unexpected noise, she will act reflexively. Such a reaction is not a matter of choice. It is an involuntary response similar to how your leg kicks when the doctor taps your knee. This is Tomkins's surprise-startle affect. However, follow-on thoughts and actions in response to the noise are choices, even though they might be quite reasonable, out of present awareness, and not much conscious thought goes into the choice.

Another example of a reflexive reaction is when a person responds with panic at the sudden recognition of a potentially serious danger. His initial panic reaction is largely knee-jerk to the abrupt and overwhelming fear. But subsequent thoughts are intentional and purposeful. Even though we can completely understand why he would continue thinking about the threat, he nonetheless has the ability to do otherwise.

One's unique history of experiences, current environmental influences, and level of ongoing emotional turmoil can have a tremendous effect on his choices, both the choices occurring out of awareness and those of which he is conscious. But other than in reflexive situations, these things do not take away the *ability* to choose or dictate what to choose. Instead, they form the basis of our desires in the moment and, therefore, what we are willing to do and what we choose to do in that moment. Whereas these historical, environmental, and emotional factors can help us understand why someone makes certain choices, and those choices might very well be justified and the best course of action at the time, they do not take away the ability to choose differently. Instead, they affect the rationale for the choices made.

If we thought people who are labeled "mentally ill" were truly not able to choose differently, how would talking with them in psychotherapy alter their ability? A psychotherapist can provide encouragement, support, and a sense of safety so she becomes willing to make risky changes in how she thinks and acts. But talking to her in psychotherapy has no effect on her abilities to choose. Instead, it affects her rationale, desires, and, therefore, her willingness to choose certain courses of action.

Some have misunderstood my critique of the concept of mental disability, claiming that I'm blaming the person for her problems, disparaging her for being lazy and not trying hard enough, and not being compassionate. I want to assure you this isn't the case. In my rejection of the mental disability concept, I am not substituting it with moral disapproval or claiming the person has a character flaw. I am merely pointing out that in most situations, one retains the ability to act and think. It can definitely seem impossible to get out of bed, to confront one's spouse, to trust another person, or to allow the day to drift away when settling down at night to sleep. But other than in cases such as brain damage, chemical intoxication, and the limits of intellectual capacity, nothing truly disables mental or behavioral ability.

In other words, nothing of a mental nature takes away our ability to choose one way or another. It is critical to make this distinction. There is an important difference between one's ability to act and one's rationale for action. Remember, this is because "mental illness" is not a thing inside us that makes us act and think in certain ways. Instead, it is the Industry's descriptive label given to the ways we choose to think and act. The same goes for our emotions and thoughts. They are not things within us dictating our choices. They are our meaningful experiences of life and the reasons for our choices.

It can be terrifying to deal with substantial challenges in life, such as when a middle-aged man believes his life is a failure and so he shuts down in despair, when a child suffers ongoing sexual and physical abuse at the hands of her parent and dissociates in an attempt to escape, or when a soldier has faced horrible carnage all around for months on end and so she takes on an intensely hypervigilant posture, even after her combat tour is over. Still, despite the intense difficulties these situations present, they are difficult because of the person's understandable desires to act in certain ways in the moments of choice. The choice might be quite reasonable, but it is not a reflection of a literal incapacity to choose otherwise. In these situations, the circumstances don't dictate our choices.

There are times when people lack knowledge or have beliefs that affect their choices. For instance, a woman who believes she is unworthy of being treated respectfully might not demand better treatment from her husband. Yet she still has the ability to protest, she just doesn't know she is worthy of doing so. Therefore, she chooses to remain silent as would be expected, but she never loses her ability to be assertive. Similarly, a man who is listening to loud music and does not hear his phone ringing would not answer it. Yet, he still has the ability to answer it, he just doesn't know it is ringing. Therefore, he chooses to continue listening to the music, even though he never loses his ability to answer his phone. In these two situations, the person isn't disabled. Instead, the rationale for action is missing, so it is quite understandable why the person wouldn't choose otherwise.

Most ideas about disability have been based on a medical model. This is when some kind of medical impairment in the person prevents him from carrying out a particular action. It would apply when a paraplegic is not able to walk up a staircase. But this model can't apply to the problems labeled "mental illness," since with those problems, there is no medical impairment.

However, a newer perspective of disability follows a *social model.* This newer model points out that many social conditions are disabling in the sense they prevent medically impaired people from taking certain actions. In other words, this model asserts these people are truly disabled because of social restrictions preventing them from carrying on a socially viable existence. They are not disabled because of their impairments, as is suggested by the medical model of disability.[6]

According to the social model, the disabling problem is the unaccommodating social structure, not the person's differential abilities. This is the idea of *ableism*, or the prejudice that non-impaired people are the norm and impaired people are abnormal, living in a society biased toward and supporting the norm, and therefore, it disables those who are impaired.

This social model distinguishes between *impairment* and *disability*. Impairment is about the person, such as paralysis, blindness, or the problems that are labeled "mental illnesses." However, the cause of the disability itself is the social context, such as stairs, sight-dependent traffic systems, and negative attitudes toward people who are labeled "mentally ill." These contextual things discriminate against and restrict one's adequate functioning and, in that sense, they are disabling.

According to the social model, the solution is to correct these societal restrictions in order to be more inclusive of those with impairments. With the first two examples, stairs and sight-dependent traffic systems, physical accommodations can be made in the form of ramps, elevators, auditory traffic announcements, and special traffic warning signs of impaired persons living in the area. Those things will make the social context more inclusive of people with those impairments, thus removing the disability and enabling them, even though their impairment remains unchanged.

Let me emphasize that the social disability model still presupposes an impairment in the person, as does the medical model, but societal restrictions of the impairment are what create the disability, not the impairment itself. However, unless one considers emotional pain and responses to that pain as impairments, this doesn't apply to those labeled "mentally ill," as they have *no demonstrable impairment* or defect. Instead, their very own attempts to escape from emotional angst is the only thing preventing them from functioning. But it would be nonsensical to say people's choices impair their functioning. Their choices and their functioning are one and the same thing.

In contrast to medical impairments such as paralysis and blindness, it is hard to envision accommodations that would aid people who are said to be "mentally ill," because with the escape strategy model I am proposing, there is no impairment that can be accommodated. Campaigns to reduce the stigma of those labeled "mentally ill" might come close. However, it is important to note that the stigma is caused by the very act of labeling the person with a "mental illness" in the first place.

As long as these pejorative labels are handed out to people struggling with distress, but no impairment, there will always be that stigma, which acts as the "disabling" social context. Those who suffer from paralysis and sightlessness are literally unable to function because of social contexts (can't walk up a flight of stairs, can't see traffic signs, etc.) and so the accommodations are critical to them. But this isn't the case with people who are labeled "mentally ill." They never lose the ability to take particular actions because they have no true impairments. There are no impairments any more than there are with other forms of discrimination.

Certainly, it is a serious problem when people are discriminated against or mistreated for any reason, and it is important to rectify this social flaw. But thinking of discrimination as a social disability would also have to apply to racial, ethnic, religious, and gender forms of discrimination as well. This would imply that one's race, ethnicity, religion, and gender are impairments. So, it would be a stretch and offensive to use the term "disability" or "impairment" to describe social inequities like these.

In the case of so-called "learning disabilities" and "attention deficits," extra time on academic tests is often offered as an accommodation because those problems are considered impairments. However, the shortfalls that get labeled with these diagnostic terms are not caused by a demonstrable neurological or other literal impairment in the student (just like with other *DSM* diagnoses). They simply reflect intellectual capacity (IQ), attention capacity (which makes up 50% of an IQ score), availability of educational resources, and historical opportunities to learn.

There are no other theoretically reasonable or evidence-based explanations for relatively poorer academic performance by some students. Furthermore, it wouldn't make sense to say that one's intellectual or attentional capacity limitations are impairments and that academic standards were the social restrictions disabling the students. Clearly, economic and educational aids such as free lunch programs and tutoring services can help to rectify systemic shortcomings in the educational system, but this isn't accommodating an impairment. It is merely increasing the resources available for the development of better learning strategies, knowledge, and skills.

Why would a neurologically nonimpaired person be given extra time on a test if the purpose of the test is to assess the limits of one's academic performance? If the purpose is to measure the student's grasp of the material relative to one's peers, then accommodations defeat the purpose of the test. Providing such accommodations would be like having a race and giving slower runners a head start. This blatantly interferes with the very purpose of testing in the first place as it makes the playing field uneven.[7] Natural variation in intellectual or athletic capacity and the limitations they may impose, are not impairments.

To make testing fair across the board, all test-takers would have to be presented with the same environmental circumstances during the test, unless of course, a true impairment such as blindness exists. Similarly, providing extra time on an academic test because of "test anxiety" or any other so-called "emotional disability" is unjustifiable as it tilts the playing field unfairly. Considering the fact that emotional distress varies among people, especially while taking a test (it is not a dichotomous issue where some people are distressed and the rest are not), we would have to give extra time to all test-takers based on each individual's level of emotional distress. This would be unwieldy. Do we measure all students' level of emotional distress prior to taking each academic test, and then adjust their subsequent academic test scores accordingly based on their levels of emotional distress?

Accordingly, to be consistent with the idea that "mental illness" is a myth and metaphor, the term "mental disability" is just as mythical and metaphorical. If there is a truly disabling impairment of some kind, it would not be a "mental disability." Instead, it would just be a disability. So, the person who "can't" get out of bed is choosing to stay in bed as one way of attempting to escape a life of despair. The person who "can't" quit drinking alcohol is choosing to continue drinking as one way of attempting to escape what life would be like without alcohol. The student who "can't" pay attention either has reached the limits of his inherent intellectual capacity, or he is choosing not to put forth full effort in attending to an otherwise disinteresting task.

But because these escape strategies are mostly adopted without conscious awareness, and they are very ingrained and difficult to change, they seem like disabilities or something *happening to* the person, which encourages the belief in mental disability. As mentioned earlier, the critical point of psychotherapy is to help the person understand the meaningful nature of her choices and to remind her she always retains the ability to do otherwise in the future. Such an approach is empowering, yet frightening.

Notwithstanding my rejection of the idea of literal mental disability, I think it is important for us to compassionately take on the task of aiding people in difficult circumstances. For one thing, this would mean giving people "a break" when they are facing those circumstances. For instance, when I see people in the midst of significant emotional distress, I am more than willing to suggest their employers give them limited time off in order to loosen their burden. I am also willing to suggest other services, such as an emotional support animal, which could be helpful in lessening their emotional load.

But I refuse to say they are disabled, or in any other way not able to work, since I think it would be intellectually dishonest. The point of our involvement with them is not to confirm or disconfirm their *ability* to work or whether they have an impairment. Instead, the point is to be considerate of their experiences and helpful when they are facing dire situations. But hopefully, these forms of assistance are temporary and do not become permanent forms of dependency. It is important to balance our interests of being compassionate with that of preventing overreliance on the system.

Financial support and official protection of people in trying times currently falls under state and federal mental disability insurance programs and school programs that offer individualized educational assistance. Because of the reality of limited funds, those programs are saddled with the difficult task of distinguishing between people who are "in need" of assistance and those who are not. But a serious problem arises when identifying those who qualify for such aid using the current systems.

These evaluations try to determine if the person warrants a label listed in the *DSM* and how the alleged illness prevents the person from functioning. However, remember the various *DSM* diagnoses are not about malfunctioning brains, other defective bodily systems, or flawed minds having a literally disabling effect. Instead, they are about a person's understandable choices in response to emotionally charged situations or inherent intellectual capacity.

If the goal of these systems ignored *DSM* diagnoses and, instead, focused on verifying the person's very real *difficulties* in living, and the authorities would assist them with those difficulties, I might be more agreeable to it. But the only path currently available to people who are struggling with life problems and who wish to obtain assistance is to be designated mentally disabled, which much of the time leads to indefinite dependency on the system.

This puts Industry professionals in another ethical double bind similar to the one I mentioned in Chapter 5 about diagnosing people so they can use their health insurance benefits. Specifically, if professionals participate in the disability and educational accommodation systems, they could be accused of acting unethically because they would be using an invalid and unreliable tool to label the person with a diagnosis that can have long-term harmful effects.

Further, a successful assessment requires one of the more "serious" diagnoses. The evaluator cannot soften the harmful effect of the diagnosis the way psychotherapists can by picking a relatively minor diagnosis merely for administrative purposes. This is because a minor diagnosis is unlikely to qualify for a disability. Also, the very act of participating in the system and making a determination of disability is tacit acceptance of these problems as literally disabling, when there is no evidence of that. But if those professionals refuse to participate in the system, people might not be able to obtain the assistance that can aid in their struggles. Given the current system, there is no solution to this double bind that would avoid ethical concerns completely.

If this were not enough of an ethical problem, the current disability system can also harm the very people it claims to help by creating a dependency on the system and a disincentive to change. For example, a person who has been diagnosed for several years, and who believes the falsehood he is suffering from an illness caused by a chemical imbalance in his brain, might reach out to the disability system in order to obtain assistance. But if he does, and he is approved for such a disability, he will then become dependent on the financial and other assistance he receives as well as his identity as a "depressed," or "learning disabled," or "schizophrenic" person, plunging him into a dilemma.

Resolving the problem would be in conflict with his financial interests and it may jeopardize his sense of identity. So, this could encourage him to live his life consistent with a disability and with what he falsely believes is his illness, seeing many problems he encounters as symptoms of illness and confirmation he is disabled. This might lock him into a perpetual life of believing he suffers from a life-long illness, that it disables him, that his only option is to manage the so-called "symptoms" and that his life is necessarily limited.

Insanity

The issue of mental disability also shows up in our courts of law. This is the idea of *insanity* and it asserts basically the same thing. In other words, it claims something other than a person's own desires and choices forces him to act contrary to the law, prevents him from acting in accordance with the law, or removes his knowledge of the law. If true, this would mean he shouldn't be held accountable for his actions.

However, as with mental disability, science has failed to demonstrate there is any such entity that controls people's choices when they commit illegal acts. Insanity doesn't make people act or prevent them from acting. Instead, it is a legal and moral label assigned to people who act in ways we don't understand, especially if those actions are bizarre or harmful. This makes it very odd that courts would rely on Industry professionals to assess insanity, as those professionals have no scientific expertise to make that legal and moral judgment.

They might be experts at bureaucratically categorizing problem behaviors with the official diagnostic guidelines and labeling the person "mentally ill." Although, we saw these diagnostic categories are unreliable and invalid, which makes such a labeling process meaningless. Besides, such a designation has no bearing on the essential legal criteria of insanity. Although the specific criteria vary among the states, in general they share the following two ideas: (1) a person does not know right from wrong, as the law defines it, or (2) the person does not have the ability to conform his or her behavior to the law.[8]

Other than in cases where chemical intoxication, brain damage, and the limited cognitive capacity of childhood and the elderly affect a person's actions, it would be rare for a person to literally not know what constitutes illegal action. I'm sure there are some laws most of us are not aware of and, therefore, we might accidentally violate them purely out of ignorance. But that doesn't take away our ability to conform to those laws if we knew about them. And, as you all know, it is a common legal principle that ignorance of the law is no defense.

Hopefully, in those cases when someone unknowingly and unintentionally violates some obscure law, the court would take that lack of knowledge and intent into consideration as mitigating factors. Besides, in cases where insanity is typically raised, the question of whether the action is a violation of the law is widely known, such as with murder and theft. If a person believes the law is an unjust and immoral law, or otherwise disagrees with it, and therefore violates it, that does not meet this first criteria of the insanity test. The person has to literally not know an act is illegal.

The only situation where a person meets the first criterion of the insanity test is when he truly believes the act isn't a violation of the law. This might apply, for instance, when a war veteran experiencing a flashback truly believes his neighbor is an enemy combatant and attacks him. In such a case, he would genuinely believe he is acting out of self-defense, within the rules of war, and his actions are legal.

However, how would an Industry professional be able to verify what another person truly believed at the time of the crime any better than the lay public, police, judge, or jury could? Just as with anyone, they must rely mostly on what the person claims he believed at the time of the incident. The rest is speculation, not science, and, in general, experts are no better than other professionals or the lay public at speculating about the truthfulness of a person's claims. In fact, their accuracy at detecting deception or truth is roughly the same as flipping a coin.[9] Thus, the very difficult question about what a defendant truly believed at the time of the offense is to be answered by the trier of fact – judge and jury, not an expert.

In addition to how unusual it would be for someone to not know an action is illegal, it would also be a rarity for someone to not have the literal capacity to obey the law. Similar to the mental disability issue, people make choices in life. While those choices can occur impulsively and out of present awareness, urges in the moment can be very difficult to inhibit, and we could easily understand and perhaps justify why a person would act contrary to the law, those things don't remove one's ability to choose one way or another. Instead, they affect one's rationale and motivation for choosing.

Even if we assumed that "difficulties" removed a person's ability to act in certain ways, how would Industry professionals know or assess what level of *mental difficulty* was required in order to confirm the person wasn't capable of following the law? Also, if one proposes difficulty removes the ability to conform to the law, it means she is asserting the existence of difficulty as a non-self entity calling the shots. This is an untenable scientific assertion and it strains reason. The mental difficulty related to insanity refers to one's experience of emotional pain. It is not analogous to physical difficulty, chemical intoxication, brain pathology, and inherent cognitive limitations.

For instance, one might be able to lift increasingly heavy weights but at some point, the weight would be so heavy the person would be *unable* to lift it. But mental difficulty is not like this. Instead, it is another way to describe one's willingness to tolerate emotional pain (or physical pain) and to continue abiding by the law, nonetheless. So, mental difficulty is the basis for a person's choice to abide by the law, not the ability to abide by it. Many people have acted contrary to these kinds of mental difficulties, such as when a speaker continues on with a presentation despite feelings of embarrassment and fear, a grieving parent pushes forward in life despite the loss of a child, and when a soldier charges a hill knowing death is nearly certain.

An exception to this would be the reflexive surprise-startle response as described in Tomkins's theory of affects and mentioned earlier in the section about mental disability. It could be considered a true inability to conform to the law. In the surprise-startle situation, one's immediate reactions to an intense and abrupt trigger occur essentially in a reflexive manner. That initial reflex is next to impossible to stop. For instance, if I sneak up behind my friend and grab his shoulder, he might automatically whirl around and strike me, depending on his history and understanding of how threatening other people are. However, with effort he would be able to inhibit his subsequent actions, once he realized it was me. And any charges I pursued against him for assaulting me would likely be dismissed or lessened.

As they do with ignorance of the law, the courts consider the emotional pain experienced in the moments of criminal behavior as mitigating factors out of compassion in determining the seriousness of a crime and, therefore, whether and to what degree of accountability to hold the person. A person who kills in the heat of passion is usually considered less culpable than one who sets out with premeditation to kill, and the verdicts and sentences reflect this consideration. Also, someone who steals food to feed his family would be considered less accountable than a person who conspires to defraud an insurance company. But from a scientific perspective, which is the perspective Industry professionals claim to be using, it is indefensible to assert an internal entity disables us from acting in lawful ways.

Notwithstanding this lack of scientific evidence for internal entities or malfunctioning brains and minds that cause "mental illness," there is still a persistent and widespread belief that strange and harmful behaviors are not the doings of sane people. Instead, there appears to be comfort in thinking some type of alien force within, other than the person, compels actions. Further, as with disability evaluations, insanity assessments are not necessarily helpful and in fact can be harmful. See the case of Bill in Chapter 8 as an example of how being judged insane can be very harmful and strip someone of constitutional rights. The outcome can be far worse than if the person is adjudicated criminally responsible for the crime.

In the present day, "mental illness" is the convenient culprit as the purported internal alien force that makes us act in ways we wouldn't otherwise act. Other alleged mental forces are also implicated. Some of these are: temperaments, personalities, traits, impulses, compulsions, obsessions, addictions, habits, urges, desires, motivations, and difficulties. But these terms do not refer to entities residing within people and that control their thoughts and actions. They are just different reified terms we use to describe what people do, think, and feel. At one point in history, and still to some extent today, this alien force was thought to be demons or other evil spirits.

Whether invoking "mental illness" or demons, this interpretation of troublesome and strange behaviors helps us avoid the otherwise frightening idea that people can do terrible and bizarre things simply because it is what they desire to do in the moments of action. Nothing is pulling the strings. Further, the fictions of these mental forces and demons have allowed us to maintain the false but comforting belief in a fundamental difference between those who are abnormal (them) and the rest of us normal people (us). This belief gives us an illusory sense of immunity from those abnormal ways. In its humanity-wide version, this is the idea of good vs. evil, and the near frantic attempts to prove one is on the good side.

But the truth is, given the right set of circumstances, each of us has the potential to experience and do very strange and sometimes horrible things that are considered quite abnormal by observers. Many of us have done things we thought we'd never do, and that we deeply regret. But after doing those things, we can see much clearer how it can happen to "normal" people. Those unfortunate enough to experience the awful conditions of war find this out the hard way in the experience of *moral injury*.[10] Given the right combination of a sense of duty, patriotism, encouragement by and bonding with others, and fear of personal harm, warfighters can act in ways they later profoundly regret. But "mental illness," disability, or insanity does not cause them to act in those ways. Instead, the various labels given to those people, most likely "post-traumatic stress disorder" in this case, are how we later describe them.

Absent the effects of physiological impairments that lead to involuntary actions (including some of the negative effects of psychiatric drugs) and cognitive limitations like how low IQ prevents an understanding of things such as social norms, there is nothing inside us that makes us do what we do, whether we call it illness, demons, disability, bad traits, urges, insanity, or difficulties. Simply put, our actions reflect our desires to act in the moments of acting, even though we can certainly understand and perhaps justify actions given those contexts and the person's state of mind. When a gun is pointed at your head, it is easy to understand why you would want to hand over your money at that moment. But you are still able to refuse, even though it might be an unwise choice.

Two Kinds of Desire

I want to point out two kinds of desire that are frequently conflated. Confusing the two creates an illusion of mental disability. The first is a sense of desire for something in the future, such as when a person says she wants to quit smoking (or be more assertive, or start exercising, or stop ruminating). The second kind is when the moments to do those things arrive, but she doesn't do them. This is frequently accompanied by saying things like, "I just can't stop smoking," which falsely suggests an inability to do so. The second kind is an *in-the-moment desire* and it is far more important than the first.

We have all experienced the first kind, but when the opportunity arrives to put the first kind to work, we don't do it. This simply means we don't desire to do it at that moment. It is not an indicator of an inability to do so. It is easy to say we want to make difficult changes in our life when the opportunity to do so hasn't yet arrived. At that point they are just future ideas, possibilities, or aspirations. This is why New Year's resolutions are so plentiful, but few are carried out. It is with such a mindset that we say things like, "I want to lose weight," as we are biting into the fifth piece of pizza.

The second kind of desire is far more difficult to muster. It reflects what we desire in those moments of choice, and in the face of the difficulties of doing so. The reason we get confused with "Why can't I [fill in the blank]?" questions is because we are not paying attention to the difference between these two types of desire. The truthful answer to that question would be we have the ability, but we don't have the desire at the moment the opportunity for action arises.

We frequently hear comments such as, "I so much want to be assertive, but when the time comes, I just can't." Saying, "I so much want…." at the beginning of this statement creates an illusion that sets up the other illusion "I can't." The person who says this isn't paying attention to what "want" really means when he says it. Wishing for something or wanting something without including the difficulties of it creates this illusion. Truly wanting or desiring something entails taking it all, not just the easier pieces of it. A more accurate statement would be, "I so much want to be assertive, if it were easier and less frightening to do, but when the time comes, I find out how difficult and scary it is and since I don't want what comes with it, I choose not to be assertive."

It is a common belief that Industry professionals can teach techniques or relay knowledge that will help people avoid the difficulty of personal change. But they quickly find out it isn't true – we can't eliminate the difficulty involved in change. This can lead to what is known in the Industry as *therapeutic resistance*, which, by the way, is another phrase borrowed from medicine. This is when the person realizes he really doesn't want the thing he had been saying he wanted because the negative consequences of it are too much.

Another common reaction to the difficulty of personal change is splitting oneself into two. This is revealed in statements such as, "I need to convince myself to stop smoking (or get out of bed, or go to bed, or be more assertive)." Think about that for a moment. How can a person act as two and have a struggle between the two with one trying to convince the other what the other doesn't want to do? If either one wins, the other loses. This means loss is destined to occur for him. Who is resisting and who is the one doing the convincing?

We can't desire something and not desire it at the exact same time. What is happening when we say things like "I have to convince myself to…" is we are sequentially considering different options, possibilities, and fantasies. We notice the desire for something, but only if it were easier in some way. Then we notice how difficult it would be to take action and all the real-world consequences that would follow. Then we think perhaps the change isn't worth it. Then we wonder what will happen if we don't change. Then we find a renewed sense of wanting to change, although without the painful consequences of doing so. This thought process overlooks the reality that personal change is hard, damn hard, and it won't be any different. The existential ultimate concerns see to that.

As long as we talk and think in this self-confrontational way about problems, we will feel constantly in a state of coercion and, thus, will unlikely take any action. While I fully understand we speak this way colloquially, it nonetheless can put us at risk for perpetual stagnation if we don't remind ourselves of its illusory nature. This is especially true if we believe we are disabled in some way, which is what typically happens – how we language something has a huge effect on how we perceive our problems.[11] We might come to believe we can't change, so why try?

These language issues must be addressed during psychotherapy if the goal is to increase the chances the person will make substantial life changes. A psychotherapist can provide assistance by addressing this language problem along with other common therapeutic practices such as relaxation skills, meditation, journaling, visualization, personal planning, organizational skills, exploring felt senses, role playing, and the value of merely venting to an empathetic ear. But don't forget these practices do not make change easier, they just provide a "map" for the journey and offer support along the way. Facing these situations is the key, being compassionate with oneself, but also being careful not to attempt excessive escape along the way. It is also important to avoid the belief that a "mental illness" in the brain or the mind is preventing or dictating human choices.

While I think this is a far more accurate assessment of what we human beings do when faced with the existential emotional distress of living, I also admit it seems to make change harder and sometimes terrifying. But this apparent increased difficulty is due to the simplicity this model exposes. It removes any supposed impairment to making choices (not the difficulties) and it places the burden squarely on the shoulders of the person who is facing the distress. This is the freedom existential ultimate concern at work. The simple-complex continuum is not the same as the easy-difficult one. Simple things can be difficult and complex things can be easy. The act of choosing is a simple act that is very difficult to do in many situations.

The key to overcoming attempts to escape the emotional pain in our lives is to recognize our desires to act in the moments that count. Aspirational comments and beliefs about our desires for the future are important but they do not rise to the level of significance, as do our desires to resist the urges to escape in the moments when those urges occur. Understanding our desires in the only reality there is – the everlasting and ever-changing experiential *now* – is essential if we want to alter our life's direction and set a new course for living with contentment and personal satisfaction.

Chapter 16

Final Thoughts

> Today the function of psychiatry, psychology and psychoanalysis threatens to become the tool in the manipulation of men. The specialists in this field tell you what the "normal" person is, and, correspondingly, what is wrong with you.... There are many exceptions to this among psychiatrists, psychologists, and psychoanalysts, but it becomes increasingly clear that these professions are in the process of becoming a serious danger....
>
> - Eric Fromm, 1956[1]

Shortly before President John Kennedy cautioned Yale University graduates about the dangers of political myths[2] and psychiatrist Thomas Szasz exposed the Industry's abuses in *The Myth of Mental Illness*,[3] social psychologist Eric Fromm warned of the Industry's growing, dangerous, and unjustified efforts to control our lives. Little has changed over the last six decades, despite the well-reasoned and serious warnings by numerous scholars and practitioners since then (Appendix A).

In fact, one could argue things have become worse. Since the strengthening of biological psychiatry in the mid 20th century, along with its chemical cures, growing political and financial incentives have hardened the battlements of the defenders of the Myth hatched over a century before with Benjamin Rush's ideas about "diseases of the mind." This pessimistic observation makes it difficult for those of us within the marginalized critical psychiatry movement to have hope for a humane transformation of the current orthodox system.

Yet, we will continue the fight. The message is clear: "mental illness" is not illness. It is a moral judgment label applied to various forms of human suffering and individual differences. Branding people with its stigmatizing labels and subjecting them to medical model interventions is dangerous. At best, the phrase "mental illness" is a metaphorical use of medical language to highlight the seriousness of the problems it attempts to describe. But if there ever was a time when this metaphor was recognized, that time has long since passed. Most people, including the bulk of Industry professionals, have adopted a belief system – yes, I said a belief system, not a scientific position – that human emotions and behaviors are matters of health and illness of the brain, mind, or both.

However, there is no empirical evidence, logic, or line of critical reasoning that supports this belief system. Unless we are willing to open up the definitional gates to the ridiculous degree that any emotionally charged human problem or troublesome behavior is considered a matter of illness to be treated within a medical model, then we must restrict the concept of illness to physiological malfunctioning of the human body. The terms "mental" and "illness" cannot be included in the same phrase and still retain a literal meaning.

The concept of "mental illness" was built upon and is maintained with illusory twists of language, pseudoscience, and moral judgments. From its very beginning in the early 19th century, it has survived without a scientific foundation, even though it has developed a scientific and medical disguise concealing this more fundamental and serious flaw. The guardians of the Myth have repeated their worn-out reasoning, over and over again, and louder and louder, until their claims have attained the undeserved status of orthodoxy. The Myth seems impenetrable and it has deflected the numerous critiques made by the more reasonable and intellectually honest professionals within the Industry.

I want to emphasize the orthodox diagnostic labels reflect moral judgments of people and they are used for bureaucratic and administrative reasons only, not for the purpose of making decisions about how to help people. The Industry's own leaders have openly admitted those diagnoses are invalid and unreliable, even though they continue to be the basis for classifying human problems as illnesses. Many of the unsuspecting and unfortunate ones who have sought out professional help with personal problems have been labeled with these harmful diagnoses and assaulted with so-called "treatment," which remain with the person throughout life like the scars of a criminal record.

Other than self-maintenance of the Industry, the only benefit of this system has been to provide social control over, and a façade of protection from, people who have been deemed inappropriate or dangerous. While identifying and protecting society from truly dangerous people is clearly a worthy goal, that role is not within the expertise of the Industry. Instead, the societal responsibility of protecting the public is the jurisdiction of legal and political institutions, with sound input from the social sciences, but it is clearly not a matter of medicine or illness, unless there is an identifiable biological malfunction responsible for their actions.

Even though many governments around the world long ago abandoned religion's moral regulation of strange behaviors, and instead started ostensibly to use the standards of medical science in the 19th century and forward, morality was never actually replaced with science as the basis for judging those people. This is because there was never any medical foundation for those human problems. Instead, medical science has been a disguise. This makes the diagnosing of "mental illness" quite problematic since each professional must use not only the Industry's loose set of shared morals as reflected in the unreliable and invalid *DSM* and *ICD*, but also his or her own personal morals to some degree, in making that judgment call.

For this reason, there is no natural delineation between "mental health" and "mental illness." Still, Industry professionals continue to be given the authority to make these moral decisions about human actions and experiences. Their attempts to use statistics to verify mental and behavioral abnormality doesn't provide them with authoritative standards since morality comes into play when trying to decide just how deviant people have to be in order for them to be considered statistically abnormal.

The Myth is also bolstered by the financial and guild interests of those who benefit from it. Drug companies, "mental health" grassroots organizations, Industry professionals and their member organizations, health insurance companies, professional journals, and medical schools all have significant interests in seeing the system continue unabated. So, it is essential for these invested groups to encourage a widespread belief that the emotional and behavioral problems are about real illnesses and medical matters that demand medical forms of attention.

Billions are spent in this effort, especially by the drug companies in their attempts to market their products to the public, fund allied organizations who act as their principal mouthpieces, and schmooze physicians, who are the gatekeepers of drugs through their prescription authority. Without "mental illness" as illness, the drugs wouldn't make much sense. Money is also directed at lawmakers, who are the only ones who have the access and power to make fundamental change in the system, or, more likely, to protect that system from change.

We seem to be living in a time of increasing distrust of science, critical reasoning, and independent thought. Instead, a great many people who feel politically impotent, socially insignificant, and offended by perceived injustices, are relying more and more on rumor, tribal mentality, and revenge. Loyalty to populist leaders and simplistic retaliatory motives against the "other" is widespread. This appears to have created a mass of people who live life from within a "reality TV" perspective, seeking easy, quick, and entertaining solutions to very difficult, drawn out, and dreary life problems.

Among the convenient targets of this righteous indignation are people who have been labeled "mentally ill," and even many others who haven't been officially labeled but who are still considered different enough to be called "crazy," "not right in the head," and sometimes even the pseudo "mental illness" designator "evil." Those people, in addition to other recently tagged groups such as immigrants, liberals, and "fake news" journalists, have become the convenient blameworthy scapegoats for our social problems.

This makes our challenge against the power of the Industry even more so difficult. At a time when ill-informed masses of people are looking for others to blame, we are suggesting the people labeled "mentally ill" are not blameworthy candidates, primarily because nothing is constitutionally wrong with them, they are not diseased, and they are not the reason for society's woes. They are more likely the product of those woes.

Still, we must continue to nip at the heels of the giants who benefit from the continuation of the Industry and of those who perpetuate the urge to find scapegoats. The big question is whether we work toward reform from within or the outright abolition of the Industry as it currently exists. The former seems more likely as the latter would require a nearly impossible amount of resources and revolutionary change. After all, human distress and troublesome behaviors are not going away and so both public and private systems have a role in offering assistance to people who struggle with those problems. The current Industry could be used as a basic scaffold for that new structure. But it is long overdue for a major renovation.

On the other hand, there is potentially a third option. Perhaps, those of us pushing for a more humane way to help people in emotional distress could just set out on our own. We can declare independence from the Industry and offer our assistance to people without the stigmatizing labels, medical language, morality-driven interests, and disrespectful interventions of the orthodox system.

It is possible to construct a humane system of helping. The elements are already in place and there are many, many of us within the professions who reject the medical model and are willing to invest our efforts to humanely help people outside that failed model. The irony is that change can happen, but only by using the standards of scientific inquiry and critical thought in challenging a system supposedly already based on science. If we can get the message to the potential consumers of the Industry's services and convince them to stop buying the medical model product, then the manufacturers of the product will go financially bankrupt. They are already intellectually bankrupt. The hard part will be to disentangle any new model from the medical establishment. That would require substantial political pressure and even a makeover of the very language used within the new system.

Understanding human emotional and behavioral problems in living as natural reactions to the existential realities of life allows for more compassion and acceptance of those who so suffer. By removing the façade of medicine, and its accompanying political power, we can restore humanity to our lives and free ourselves from the authoritarian paternalism of the present-day Industry priesthood, leaving religion to the religious. It is only through this humane view of human struggles that we can fully appreciate the power of individual choice, respect for human dignity, and the entitlement of self-determination.

Epilogue

As this book goes to press, the world is experiencing a crisis of historic proportion. A new and deadly strain of coronavirus has emerged. It has infected more than seven million people in over 200 countries and the rising death toll has surpassed 400,000. In the United States, where more than a quarter of those deaths have occurred, patchwork efforts have apparently succeeded in slowing its deadly spread. But we're far from safe. The virus is still active and on the move. The resulting grief, social disruption, and economic plight will continue to be felt for years.

We naturally want to know as much as we can about COVID-19. How did it arise in humans? How does it spread? How fatal is it? How do we protect ourselves from it? How do we cure it? We also question whether our leaders are doing their best to coordinate and promote community health in the face of this unseen enemy.

In an attempt to find the answers to these questions, many are wondering who to believe. But I think a better way to answer the questions and inform ourselves is to wonder: How to believe? We must critically and dispassionately examine claims about the disease, rather than accept them just because they happen to support a certain narrative or because they are alarming. Some sources of information are more credible than others. Some details make more sense than others. Some facts are more substantiated than others. Some claims are more logical than others. But it can take a lot of time and effort to be well-informed this way, and many people are not able or willing to make the investment. This leaves them in a world of gossip and distrust.

Still, even the most informed person will face an element of uncertainty. It is not possible to know everything. This necessarily leaves us with a lingering sense of fear, about which we can do nothing but accept. Thus, faith in the process is crucial - being willing to go forward despite this uncertainty and fear, to learn what we can, to do what we can, and to carry on with our lives, nonetheless.

However, in an attempt to reduce uncertainty and fear, some try to fill in the gaps between what they know and what they don't. But they do so by entertaining dubious and sensational theories that tend to pit friend against friend, neighbor against neighbor, and citizen against citizen. These theories serve no purpose but to confuse and misdirect us in our attempts to handle the crisis. The more theories, the more confusion. This is the fuel that drives a rising and widespread sense of angst that the Industry predicts will cause an epidemic of "anxiety disorders" in the near future.

But don't fall prey to the Industry's urge to label you during this deadly time. Your fear in response to uncertainty is natural and expected. It is neither a "mental illness" nor an "anxiety disorder," and it doesn't need to be "treated" or eliminated. It is meaningful. It is not the problem. *The problem* lies in what you do in response to the fear. Find out what you can about the virus. Do your best to discriminate between facts and rumors. Be willing to admit when you just don't know. Above all, stop looking for a scapegoat to blame. Don't get caught in the never-ending cycle of hypervigilance, interpersonal suspicion, and wild speculation. Doing so can be just as destructive as the virus itself.

Appendix A

Selected Bibliography

Angell, M. (2005). *The Truth About the Drug Companies: How They Deceive Us and What to Do About It.* New York, NY: Random House.

Baughman, F. (2006). *The ADHD Fraud: How Psychiatry Makes "Patients" of Normal Children.* Bloomington, IN: Trafford Publishing.

Boyle, M. (1993). *Schizophrenia: A Scientific Delusion.* Abingdon, U.K.: Routledge.

Breggin, P. (1991). *Toxic Psychiatry: Why Therapy, Empathy and Love Must Replace the Drugs, Electroshock, and Biochemical Theories of the "New Psychiatry".* New York, NY: St. Martin's Press.

Breggin, P. (1995). *Talking Back to Prozac: What Doctors Won't Tell You About Today's Most Controversial Drug.* New York, NY: St. Martin's Press.

Breggin, P. (2001). *Talking Back to Ritalin: What Doctors Aren't Telling You About Stimulants and ADHD.* Cambridge, MA: Da Capo Press, Inc.

Breggin, P. (2008). *Medication Madness: A Psychiatrist Exposes the Dangers of Mood-Altering Medications.* New York: St. Martin's Press.

Breggin, P. & Cohen, D. (2000). *Your Drug May Be Your Problem: How and Why to Stop Taking Psychiatric Medications.* Cambridge, MA: Da Capo Press, Inc.

Caplan, P. (1996). *They Say You're Crazy: How the World's Most Powerful Psychiatrists Decides Who's Normal.* Cambridge, MA: Da Capo Lifelong Books.

Caplan, P. & Cosgrove, L. (Eds.). (2004). *Bias in Psychiatric Diagnosis.* Lanham, MD: Jason Aronson.

Colbert, T. (1996). *Broken Brains or Wounded Hearts: What Causes Mental Illness.* Orange, CA: Kevco Publishing.

Colbert, T. (2017). *The Four False Pillars of Biopsychiatry.* Orange, CA: Kevco Publishing.

Coleman, L. (1984). *The Reign of Error: Psychiatry, Authority, and Law.* New York, NY: Beacon Press.

Frances, A. (2013). *Saving Normal: An Insider's Revolt Against Out-Of-Control Psychiatric Diagnosis, DSM-5, Big Pharma, and the Medicalization of Ordinary Life.* New York, NY: William Morrow.

Gottstein, J. (2008). Involuntary commitment and forced psychiatric drugging in the trial courts: Rights violations as a matter of course. *Alaska Law Review, 25(51)*, 51-105. Retrieved from: http://psychrights.org/Research/Legal/25AkLRev51Gottstein2008.pdf.

Gottstein, J. (2020). *The Zyprexa Papers.* Anchorage, AK: Jim Gottstein.

Gøtzsche, P. (2013). *Deadly Medicines and Organised Crime: How Big Pharma Has Corrupted Healthcare.* Boca Raton, FL: CRC Press.

Gøtzsche, P. (2015). *Deadly Psychiatry and Organised Denial.* London, UK: Art People.

Greenberg, G. (2013). *The Book of Woe: The DSM and the Unmaking of Psychiatry.* New York, NY: Blue Rider Press.

Hagen, M. (1997). *Whores of the Courts: The Fraud of Psychiatric Testimony and the Rape of American Justice.* New York: HarperCollins.

Harrington, A. (2019). *Mind Fixers: Psychiatry's Troubled Search for the Biology of Mental Illness.* New York, NY: W. W. Norton & Co.

Healy, D. (2004). *The Creation of Psychopharmacology.* Cambridge, MA: Harvard University Press.

Healy, D. (2006). *Let Them Eat Prozac.* New York, NY: New York University Press.

Horowitz, A. (2003). *Creating Mental Illness.* Chicago, IL: University of Chicago Press.

Horowitz, A. & Wakefield, J. (2012). *The Loss of Sadness: How Psychiatry Transformed Normal Sorrow into Depressive Disorder.* Oxford, UK: Oxford University Press.

Jackson, G. (2005). *Rethinking Psychiatric Drugs: A Guide for Informed Consent.* Bloomington, IN: Author-House.

Jackson, G. (2009). *Drug-Induced Dementia: A Perfect Crime.* Bloomington, IN: Author-House.

Joseph, J. (2004). *The Gene Illusion: Genetic Research in Psychology and Psychiatry Under the Microscope.* New York: Algora Publishing.

Joseph, J. (2017). *Schizophrenia and Genetics: The End of an Illusion.* Pennsauken, NJ: Bookbaby.

Kirk, S.; Gomory, T.; & Cohen, D. (2015). *Mad Science: Psychiatric Coercion, Diagnosis, and Drugs.* Abingdon, U.K.: Routledge.

Kirsch, I. (2011). *The Emperor's New Drugs: Exploding the Antidepressant Myth.* New York, NY: Basic Books.

Kutchins, H. & Kirk, S. (1997). *Making Us Crazy: DSM: The Psychiatric Bible and the Creation of Mental Disorders.* New York: Free Press.

Levine, A. (2017). *Mental Health Inc.: How Corruption, Lax Oversight and Failed Reforms Endanger Our Most Vulnerable Citizens.* New York, NY: Harry N. Abrams.

Levine, B. (2003). *Commonsense Rebellion: Taking Back Your Life from Drugs, Shrinks, Corporations, and a World Gone Crazy.* New York, NY: Continuum.

Maisel, E. (2012). *Rethinking Depression: How to Shed Mental Health Labels and Create Personal Meaning.* Novalto, CA: New World Library.

Maisel, E. (2016). *The Future of Mental Health: Deconstructing the Mental Disorder Paradigm.* Abingdon, UK: Routledge.

Moncrieff, J. (2008). *The Myth of the Chemical Cure: A Critique of Psychiatric Drug Treatment.* Basingstoke, U.K.: Palgrave MacMillan.

Moncrieff, J.; Cohen, D.; & Porter, S. (2013). The psychoactive effects of psychiatric medication: The elephant in the room. *Journal of Psychoactive Drugs, 45(5)*, 409-415. https://doi:10.1080/02791072.2013.845328.

Morgan, R. (Ed.). (2005). *The Iatrogenics Handbook: A Critical Look at Research & Practice in the Helping Professions.* Albuquerque, NM: Morgan Foundation.

Morgan, R. (Ed.) (1999). *Electroshock: The Case Against.* Albuquerque, NM: Morgan Foundation.

Moynihan, R. & Cassels, A. (2006). *Selling Sickness: How the World's Biggest Pharmaceutical Companies Are Turning Us All into Patients.* New York, NY: Nation Books.

Newman, F. & Holzman, L. (2006). *Unscientific Psychology: A Cultural-Performatory Approach to Understanding Human Life.* Bloomington, IN: iUniverse, Inc.

Ross, C. & Pam, A. (1995). *Pseudoscience in Biological Psychiatry: Blaming the Body.* Hoboken, NJ: John Wiley & Sons.

Sharpe, K. (2012). *Coming of Age on Zoloft: How Antidepressants Cheered Us Up, Let Us Down, and Changed Who We Are.* New York, NY: Harper Perennial.

Sheller, S.; Kirkpatrick, S.; & Mondics, C. (2019). *Big Pharma, Big Greed: The Inside Story of One Lawyer's Battle to Stem the Flood of Dangerous Medicines and Protect Public Health.* Washington, DC: Strong Arm Press.

Simon, L. (2019). *Psycho"therapy" and the Stories We Live By.* New York, NY: Bookbaby.

Sinaikin, P. (2010). *Psychiatryland: How to Protect Yourself from Pill-Pushing Psychiatrists and Develop a Personal Plan for Optimal Mental Health.* Bloomington, IN: iUniverse, Inc.

Smedslund, J. (2012). The bricoleur model of psychological practice. *Theory & Psychology, 22(5),* 643-657. https://doi.org/10.1177/0959354312441277.

Szasz, T. (1961). *The Myth of Mental Illness: Foundations of a Theory of Personal Conduct.* New York: Harper & Row.

Szasz, T. (1970). *The Manufacture of Madness: A Comparative Study of the Inquisition and the Mental Health Movement.* New York: Harper & Row.

Szasz, T. (1984). *The Therapeutic State: Psychiatry in the Mirror of Current Events.* Amherst, NY: Prometheus Books.

Szasz, T. (2007). *Medicalization of Everyday Life: Selected Essays.* Syracuse, NY: Syracuse University Press.

Szasz, T. (2008). *Psychiatry: The Science of Lies.* Syracuse, NY: Syracuse University Press.

Szasz, T. (2009). *Coercion as Cure: A Critical History of Psychiatry.* Abingdon, U.K.: Routledge.

Valenstein, E. (2002). *Blaming the Brain: The Truth About Drugs and Mental Health.* New York: Free Press.

Whitaker, R. (2010). *Mad in America: Bad Science, Bad Medicine, and the Enduring Mistreatment of the Mentally Ill (2nd Ed.).* New York, NY: Basic Books.
Whitaker, R. (2011). *Anatomy of an Epidemic: Magic Bullets, Psychiatric Drugs, and the Astonishing Rise of Mental Illness in America.* New York, NY: Broadway Books.

Whitaker, R. & Cosgrove, L. (2015). *Psychiatry Under the Influence: Institutional Corruption, Social Injury, and Prescriptions For Reform.* Basingstoke, U.K.: Palgrave Macmillan.

Williams, P. (2012). *Rethinking Madness: Towards a Paradigm Shift in Our Understanding and Treatment of Psychosis.* San Francisco, CA: Sky's Edge Publishing.

Appendix B

Mental Illness Glossary

Abnormal – Morally inappropriate.

Addiction – A strong desire to do something soothing.

Alcoholism – Drinking too much alcohol.

Anxiety – Mental and physical hypervigilance.

Bipolar disorder – Trying to exceed human limitations.

Chemical imbalance (mythical) – A baseless assumption that a surplus or deficit of brain chemicals cause "mental illness."

Chemical imbalance (real) – A disruption of normal brain chemistry caused by mind-altering drugs, including psychiatric drugs.

Clinic – A clinician's office location.

Clinical – Occurring in a clinician's office.

Clinician – A professional who works in a clinic.

Counselor, Psychotherapist – A person who tries to help others who have life problems, usually in exchange for money.

Counseling, Psychotherapy – What counselors and psychotherapists do – talking.

Depression – Shutting down in passivity.

Diagnosis – With "mental illness," it is the name given to a problem. With real illness, it is the name given to a bodily disease process.

Dysfunctional – Inappropriate.

Medical necessity – Warranting reimbursement from health insurance companies.

Mental disease – See "mental illness."

Mental disorder – See "mental illness."

Mental health – The condition in which a person is free of difficult life problems.

Mental illness – The condition in which a person is facing difficult life problems.

Mind – A person's ongoing experiences. Inferred by that person's conduct and actions.

Normal – Morally appropriate

Pathological – Morally inappropriate.

Patient – A person who seeks out the help of a true medical professional.

Personality disorder – A broad and chronic style of living that can cause problems.

Psychiatrist – A physician with specialized training in how to control people who are complaining about life problems by getting them to stop complaining.

Psychological tests – Opinion surveys, performance measures, or speculations about a person.

Psychologist – A social scientist with specialized training in experiential and behavioral aspects of human living. (Clinical Psychologist – A psychologist with special training in how to control people who are complaining about life problems by getting them to stop complaining.)

Psychopathology – See "mental illness."

Psychosis – Abandonment of consensual reality.

Symptoms – With "mental illness," a person's stated or manifested complaints about life problems. With real illness, what patients experience because of disease.

Syndrome – A grouping of problems.

Treatment – With "mental illness," a professional's attempt to stop a person from complaining about life problems. With real illness, addressing disease processes of the body and attempting to alleviate them.

Treatment (humane form) – A professional's attempt to help someone deal with life problems and achieve a sense of overall contentment and satisfaction with life.

Appendix C

False Positives and Screening Tools

(Warning: For convenience sake, medical language is used in this explanation.)

- An 80% accurate depression screening tool.
- A tool's accuracy is stated in two ways:
  - *Sensitivity* is the accuracy of detecting a true case (i.e., the person is depressed).
  - *Specificity* is the accuracy of detecting a false case (i.e., the person is not depressed).
- 3.2% rate of depression for children and adolescents.
- Hypothetical sample of 1,000 kids.
- 2 X 2 contingency table:

Is the person depressed?

	Yes	No	
Screening results: Positive	26	194 (false positives)	220
Negative	6 (false negatives)	774	780
	32	968	1,000

- Discussion:
  - In the hypothetical population of 1,000 children and adolescents with a 3.2% base rate of depression, 32 will be depressed ($3.2\%_{\text{base rate}}$ X $1{,}000 = 32_{\text{depressed}}$) and the remaining 968 will not be depressed.
  - An 80% accurate screening tool will accurately identify 26 of the 32 truly depressed kids ($32_{\text{depressed}}$ X $80\%_{\text{accuracy}} = 26_{\text{identified}}$).
  - But it will misidentify 6 truly depressed kids as not being depressed ($32_{\text{depressed}} - 26_{\text{identified}} = 6_{\text{misidentified}}$) and thus not offered assistance.
  - The 80% accurate screening tool will accurately identify 774 of the 968 not depressed kids ($968_{\text{not depressed}}$ X $80\%_{\text{accuracy}} = 774_{\text{identified}}$).
  - But it will misidentify 194 not depressed kids as being depressed ($968_{\text{not depressed}} - 774_{\text{identified}} = 194_{\text{misidentified}}$).

While 80% of all truly depressed kids would be accurately identified, and 80% of all truly not depressed kids would be accurately identified, 88% of all those identified as being depressed using this screening tool would not actually be depressed. These are the false positives ($26_{\text{truly depressed}} + 194_{\text{not depressed}} = 220_{\text{identified depressed}}$; $194_{\text{not depressed}} \div 220_{\text{identified depressed}} = 88\%$). This means that only about one out of every 10 children identified as depressed will truly be depressed. Nine will not be depressed but will still be subjected to the stigmatizing label and unnecessary treatment.

Appendix D

Hypothetical Psychotherapy Effect Size

(Warning: For convenience sake, medical language is used in this explanation.)

- Two groups
  - Psychotherapy group – undergoes psychotherapy
  - Control group – has no psychotherapy
  - 30 people in each
- Each person rated on 9-point scale showing level of depression
  - Lower scores indicate less depression
  - Higher scores indicate more depression
- Ratings collected before and after treatment
- Dataset
  - Both groups started out with exact scores
  - Scores that were worse after the study are underlined
  - Before/after scores separated by a slash (/)
  - Treatment group: 5/7, 3/1, 7/5, 6/8, 5/3, 3/1, 3/1, 2/4, 8/6, 7/5, 6/4, 5/3, 3/1, 4/6, 5/3, 7/5, 7/9, 9/7, 8/6, 3/1, 3/1, 6/8, 4/2, 7/5, 8/6, 3/5, 3/5, 8/6, 9/7, 6/4.
    - 22 less depressed after treatment
    - 8 more depressed after treatment
  - Control group: 5/5, 3/5, 7/7, 6/8, 5/5, 3/5, 3/3, 2/2, 8/8, 7/9, 6/8, 5/5, 3/3, 4/4, 5/7, 7/9, 3/3, 9/9, 8/8, 3/3, 3/3, 6/6, 4/4, 7/9, 8/8, 3/3, 3/3, 8/8, 9/9, 6/6.
    - 8 more depressed while they waited
    - 22 remained the same

- The following statistics are derived from this dataset using https://www.socscistatistics.com:

	Treatment	Control
Mean (M)	4.50	5.83
Standard Deviation (SD)	2.374	2.365
Cohen's d*	.56 (medium magnitude)	

*The effect size computation assumes that the two groups represent normally distributed (bell curve) populations. When this assumption is not met, the effect size statistic is to be interpreted with caution. This analysis assumes that if we measured the depression scores of two very large groups of people (e.g., 100,000 each) their distributions would be approximately normal. I think this is a safe assumption since there doesn't appear to be any reason to doubt that those distributions would vary from a normal distribution. In other words, depression appears to follow a normal distribution similar to how height, weight, and most any other human characteristic does. Just to gauge, though, I calculated (but only based on the samples above) measures to get a sense of whether they are from normally distributed theoretical populations. These are measures of *skewness* (if the distribution is symmetrical) and *kurtosis* (how peaked or flat is the distribution). The skewness was .06 and the kurtosis was -1.3. Both these are within the guidelines of +/- 2 for skewness and +/- 7 for kurtosis. (West, S.; Finch, J.; Curran, P. {1995}. Structural equation models with nonnormal variables: problems and remedies. In: Hoyle, R., editor. *Structural Equation Modeling: Concepts, Issues and Applications.* Newbery Park, CA: Sage, pp. 56–75.)

- Treatment group has lower depression (average) than the control group; shows that treatment "worked"
- Despite the medium effect size, the practical significance is questionable
  - Only a 1.3 score difference – between 4.5 and 5.8 for treatment and control groups, respectively
  - Both are less than one point away from midpoint on 9-point scale
  - Treatment resulted in worsened depression for 8 people (27% of group)
  - Medium effect size of .56 = correlation of .27

        - Correlation squared ($R2$) = Percent of variance explained = .073
        - Only 7% of the change in depression is attributable to treatment
        - 93% attributed to factors not being studied
    - Large effect size of .80 still only has R2 of .14
        - Only 14% of change in depression would be due to treatment; 86% to other factors not being studied
- Study results such as these would be used to demonstrate standard of care but, even so, they indicate that such treatment might harm and won't help much.

Notes

Introduction

[1] Kennedy, J. (1962). Commencement Address at Yale University, June 11, 1962. Online by Gerhard Peters and John T. Woolley, *The American Presidency Project*. Retrieved from: http://www.presidency.ucsb.edu/ws/?pid=29661.
[2] I'll refer to the "mental health" industry as just "the Industry." This is similar to how George Orwell used the "Ministry" (e.g., the "Ministry of Love") in his novel *1984* in order to designate its all-powerful, controlling, but deceptive nature.
[3] Szasz, T. (1961). *The Myth of Mental Illness: Foundations of a Theory of Personal Conduct*. New York: Harper & Row.
[4] As will be highlighted many times in this book, we can either put on blinders and adopt a belief system about things, regardless of the evidence, or we can pay attention to the evidence in our lives and make conclusions based on that evidence. See Chapter 12 for a far more detailed examination of this issue.
[5] Ventriglio, A.; Torales, J.; & Bhugra, D. (2016). Disease versus illness: What do clinicians need to know? *International Journal of Social Psychiatry, 63(1)*, 3-4. https://doi.org/10.1177/0020764016658677.
[6] Conrad, P. (2007). *The Medicalization of Society: On the Transformation of Human Conditions into Treatable Disorders*. Baltimore, MD: Johns Hopkins University Press; Szasz, T. (2007). *The Medicalization of Everyday Life: Selected Essays*. Syracuse, NY: Syracuse University Press.
[7] Buoli, M. & Giannuli, A. (2017). The political use of psychiatry: A comparison of totalitarian regimes. *International Journal of Social Psychiatry, 63(2)*, 169-174. https://doi.org/10.1177/0020764016688714
[8] Grohol, J. (2016). Mental Health Professionals: US Statistics. *Psych Central.* Retrieved from: https://psychcentral.com/lib/mental-health-professionals-us-statistics/.
[9] Yalom, I. (2017). *The Gift of Therapy: An Open Letter to a New Generation of Therapists and Their Patients*. New York, NY: HarperCollins Publishers. [Kindle version: Chapter 27, paragraph 1].

Part I: The Disguise

[1] Paz, O. (1991). *The Monkey Grammarian*. Chapter 4. New York, NY: Arcade Publishing.
[2] Leifer, R. (2017). Imposters, liars, and thugs: The face behind the medical mask of psychiatry. *Ethical Human Psychology & Psychiatry: An International Journal of Critical Inquiry, 19(3)*, 176-181. https:// https://doi.org/10.1891/1559-4343.19.3.176.

Chapter 1: Illusions of Language

[1] Wittgenstein, L. (1953). *Philosophical Investigations*. London: Blackwell.
[2] Gomory, T.; Cohen, D.; & Kirk, S. (2013). Madness or Mental Illness? Revisiting Historians of Psychiatry. *Current Psychology, 32*, 119-135.
[3] This was the late Sandy Kerr, Ph.D., at the Florida State University. Sandy was a mathematician and psychologist. He offered a unique mentorship that encouraged independent and critical thinking, self-confidence, and a form of helping people in a empathetic, non-pathologizing, way. His guidance was unmatched.
[4] Poyani (2012, December). *George Carlin – Euphemisms* [Video File]. Retrieved from: https://www.youtube.com/watch?v=vuEQixrBKCc.

Chapter 2: The Invention of a Myth

[1] More formally, there are "signs" and "symptoms." Signs are the things that the physician observes about a patient. Symptoms are the things that the patient experiences and reports to the physician. Just for simplicity sake, I'll refer to both as symptoms.

[2] This obviously excludes the cases where a person is faking or exaggerating for some financial gain or to gain the attention of others. Further, it would be a fool's errand to try to determine if a person genuinely believed he was experiencing pain, but really wasn't. How would we ever verify if he really was or wasn't experiencing pain if he truly believes he is?

[3] Ventriglio, A.; Torales, J.; & Bhugra, D. (2016). Disease versus illness: What do clinicians need to know? *International Journal of Social Psychiatry, 63(1)*, 3-4. https://doi.org/10.1177/0020764016658677.

[4] Crozatti, L.; Britto, M.; Lopez, B.; & Campos, F. (2015). Atypical behavioral and psychiatric symptoms: Neurosyphilis should always be considered. *Autopsy and Case Reports, 5(3)*, 43-47. https:// 10.4322/acr.2015.021.

[5] Fallon, B. & Nields, J. (1994). Lyme's disease: A neuropsychiatric illness. *American Journal of Psychiatry, 151(11)*, 1571-1583. https:// DOI:10.1176/ajp.151.11.1571.

[6] Hage, M. & Azar, S. (2012). The link between thyroid function and depression. *Journal of Thyroid Research*. https:// doi.org/10.1155/2012/590648.

[7] Richards, G. & Smith, A. (2015). Caffeine consumption and self-assessed stress, anxiety, and depression in secondary school children. *Journal of Psychopharmacology, 29(12)*, 1236-1247. https:// 10.1177/0269881115612404.

[8] Nigg, J. (2016). Understanding the link between lead toxicity and ADHD. *Psychiatric Times, 33(9)*. Retrieved from: http://www.psychiatrictimes.com/special-reports/understanding-link-between-lead-toxicity-and-adhd.

[9] American Psychiatric Association. (2013). *Diagnostic and Statistical Manual of Mental Disorders* (5th Edition). Washington, DC: American Psychiatric Association.

[10] Ibid, p. 602.

[11] Ibid.

[12] Ibid.

[13] Ibid, p. 499 (alcohol withdrawal).

[14] Ibid, p. 378.

[15] Ibid, p. 175 (depression).

[16] Ibid, p. 145 (bipolar disorder).

[17] Pescosolido, B. (2013). The public stigma of mental illness: What do we think; what do we know; what can we prove? *Journal of Health and Social Behavior, 54(1)*, 1-21. https://doi.org/10.1177/0022146512471197.

[18] Pies, R. (2011, July). Psychiatry's New Brain-Mind and the Legend of the "Chemical Imbalance". *Psychiatric Times.* Retrieved from: http://www.psychiatrictimes.com/couch-crisis/psychiatrys-new-brain-mind-and-legend-chemical-imbalance.

[19] I choose not to call them psychiatric "medicines" or "medications" as they do not medicate anything. They are more honestly described as drugs or chemicals, the same as how we would describe arsenic or opium.

[20] Pies, R. (2019, April). Debunking the two chemical imbalance myths, again. *Psychiatric Times, 36(8).* Retrieved from: https://www.psychiatrictimes.com/depression/debunking-two-chemical-imbalance-myths-again.

[21] Hickey, P. (2019, July). The Chemical Imbalance Theory: Dr. Pies Returns, Again. Blog entry at Mad in America. Retrieved from: https://www.madinamerica.com/2019/07/chemical-imbalance-theory-dr-pies-returns-again/; McLaren, N. (2019, September). Pies' Polemic and the Question of Theories in Psychiatry, Again. Blog entry at Mad in America. Retrieved from: https://www.madinamerica.com/2019/09/pies-polemic-and-the-question-of-theories-in-psychiatry-again/.

[22] Insel, T. (2011). Post by Former NIMH Director Thomas Insel: Mental Illness Defined as Disruption in Neural Circuits. Retrieved from: https://www.nimh.nih.gov/about/directors/thomas-insel/blog/2011/mental-illness-defined-as-disruption-in-neural-circuits.shtml.

[23] Harvard Health Publishing. (2019, June). What Causes Depression? Retrieved from: https://www.health.harvard.edu/mind-and-mood/what-causes-depression

[24] American Psychiatric Association. (2019). What Is Depression? Retrieved from: https://www.psychiatry.org/patients-families/depression/what-is-depression.

[25] Spiegel, A. (2014, January). When It Comes To Depression, Serotonin Isn't The Whole Story. *National Public Radio.* Retrieved from: https://www.npr.org/sections/health-shots/2012/01/23/145525853/when-it-comes-to-depression-serotonin-isnt-the-whole-story.

[26] Ibid.

[27] Breggin, P. (1991). *Toxic Psychiatry: Why Therapy, Empathy and Love Must Replace the Drugs, Electroshock, and Biochemical Theories of the "New Psychiatry".* New York, NY: St. Martin's Press.

[28] Pandya, M.; Altinay, M.; Malone, D.; & Anand, A. (2012). Where in the brain is depression? *Current Psychiatry Reports, 14(6)*, 634-642. https:// https://dx.doi.org/10.1007%2Fs11920-012-0322-7.

[29] Bremner, J. (2006). Traumatic stress: Effects on the brain. *Dialogues in Clinical Neuroscience, 8(4)*, 445-461.

[30] Ho, J.; Zhao, M.; Zhang, W.; Song, L.; Wu, W.; Wang, J.;…& Li, H. (2014). Resting-state functional connectivity abnormalities in patients with obsessive-compulsive disorder and their healthy first-degree relatives. *Journal of Psychiatry & Neuroscience, 39(5)*, 304-311. https:// https://dx.doi.org/10.1503%2Fjpn.130220.

[31] Sun, H.; Chen, Y.; Huang, Q.; Lui, S.:Huang, X.; Shi, Y.;…& Gong, Q. (2017). Psychoradiologic Utility of MR Imaging for Diagnosis of Attention Deficit Hyperactivity Disorder: A Radiomics Analysis. *Radiology, 287(2)*. https://doi.org/10.1148/radiol.2017170226.

[32] Hunter, N. & Schultz, W. (2017). White Paper: Brain Scan Research. *Ethical Human Psychology and Psychiatry: An International Journal of Critical Inquiry, 18(1)*, 9-19, p. 11. https://dx.doi.org/10.1891/1559-4343.18.1.29.

[33] Kolb, B.; Gibb, R.; & Robinson, T. (2003). Brain plasticity and behavior. *Current Directions in Psychological Science, 12(1)*, 1-5. https://doi.org/10.1111/1467-8721.01210.

[34] Bianco, R.; Novembre, G.; Keller, P.; Villringer, A.; & Sammler, D. (2018). Musical genre dependent behavioural and EEG signatures of action planning. A comparison between classical and jazz pianists. *NeuroImage, 169*, 383-394. https:// DOI: 10.1016/j.neuroimage.2017.12.058.

[35] Lu, J.; Yang, H.; Zhang, X.; He, H.; Luo, C.; & Yao, D. (2015). The brain functional state of music creation: An fMRI study of composers. *Scientific Reports, 5, 12277*. https:// doi: 10.1038/srep12277.

[36] Sadato, N; Pascual-Leone, A.; Grafman, J.; Deiber, M.; Ibañez, V.; & Hallett, M. (1998). Neural networks for Braille reading by the blind. *Brain, 121*, 1213-1229. Retrieved from: https://www.ncbi.nlm.nih.gov/pubmed/9679774.

[37] Luders, E.; Kurth, F.; Mayer, E.; Toga, A.; Narr, K.; & Gaser, C. (2012). The unique brain anatomy of meditation practitioners: alterations in cortical gyrification. *Frontiers in Human Neuroscience, 6 (34)*. https://doi.org/10.3389/fnhum.2012.00034.

[38] Pereira, F.; Detre, G.; & Botvinick, M. (2011). Generating text from functional brain images. *Frontiers in Human Neuroscience, 5*. https://doi.org/10.3389/fnhum.2011.00072.

[39] Schreiber, D.: Fonzo, G.; Simmons, A.; Dawes, C.; Flagan, T.; Fowler, J.; & Paulus, M. (2013). Red brain, blue brain: Evaluative processes differ in democrats and republicans. *PLOS ONE, 8(2)*: e52970. https://doi.org/10.1371/journal.pone.0052970.

[40] Gillihan, S. (2016). Using brain scans to diagnose mental disorders: Unfortunately, the science isn't there. *Psychology Today*. Retrieved from: https://www.psychologytoday.com/us/blog/think-act-be/201605/using-brain-scans-diagnose-mental-disorders; Sawyer, K. (2013, October). Brain imaging: What good is it? *Psychology Today*. Retrieved from: https://www.psychologytoday.com/us/blog/zig-zag/201310/brain-imaging-what-good-is-it.

[41] Bennet, C; Baird, A.; Miller, M.; & Wolford, G. (2010). Neural correlates of interspecies perspective taking in the post-mortem Atlantic salmon: An argument for proper multiple comparisons correction. *Journal of Serendipitous and Unexpected Results*, 1(1), 1-5. https:// http://dx.doi.org/10.1016/S1053-8119(09)71202-9.

[42] Schmitz, T.; Correia, M.; Ferreira, C.; Prescott, A.; & Anderson, M. (2017). Hippocampal GABA enables inhibitory control over unwanted thoughts. *Nature Communications, 8(1311)*. http://doi:10.1038/s41467-017-00956-z.

[43] Mattejat, F. (2008). The children of mentally ill parents. *Deutsches Ärzteblatt International, 105(23)*, 413-418. https://doi:10.3238/arztebl.2008.0413.

[44] Glasser, M.; Kolvin, I.; Campbell, D.; Glasser, A.; Leitch, I; & Farrelly, S. (2001). Cycle of child sexual abuse: links between being a victim and becoming a perpetrator. *British Journal of Psychiatry, 179*, 482-494. https://https://doi.org/10.1192/bjp.179.6.482.

[45] Johnson, J. & Leff, M. (1999). Children of substance abusers: Overview of research findings. *Pediatrics, 103(5),* 1085-1099. Retrieved from: https://pediatrics.aappublications.org/content/pediatrics/103/Supplement_2/1085.full.pdf.

[46] Joseph, J. (2017). *Schizophrenia and Genetics: The End of an Illusion*. Pennsauken, NJ: Bookbaby.

[47] The environment plays two roles. First, one's environment influences a person's learning and psychological development, to include whether or not they develop problems in life that get diagnosed as "mental illness." Second, the environment directly affects gene expression, meaning whether genes are "turned on" or not. Consequently, a particular genetic risk doesn't always reveal itself unless the right environmental conditions are present. This second role of the environment is called *epigenetics*. This makes it particularly difficult to tease apart the true effects of genes (nature) and the effects of the environment (nurture).

[48] For example: Fosse, R.; Joseph, J; & Richardson, K. (2015). A critical assessment of the equal-environment assumption of the twin method for schizophrenia. *Frontiers in Psychiatry, 6(62)*. http://doi.org/10.3389/fpsyt.2015.00062; Hahn, P. (2019). *Madness and Genetic Determinism: Is Mental Illness in Our Genes?* London, UK: Palgrave Macmillan; Joseph, J. (2004). *The Gene Illusion: Genetic Research in Psychology and Psychiatry Under the Microscope*. New York: Algora Publishing; Joseph, J. (2017). *Schizophrenia and Genetics: The End of an Illusion*. Pennsauken, NJ: Bookbaby; Ross, C. (2018). How the incorrect belief that eating disorders are predominantly genetic is maintained. *Ethical Human Psychology and Psychiatry, 20(2)*, 73-78. https:dx.doi.org/10.1891/1559-4343.20.2.73.

[49] Blanck, P. (Ed.). (1993). *Studies in Emotion and Social Interaction. Interpersonal Expectations: Theory, Research, and Applications*. New York, NY, US: Cambridge University Press; Paris, France: Editions de la Maison des Sciences de l'Homme.

[50] Vandeleur, C.; Rothen, S.; Gholam-Rezaee, M.; Castelao, E.; Vidal, S.; Favre, S.; Ferrero, F.; et al. (2012). Mental disorders in offspring of parents with bipolar and major depressive disorders. *Bipolar Disorder, 14(6)*. 641-653. https://doi:10.1111/j.1399-5618.2012.01048.x.

[51] Joseph, J. & Leo, J. (2006). Genetic Relatedness and the Lifetime Risk for Being Diagnosed with Schizophrenia: Gottesman's 1991 Figure 10 Reconsidered. *The Journal of Mind and Behavior, 27(1)*, 73-90. Retrieved from: https://www.researchgate.net/publication/286015176_Genetic_Relatedness_and_the_Lifetime_Risk_for_Being_Diagnosed_with_Schizophrenia_Gottesman%27s_1991_Figure_10_Reconsidered.

[52] Cross-Disorder Group of the Psychiatric Genomics Consortium. (2013). Identification of risk loci with shared effects on five major psychiatric disorders: a genome-wide analysis. *Lancet, 381*, 1371-1379. http://dx.doi.org/10.1016/S0140-6736(12)62129-1.
[53] National Institutes of Health. (2013, March). Common Genetic Factors Found in 5 Mental Disorders. Retrieved from: https://www.nih.gov/news-events/nih-research-matters/common-genetic-factors-found-5-mental-disorders.
[54] Gandal, M.; Haney, J.; Parikshak, M.; Leppa, V.; Ramaswami, G.; & Hart, C. (2018). Shared molecular neuropathology across major psychiatric disorders parallels polygenic overlap. *Science, 359(6376)*, 693-697. http://doi:10.1126/science.aad6469.
[55] Barrès, R.; Yan, J.; Egan, B.; Treebak, J.; Rasmussen, M.; Fritz, T.;...& Zierath, J. (2012). Acute exercise remodels promoter methylation in human skeletal muscle. *Cell Metabolism, 15(3)*, 405-411. http://doi: 10.1016/j.cmet.2012.01.001.
[56] Robinson, G.; Fernald, R.; & Clayton, D. (2008). Genes and social behavior. *Science, 322(5903)*, 896-900. https://doi: 10.1126/science.1159277.

Chapter 3: Psychological Testing

[1] Wechsler, D. (2008). Wechsler Adult Intelligence Scale (4th Ed.) (WAIS-IV) [Assessment Instrument]. San Antonio, TX: Pearson Corp.
[2] Butcher, J.; Graham, J.; Ben-Porath, Y.; Tellegen, A; Dahlstrom, W.; & Kaemmer, B. (2009). Minnesota Multiphasic Personality Inventory (2nd Ed.) (MMPI-2) [Assessment Instrument]. Minneapolis, MN: University of Minnesota Press.
[3] Capricorn Horoscope. 2019, February). Retrieved from: https://www.horoscope.com/us/horoscopes/general/horoscope-general-daily-today.aspx?sign=10
[4] Exner, J.E. (2003). *The Rorschach: A Comprehensive System, Vol. 1: Basic Foundations* (4th ed.). New York, NY: Wiley.
[5] Framingham, J. (2016). Rorschach Inkblot Test. *Psych Central.* Retrieved from: https://psychcentral.com/lib/rorschach-inkblot-test/.
[6] Garb, H.; Wood, J.; Lilienfeld, S.; & Nezworski, M. (2002). Effective use of projective techniques in clinical practice: Let the data help with selection and interpretation. *Professional Psychology: Research and Practice, 33(5)*, 454-463. https://doi:10.1037//0735-7028.33.5.454.; Vincent, K. & Harman, M. (1991). The Exner Rorschach: An analysis of its clinical validity. *Journal of Clinical Psychology, 47(4)*, 596-599. https:// https://doi.org/10.1002/1097-4679(199107)47:4<596::AID-JCLP2270470420>3.0.CO;2-8.
[7] Meyer, G.; Viglione, D.; Mihura, J.; Erard, R.; & Erdberg, P. (2011). *Rorschach Performance Assessment System: Administration, Coding, Interpretation, and Technical Manual.* Toledo, OH: Rorschach Performance Assessment System.
[8] Aubrey, A. (2018, February). Pediatricians Call For Universal Depression Screening For Teens. *NPR.* Retrieved from: https://www.npr.org/sections/health-shots/2018/02/26/588334959/pediatrians-call-for-universal-depression-screening-for-teens.

[9] National Alliance on Mental Illness. (2019). Mental Health Screening. Retrieved from: https://www.nami.org/Learn-More/Mental-Health-Public-Policy/Mental-Health-Screening.

[10] McGinnis, R.; McGinnis, E.; Hruschak, N.; Lopez-Duran, N.; Fitzgerald, K.; Rosenblum, K.; & Muzik, M. (2019). Rapid detection of internalizing diagnosis in young children enabled by wearable sensors and machine learning. *PLOS One*. https://doi.org/10.1371/journal.pone.0210267.

[11] Grohol, J. (2017). Short Autism Screening Quiz. *Psych Central.* Retrieved from: https://psychcentral.com/quizzes/autism-quiz/.

[12] Blanck, P. (Ed.). (1993). *Studies In Emotion and Social Interaction. Interpersonal Expectations: Theory, Research, and Applications*. New York, NY, US: Cambridge University Press; Paris, France: Editions de la Maison des Sciences de l'Homme.

[13] Centers for Disease Control and Prevention (2019). Children's Mental Health. Retrieved from: https://www.cdc.gov/childrensmentalhealth/data.html.

[14] Lavigne, J.; Feldman, M.; & Meyers, K. (2016). Screening for Mental Health Problems: Addressing the Base Rate Fallacy for a Sustainable Screening Program in Integrated Primary Care. *Journal of Pediatric Psychology, 41(10)*, 1081-1090. https://doi.org/10.1093/jpepsy/jsw048.

[15] U.S. Census Bureau. (2016). Quick Facts. Retrieved from: https://www.census.gov/quickfacts/fact/table/US/AGE295216#viewtop.

[16] Aubrey, A. (2018, February). Pediatricians Call For Universal Depression Screening For Teens. *NPR.* Retrieved from: https://www.npr.org/sections/health-shots/2018/02/26/588334959/pediatrians-call-for-universal-depression-screening-for-teens.

[17] National Institute of Mental Health (2018, May). Schizophrenia. Retrieved from: https://www.nimh.nih.gov/health/statistics/schizophrenia.shtml#part_154880.

[18] For example, see King, A. (2011, December). Mother Under Siege. BLAC. Retrieved from: https://www.blacdetroit.com/people-places/mother-under-siege.

[19] Fava, G. & Rafanelli, C. (2019). Iatrogenic factors in psychopathology. *Psychotherapy and Psychosomatics, 88*, 129-140. https://doi.org/10.1159/000500151.

[20] Autism Science Foundation. (2018). How Common Is Autism? Retrieved from: https://autismsciencefoundation.org/what-is-autism/how-common-is-autism/.

[21] Ibid.

[22] Centers for Disease Control and Prevention. (2016). CDC Estimates 1 in 68 School-Aged Children Have Autism; No Change From Previous Estimate. Retrieved from: https://www.cdc.gov/media/releases/2016/p0331-children-autism.html.

[23] Pierce, K.; Gazestani, V.; Bacon, E.; Barnes, C.; Cha, D.; Nalabolu, S. Lopez, L.; et al. (2019). Evaluation of the Diagnostic Stability of the Early Autism Spectrum Disorder Phenotype in the General Population Starting at 12 Months. *JAMA Pediatrics.* Published online April 29, 2019. https://doi:10.1001/jamapediatrics.2019.0624.

[24] See Wilson, J. & Jungner, G. (1968). *Principles and Practice of Screening for Disease.* Geneva, Switzerland: World Health Organization. Retrieved from:

https://www.who.int/ionizing_radiation/medical_radiation_exposure/munich-WHO-1968-Screening-Disease.pdf.

[25] Rabin, R.; Jennings, J.; Campbell, J.; & Bair-Merritt, M. (2010). Intimate Partner Violence Screening Tools. *American Journal of Preventive Medicine, 36(5)*, 439-445. https://doi.org/10.1016/j.amepre.2009.01.024.

[26] Stevens, L. & Sheaffer, B. (2007). Screening for Sexual Violence: Gaps in Research and Recommendations for Change. Applied Research Forum National Online Resource Center on Violence Against Women. Retrieved from: https://vawnet.org/sites/default/files/materials/files/2016-09/AR_ScreeningforSV.pdf.

[27] Quinsey, V.; Harris, G.; Rice, M.; & Cormier, C. (2015). *Violent Offenders: Appraising and Managing Risk (3rd Edition).*

[28] Lavigne, J.; Feldman, M.; & Meyers, K. (2016). Screening for Mental Health Problems: Addressing the Base Rate Fallacy for a Sustainable Screening Program in Integrated Primary Care. *Journal of Pediatric Psychology, 41(10)*, 1081-1090. https://doi.org/10.1093/jpepsy/jsw048.

Chapter 4: The Essence of Abnormality

[1] Dittmann, M. (2005, July/August). Hughes's germ phobia revealed in psychological autopsy. *Monitor on Psychology*. Retrieved from: https://www.apa.org/monitor/julaug05/hughes.

[2] Image by M. W. Toews, Free to use. Wikimedia Commons - https://commons.wikimedia.org/wiki/File:Standard_deviation_diagram.svg.

[3] Conners, C. K. (2008). Conners 3rd Edition [Measurement Instrument]. Toronto, Ontario, Canada: Multi-Health Systems.

Chapter 5: Classifying Immorality

[1] Cartwright, S. (1851). Diseases and Peculiarities of the Negro Race. *DeBow's Review, 11*.
[2] Sheffer, E. (2018). *Asperger's Children: The Origins of Autism in Nazi Vienna*. New York: W. W. Norton & Company.

[3] The term "autism" was actually coined in 1911 by the German psychiatrist Eugene Bleuler as explained in Evans, B. (2013). How autism became autism: The radical transformation of a central concept of child development in Britain. *History of the Human Sciences, 26(3)*, 3-31. http://doi: 10.1177/0952695113484320.

[4] Ibid.

[5] Burton, N. (2015, September). When homosexuality stopped being a mental disorder: Not until 1987 did homosexuality completely fall out of the DSM. *Psychology Today*. Retrieved from: https://www.psychologytoday.com/us/blog/hide-and-seek/201509/when-homosexuality-stopped-being-mental-disorder.

[6] Drescher, J. (2015). Out of DSM: Depathologizing homosexuality. *Behavioral Sciences*, 5(4): 565–575. http://doi: 10.3390/bs5040565.

[7] I suppose it is possible for a majority of people to suffer from a true illness, such as a widespread virus and, therefore, it could be considered statistically normal. In such a situation, normality and pathology would be synonymous. However, this hasn't happened with any one type of illness. Even the Black Death of the 14th century affected only about a third of the European population. However, 95% of the world's population now suffers from some type of health problem, making "health problems" normal (see https://www.sciencedaily.com/releases/2015/06/150608081753.htm).

[8] Caplan, P. (1995). *They Say You're Crazy: How the World's Most Powerful Psychiatrists Decide Who's Normal.* Boston, MA: Addison-Wesley. This same information was also reported later in Kutchins, H. & Kirk, S. (1997). *Making Us Crazy: DSM: The Psychiatric Bible and the Creation of Mental Disorders.* New York: Free Press.

[9] Ibid, p. 91.

[10] Lord, C.; Petkova, E.; Hus V.; et al. (2012). A Multisite Study of the Clinical Diagnosis of Different Autism Spectrum Disorders. *Archives of General Psychiatry, 69(3)*, 306–313. doi:10.1001/archgenpsychiatry.2011.148.

[11] Telethon Kids Institute. (2020). Researchers call for the term 'high functioning autism' to be consigned to history. Retrieved from: https://www.telethonkids.org.au/news--events/news-and-events-nav/2019/june/researchers-call-for-term-high-functioning-autism/.

[12] Human Rights Watch. (2019, May). New health guidelines propel transgender rights: World Health Organization removes 'Gender Identity Disorder" diagnosis. Retrieved from: https://www.hrw.org/news/2019/05/27/new-health-guidelines-propel-transgender-rights.

[13] Ravitz, J. (2019, May). Transgender people are not mentally ill, the WHO decrees. CNN. Retrieved from: https://www.cnn.com/2019/05/28/health/who-transgender-reclassified-not-mental-disorder/index.html.

[14] Ibid.

[15] American Psychiatric Association. (2013). *The Diagnostic and Statistical Manual of Mental Disorders (5th Edition).* Washington, DC: American Psychiatric Association.
The *DSM* is currently in its 7th edition since 1952, even though the current edition is called *DSM-5*. This is because *DSM-III* and *DSM-IV* were each revised once without changing the edition number. Also, you'll note that with the current edition, they changed from Roman numerals to Arabic. The reason given was that Roman numerals somehow limit responsiveness to "breakthroughs in research" and "scientific advances," whereas Arabic numerals are claimed to not be limiting and subsequent editions can be designated 5.1, 5.2, and so on. I don't understand this reasoning as it would be just as easy to code them V.1, V.2, etc. (see DSM-5: Frequently Asked Questions at https://www.psychiatry.org/psychiatrists/practice/dsm/feedback-and-questions/frequently-asked-questions).

[16] Currently in its 10th edition – *ICD-10*.

[17] American Psychiatric Association. (2018). Diagnostic and Statistical Manual of Mental Disorders. Retrieved from: https://www.psychiatry.org/psychiatrists/practice/dsm.

[18] American Psychiatric Association. (2013). *The Diagnostic and Statistical Manual of Mental Disorders (5th Edition).* Washington, DC: American Psychiatric Association, p. xli.

[19] Sadler, J. (2010, October). Catching the right fish. *Psychiatric Times.* Retrieved from: http://www.psychiatrictimes.com/dsm-5/catching-right-fish.

[20] American Psychiatric Association. (2013). *The Diagnostic and Statistical Manual of Mental Disorders (5th Edition).* Washington, DC: American Psychiatric Association, p. 20.

[21] Retrieved from: https://www.horoscope.com/us/horoscopes/general/horoscope-general-daily-today.aspx?sign=10.

[22] American Psychiatric Association. (2013). *The Diagnostic and Statistical Manual of Mental Disorders (5th Edition).* Washington, DC: American Psychiatric Association, p. 160.

[23] Cooper, R. (2014). How reliable is the DSM-5? Blog entry at Mad in America. Retrieved from: https://www.madinamerica.com/2014/09/how-reliable-is-the-dsm-5/; Kirk, S. & Kutchins, H. (1992). *The Selling of DSM: The Rhetoric of Science in Psychiatry.* New Brunswick, NJ: Aldine Transaction.; Regier D. A., Narrow W.; Clarks D.; Kraemer H.; Kuramoto S.; Kuhl E.; & Kupfer D. (2013). DSM-5 field trials in the United States and Canada, Part II: Test-retest reliability of selected categorical diagnoses. *American Journal of Psychiatry, 170*, 59-70. https://doi:10.1176/appi.ajp.2012.12070999.

[24] Allsop, K.; Read, J.; Corcoran, R.; & Kinderman, P. (2019). Heterogeneity in psychiatric diagnostic classification. *Psychiatric Research, 279*, 15-22. https://doi.org/10.1016/j.psychres.2019.07.005.

[25] Frances, A. (2013, July). Should social workers use the DSM-5. *SWHELPER.* Retrieved from: https://www.socialworkhelper.com/2013/06/07/should-social-workers-use-dsm-5/.

[26] Caplan, P. (2015). Conflict of interest at the top of the psychiatric apparatus. *Aporia, 7(1).* https://doi.org/10.18192/aporia.v7i1.3486.

[27] British Psychological Society. (2020). Membership and Standards Board 2017. Retrieved from: https://www.bps.org.uk/how-we-work/membership-and-standards-board-2017.

[28] British Psychological Society. (2011). Response to the American Psychiatric Association: DSM-5 Development. Retrieved from: http://whatcausesmentalillness.com/images/110630britishpsychologicalassnresponse2dsm-5.pdf.

[29] Robbins, B.; Kamens, S.; & Elkins, D. (2017). DSM reform efforts by the Society for Humanistic Psychology. *Journal of Humanistic Psychology*, 1-23. https://doi.org/10.1177/0022167817698617.

[30] International Society for Ethical Psychology and Psychiatry. (2017). ISEPP Demands Ethical Guidance on the DSM: In the Face of an Ethical Double Bind, ISEPP Petitions Leading Professional Mental Health Member Organizations. *PRNewswire.* Retrieved from: https://www.prnewswire.com/news-releases/english-releases/isepp-demands-ethical-guidance-on-the-dsm-300504497.html.

[31] These were: International Society for Psychological and Social Approaches to Psychosis, United States Chapter; Center for Loss and Trauma; National Coalition for Mental Health Recovery; MindFreedom International; Hearing Voices Network USA; MISS Foundation; Volunteers in Psychotherapy; and Warfighter Advance.

[32] Because of the orthodox belief in "mental illness" as real illness, one of the benefits of health insurance policies is to pay for "mental health services." I am one of many who accept these insurance payments while still denying that the services I provide are truly healthcare services. This might sound hypocritical to you. However, what I do – helping people with problems by talking to them – fits the insurance company definition of healthcare. If that is how they want to define healthcare, then I'll accept their payments and I am not misrepresenting what I do. You might also be wondering why I am pushing so hard to convince people that these problems in living are not illnesses because, if I am successful, it might be counter to my financial interests. It might result in health insurance companies removing "mental healthcare" as a covered service and, therefore, many people would decide not to seek out psychotherapy services because of the cost and, thus, I would put myself out of business. But I think this would be a small price to pay for the greater benefit of treating people humanely.

[33] Personal email communication with Dr. Jaren L. Skillings, Ph.D., ABPP, Chief of Professional Practice, American Psychological Association, September 26, 2019.

[34] Ibid.

[35] Caplan, P. (1995). *They Say You're Crazy: How the World's Most Powerful Psychiatrists Decide Who's Normal.* Boston, MA: Addison-Wesley.

[36] For instance, Caplan, P. (2012). Will the APA Listen to the Voices of Those Harmed by Psychiatric Diagnosis? Blog entry at Mad in America. Retrieved from: https://www.madinamerica.com/2012/10/will-the-apa-listen-to-the-voices-of-those-harmed-by-psychiatric-diagnosis/.

[37] The Fast for Freedom was sponsored by MindFreedom (www.mindfreedom.org) and received funding from the University of California, Los Angeles (UCLA). See https://hssm.semel.ucla.edu/wheres_evidence.

[38] See examples in Johnstone, L. (2014). *A Straight Talking Introduction To Psychiatric Diagnosis.* Monmouth, England: PCCS Books.

[39] Rosenhan, D. (1973). On being sane in insane places. *Science, 179 (4070)*, 250-258.

[40] This study was critiqued in Cahalan, S. (2019). *The Great Pretender: The Undercover Mission that Changed Our Understanding of Madness.* New York, NY: Grand Central Publishing. In it, Cahalan expresses great concern about some of the study's results possibly being fabricated. However, in a recent interview with *Psychiatric Times*, she said: "I still think that the idea of seeing a patient, not just a diagnostic label, is an extremely valuable lesson. I also believe that his [Rosenhan's] statements about being primed to see certain behaviors as pathological in certain contexts and perfectly normal in others is something that all doctors should be aware of. Those parts of the paper, I believe, still have value." Aftab, A. (2020, February). 50 shades of misdiagnosis. *Psychiatric Times.* Retrieved from: https://www.psychiatrictimes.com/qas/50-shades-misdiagnosis.

[41] Insel, T. (2012). Post by Former NIMH Director Thomas Insel: Words Matter. Retrieved at https://www.nimh.nih.gov/about/directors/thomas-insel/blog/2012/words-matter.shtml.

[42] Insel, T. (2013, April). Post by Former NIMH Director Thomas Insel: Transforming Diagnosis. Retrieved at https://www.nimh.nih.gov/about/directors/thomas-insel/blog/2013/transforming-diagnosis.shtml.

[43] Hyman, S. (2013, May). Psychiatry Framework Seeks to Reform Diagnostic Doctrine. *Nature.* Retrieved at https://www.nature.com/news/psychiatry-framework-seeks-to-reform-diagnostic-doctrine-1.12972.

[44] Casey, B.; Craddock, N.; Cuthbert, B.; Hyman, S.; Lee, F.; & Ressler, K. (2013). DSM-5 and RDoC: progress in psychiatry research? *Nature Reviews Neuroscience, 14(11)*, 810-814. https://doi:10.1038/nrn3621.

[45] Frances, A. (2010, December). Inside the battle to define mental illness. *Wired.* Retrieved from https://www.wired.com/2010/12/ff_dsmv/.

[46] Kotov, R.; Krueger, R.; Watson, D.; Achenbach, T.; Althoff, R.; Bagby, R.;...& Zimmerman, M. (2017). The Hierarchical Taxonomy of Psychopathology (HiTOP): A dimensional alternative to traditional nosologies. *Journal of Abnormal Psychology, 126(4).* 454-477. https://doi:10.1037/abn0000258.

[47] Ibid, p. 456.

[48] Ibid, p. 458.

[49] Ibid, p. 458.

[50] Rubin, J. (2017). Classification and Statistical Manual of Mental Health Concerns: A proposed practical scientific alternative to the *DSM* and *ICD*. *Journal of Humanistic Psychology, 58*, 93-114. https://doi.org/10.1177/0022167817718079.

[51] Ibid, p. 107.

[52] Ibid.

[53] American Psychological Association. (2013, July/August). NIMH funding to shift away from DSM categories. *Monitor on Psychology, 44(7),* 10. Retrieved from: https://www.apa.org/monitor/2013/07-08/nimh.

Chapter 6: Life as Illness

[1] Rush, B. (1812). *Medical Inquiries and Observations Upon the Diseases of the Mind.* Philadelphia: Kimber & Richardson. Retrieved from: https://archive.org/details/2569037R.nlm.nih.gov.

[2] Ibid, p. 9.

[3] American Psychiatric Association. (1980). *Diagnostic and Statistical Manual of Mental Disorders* (3rd Edition). Washington, DC: American Psychiatric Association.

[4] Blashfield, R.; Keely, J.; Flanagan, E.; & Miles, S. (2014). The Cycle of Classification: DSM-I Through DSM-5. *Annual Review of Clinical Psychology, 10*, 25-51. p. 32.

[5] Blain, D. & Barton, M. (1979). *The History of American Psychiatry: A Teaching and Research Guide.* Washington, DC: American Psychiatric Association. p. 12.

[6] National Institute of Health. (2015). *Diseases of the Mind: Highlights of American Psychiatry Through 1900: The 1840s: Early Professional Institutions and Lay Activism*. Retrieved from: https://www.nlm.nih.gov/hmd/diseases/professional.html.

[7] Ibid.

[8] Ibid.

[9] American Psychiatric Association. (2018). DSM History. Retrieved from: https://www.psychiatry.org/psychiatrists/practice/dsm/history-of-the-dsm.

[10] Hoff, P. (2015). The Kraepelinian tradition. *Dialogues in Clinical Neuroscience, 17(1)*, 31-41.

[11] American Psychiatric Association. (2018). DSM History. Retrieved from: https://www.psychiatry.org/psychiatrists/practice/dsm/history-of-the-dsm.

[12] American Psychiatric Association. (1952). *Diagnostic and Statistical Manual of Mental Disorders*. Washington, DC: American Psychiatric Association.

[13] Blashfield, R.; Keeley, J.; Flanagan, E.; & Miles, S. (2014). The cycle of classification: The DSM-I through DSM-5. *Annual Review of Clinical Psychology, 10*, 25-51. p. 32. https://doi:10.1146/annurev-clinpsy-032813-153639.

[14] For example, see Kastelmacher, A. (2015, January). Meet The "Designer" Strains Of Marijuana Bred In Israel To Treat A Wide Range Of Illnesses. *NoCamels*. Retrieved from: http://nocamels.com/2015/01/medical-marijuana-designer-strains-illnesses-research/.

[15] This was Mary Neal Vieten, Ph.D., ABPP, personal communication. In her position as the founder of Warfighter Advance (www.warfighteradvance.org), Dr. Vieten is well versed in how psychiatric chemicals affect veterans and military members, to include marijuana. Her suggestion about wine, while joking, makes as much sense as using marijuana, other recreational and illicit drugs, and psychiatric drugs as "medications."

[16] American Psychiatric Association. (2013). *The Diagnostic and Statistical Manual of Mental Disorders (5th Edition)*. Washington, DC: American Psychiatric Association, p. 602.

[17] American Psychiatric Association. (2013). Mild Neurocognitive Disorder. Retrieved from: https://www.psychiatry.org. APA_DSM-5-Mild-Neurocognitive-Disorder.pdf.

[18] American Psychiatric Association. (2013). *The Diagnostic and Statistical Manual of Mental Disorders (5th Edition)*. Washington, DC: American Psychiatric Association, p. 156.

[19] Ibid, p. 350.

[20] Centers for Disease Control and Prevention. (2017). Obesity and Overweight. Retrieved from: https://www.cdc.gov/nchs/fastats/obesity-overweight.htm.

[21] American Psychiatric Association. (2013). *The Diagnostic and Statistical Manual of Mental Disorders (5th Edition)*. Washington, DC: American Psychiatric Association, p. 708.

[22] See Associated Press. (2005, July). More Troops Developing Latent Mental Disorders. Retrieved from: http://www.nbcnews.com/id/8743574/ns/health-mental_health/t/more-troops-developing-latent-mental-disorders/#.WrHGN2aZPOQ.

[23] Insel, T. (2013, July). Post by Former NIMH Director Thomas Insel: Getting Serious About Mental Illnesses. Retrieved from: https://www.nimh.nih.gov/about/directors/thomas-insel/blog/2013/getting-serious-about-mental-illnesses.shtml.

[24] Ibid.

[25] American Psychiatric Association. (2013). *The Diagnostic and Statistical Manual of Mental Disorders (5th Edition)*. Washington, DC: American Psychiatric Association, p. 20.

[26] Ibid, p. 783.

[27] Ibid.

[28] Ibid, p. 791.
[29] Ibid, p. 798.
[30] Ibid, p. 795.
[31] Kamens, S. (2013). Attenuated Psychosis Syndrome Was Not Actually Removed from DSM-5. Global Summit on Diagnostic Alternatives. Retrieved from: http://dxsummit.org/archives/1728.
[32] Mitchell, D.; Knight, C; Hockenberry, J.; Teplansky, R.; & Hartman, T. (2014). Beverage caffeine intake in the U.S. *Food and Chemical Technology, 63*. 136-142. https://doi:10.1016/j.fct.2013.10.042.

Chapter 7: The Maintenance of a Myth

[1] Sheller, S. (2019). *Big Pharma, Big Greed: The Inside Story of One Lawyer's Battle to Stem the Flood of Dangerous Medicines and Protect Public Health*. Washington, DC: Strong Arm Press.
[2] Statista. (2018). Top psychiatric drugs in the United States by sales 2016. Retrieved at https://www.statista.com/statistics/452464/top-psychiatric-drugs-by-sales-in-the-us/.
[3] Public Citizen. (2016, March). Twenty-Five Years of Pharmaceutical Industry Criminal and Civil Penalties: 1991 through 2015. Retrieved from: https://www.citizen.org/our-work/health-and-safety/twenty-five-years-pharmaceutical-industry-criminal-and-civil-penalties-1991-through-2015.
[4] Zaveri. M. & Thomas, K. (2019, October). Johnson & Johnson Hit With $8 Billion Jury Verdict in Risperdal Suit. *New York Times*. Retrieved from: https://www.nytimes.com/2019/10/08/health/johnson-and-johnson-risperdal-verdict.html. Of course, Risperdal causes far more physiological harm than gynecomastia. This case is singled out because of the enormous penalty, even though the court later reduced it to 6.8 million.
[5] Angell, M. (2005). *The Truth About the Drug Companies: How They Deceive Us and What to Do About It*. New York, NY: Random House Trade Paperbacks; Swanson, A. (2015, Feb). Big pharmaceutical companies are spending far more on marketing than research. *Washington Post*. Retrieved from https://www.washingtonpost.com/news/wonk/wp/2015 /02/11/big-pharmaceutical-companies-are-spending-far-more-on-marketing-than-research/?utm_term=.753471e7fb66.
[6] Pew Charitable Trusts (2013, November). Persuading the Prescribers: Pharmaceutical Industry Marketing and its Influence on Physicians and Patients. Retrieved from: http://www.pewtrusts.org/en/research-and-analysis/fact-sheets/2013/11/11/persuading-the-prescribers-pharmaceutical-industry-marketing-and-its-influence-on-physicians-and-patients.
[7] Ibid.
[8] Fickweiler, F.; Fickweiler, W.; & Urbach, E. (2017). Interactions between physicians and the pharmaceutical industry generally and sales representatives specifically and their association with physicians' attitudes and prescribing habits: a systematic review. *BMJ Open, 7(9)*. http://doi.org/10.1136/bmjopen-2017-016408.

[9] Elliot, C. (2010, September). The Secret Lives of Big Pharma's "Thought Leaders." *The Chronicle of Higher Education*. Retrieved from : https://www.chronicle.com/article/The-Secret-Lives-of-Big/124335.

[10] Langdon-Neuner, E. (2008, January-December). Medical ghost writing. *Mens Sana Monograph, 6(1)*, 257-273. http://doi.org/10.4103/0973-1229.33006.

[11] Harris, G. (2008, October). Top Psychiatrists Didn't Report Drug Makers' Pay. *New York Times*. Retrieved from: http://www.nytimes.com/2008/10/04/health/policy/04drug.html.

[12] Cosgrove, L.; Krimsky, S.; Vijayaraghavan, M.; & Schneider, L. (2006). Financial ties between *DSM-IV* panel members and the pharmaceutical industry. *Psychotherapy and Psychosomatics, 75(3)*, 154-160. https:// doi:10.1159/000091772.

[13] Cosgrove L. & Krimsky S. (2012). A comparison of *DSM*-IV and *DSM*-5 panel members' financial associations with industry: A pernicious problem persists. *PLoS Med 9(3)*. https://doi.org/10.1371/journal.pmed.1001190.

[14] Wilson, M. (2017, February). Lobbying's top 50: Who's spending big. *The Hill*. Retrieved from: http://thehill.com/business-a-lobbying/business-a-lobbying/318177-lobbyings-top-50-whos-spending-big.

[15] McGreal, C. (2017). How big pharma's money – and its politicians – feed the U.S. opioid crisis. *The Guardian*. Retrieved from: https://www.theguardian.com/us-news/2017/oct/19/big-pharma-money-lobbying-us-opioid-crisis.

[16] Harris, G. (2009, October). Drug Makers Are Advocacy Groups Biggest Donors. *New York Times*. Retrieved from: http://www.nytimes.com/2009/10/22/health/22nami.html.

[17] Carey, B. & Harris, G. (2008, July). Psychiatric Group Faces Scrutiny Over Drug Industry Ties. *New York Times*. Retrieved from: http://www.nytimes.com/2008/07/12/washington/12psych.html?_r=2&hp=&adxnnl=1&oref=slogin&adxnnlx=1215861580-UEthRxliLs0ysOwdaGG1Ug&oref=slogin.

Chapter 8: Rebranding Immorality as Illness

[1] Fancher, R. (1995). *Cultures of Healing: Correcting the Image of American Mental Health Care*. New York: W. H. Freeman/Times Books/Henry Holt & Co.

[2] See the popular account of Nellie Bly (Elizabeth Cochrane) in Bly, N. (n.d.). *Ten Days in A Mad-House: Illustrated and Annotated: A First-Hand Account of Life At Bellevue Hospital on Blackwell's Island in 1887*. New York, NY: Ian L. Muro, Publisher.

[3] Mosher, L. (1999). Soteria and other alternatives to acute psychiatric hospitalization: A personal and professional review. *The Journal of Nervous and Mental Disease, 187(3)*, 142-149. Retrieved from: doi:10.1097/00005053-199903000-00003.

[4] Seikkula, J.; Aaltonen, J.; Alakare, B.; Haarakangas, K.; Keränen, J.; & Lehtinen, K. (2006). Five-year experience of first-episode nonaffective psychosis in open-dialogue approach: Treatment principles, follow-up outcomes, and two case studies. *Psychotherapy Research, 16(2)*, 214-228. https://https://doi.org/10.1080/10503300500268490.

5 http://www.warfighteradvance.org.

6 Quinsey, V.; Harris, G.; Rice, M.; & Cormier, C. (2015). *Violent Offenders: Appraising and Managing Risk (3rd Edition)*. Washington, DC: American Psychological Association; Melton, G., Petrila, J., Poythress, N., & Slobogin, C. (2017). *Psychological Evaluations for the Courts: A Handbook for Mental Health Professionals and Lawyers (4th Edition)*. New York, NY: Guilford Press. pp. 306-307.

7 Ibid.

8 Sharac, J.; McCrone, P.; Sabes-Figuera, R.; Csipke, E.; Wood, A.; & Wykes, T. (2010). Nurse and patient activities and interaction on psychiatric inpatient wards: A literature review. *International Journal of Nursing Studies, 47(7)*, 909-919. https://doi:10.1016/j.ijnurstu.2010.03.012.

9 Bill's mother, personal communication. His mother related her personal experiences with the case in addition to what is publicly available through court documents. Bill's real identity is concealed for his privacy. He assented to his story being included in this book, although he did not endorse this rendition of events. Due to his fear of reprisal, he did not wish to personally contribute information.

10 Information detailed here was obtained from Mary Neal Vieten, personal communication. Mary has been in contact with Jane as a fellow veteran over the past several months. Jane's real identity is withheld for her privacy. Jane consented to this information being included in this book.

11 Kirk, S.; Gomory, T.; & Cohen, D. (2015). *Mad Science: Psychiatric Coercion, Diagnosis, and Drugs*. Abingdon, U.K.: Routledge.

12 Szasz, T. (1970). *The Manufacture of Madness: A Comparative Study of the Inquisition and the Mental Health Movement*. New York: Harper & Row.

13 Szasz, T. (1984). *The Therapeutic State: Psychiatry in the Mirror of Current Events*. Amherst, NY: Prometheus Books.

14 Wallman, B.; McMahon, P.; O'Matz, M.; & Bryan, S. (2018, February). School shooter Nikolas Cruz: A lost and lonely killer. *South Florida Sun Sentinel*. Retrieved from: https://www.sun-sentinel.com/local/broward/parkland/florida-school-shooting/fl-florida-school-shooting-nikolas-cruz-life-20180220-story.html.

15 Melton, G., Petrila, J., Poythress, N., & Slobogin, C. (2017). *Psychological Evaluations for the Courts: A Handbook for Mental Health Professionals and Lawyers (4th Edition)*. New York, NY: Guilford Press. pp. 306-307.

16 Ruby, C. (2016). White Paper: Psychiatric Drugs and Violence. *Ethical Human Psychology and Psychiatry: An International Journal of Critical Inquiry. 18(1)*. p. 29-35. https://dx.doi.org/10.1891/1559-4343.18.1.29.

17 American Psychological Association. (2017). Ethical Principals of Psychologists and Code of Conduct. Retrieved from: http://www.apa.org/ethics/code/.

18 Channing L. Bete Co., Inc. (1999). *What Everyone Should Know about Good Mental Health*.

19 Ibid, p. 2.

20 Ruby, C. (1998). The psychology of terrorism: A survey of its causes and effects. Washington, DC: Air Force Office of Special Investigations. Presented at the Air Force Behavioral Sciences Symposium, Sheppard AFB, TX, April 1998.

[21] Evans, D. & McGreevy, P. (2011). An investigation of racing performance and whip use by jockeys in thoroughbred races. *PLOS One*. https://doi.org/10.1371/journal.pone.0015622.

[22] Seligman, M. (1972). Learned helplessness. *Annual Review of Medicine, 23*, 407-412. https://doi.org/10.1146/annurev.me.23.020172.002203.

[23] I'm certain I read this in *The Wisdom of Insecurity: A Message for An Age of Anxiety* by Alan W. Watts, a philosopher and teacher of Zen Buddhism. But for the life of me I can't find a citation for the quote. (Watts, A. (1968). *The Wisdom of Insecurity: A Message for An Age of Anxiety*. New York, NY: Vintage Books.)

[24] See Coleman, L. (1984). *The Reign of Error: Psychiatry, Authority, and Law*. New York, NY: Beacon Press.

Chapter 9: Stop Complaining

[1] Stetka, B. & Watson, J. (2016, April). Odd and outlandish psychiatric treatments through history. *Medscape Psychiatry*. Retrieved from: https://www.medscape.com/features/slideshow/odd-psychiatric-treatments#page=1.

[2] Retrieved from: https://www.medscape.com/public/about.

[3] Cormier, Z. (2015, June). A history of the ice pick lobotomy. *Motherboard*, Retrieved from: https://motherboard.vice.com/en_us/article/kbzj8a/a-history-of-the-lobotomy.

[4] See http://www.ect.org/resources/machines.html.

[5] See http://www.elcosh.org/document/1624/888/d000543/section2.html.

[6] Spangler, W.; Cosgrove, G.; Ballantine, H.; Cassem, E.; Rauch, S.; Nierenberg, A.; & Price, B. (1996). Magnetic resonance image-guided stereotactic cingulotomy for intractable psychiatric disease. *Neurosurgery, 38(6)*. 1076-1078. https://doi:10.1097/00006123-199802000-00161.

[7] Shorter, E. (2013, October). Shock Therapy. *Psychology Today*. Retrieved from: https://www.psychologytoday.com/blog/how-everyone-became-depressed/201310/shock-therapy; Shorter, E. (2013, December). Electroconvulsive Therapy in Children. *Psychology Today*. Retrieved from: https://www.psychologytoday.com/blog/how-everyone-became-depressed/201312/electroconvulsive-therapy-in-children.

[8] Dubey, C. (2017). Electroconvulsive Therapy and Brain Damage: Survey of the Evidence from a Philosophical Promontory. *Ethical Human Psychology and Psychiatry: An International Journal of Critical Inquiry, 19 (1)*, 24-50. https://doi:10.1891/1559-4343.19.1.24; McLaren, N. (2017). Electroconvulsive therapy: A critical perspective. *Ethical Human Psychology & Psychiatry: An International Journal of Critical Inquiry. 19(2)*, 91-104. https://doi:10.1891/1559-4343.19.2.91; Morgan, R. (Ed.) (2005). *Electroshock: The Case Against.* North Charleston, SC/Grass Valley, CA: Book Surge & Morgan Foundation Publishers.

[9] American Association of Neurological Surgeons. (2019). Deep Brain Stimulation. Retrieved from: https://www.aans.org/en/Patients/Neurosurgical-Conditions-and-Treatments/Deep-Brain-Stimulation.

[10] Amon, A. & Alesch, F. (2017). Systems for deep brain stimulation: Review of technical features. *Journal of Neurotransmission, 124(9)*, 1083-1091.

[11] Burn, D. (2004). Neuropsychiatric complications of medical and surgical therapies for Parkinson's disease. *Journal of Geriatric Psychiatry and Neurology, 17(3)*, 172-180. s://doi.org/10.1177/0891988704267466.

[12] Hengartner M.; Angst, J.; & Rössler, W. (2018). Antidepressant use prospectively relates to a poorer long-term outcome of depression: Results from a prospective community cohort study over 30 years. *Psychotherapy and Psychosomatics*. https://doi.org/10.1159/000488802;
Whitaker, R. (2011). *Anatomy of an Epidemic*. New York, NY: Broadway Books.

[13] Miller, S. (2016, December). 1 in 6 Americans Take A Psychiatric Drug. *Scientific American*. Retrieved from: https://www.scientificamerican.com/article/1-in-6-americans-takes-a-psychiatric-drug/.

[14] U.S. Census Bureau. (2014). Annual Estimates of the Resident Population for Selected Age Groups by Sex for the United States, States, Counties, and Puerto Rico Commonwealth and Municipios: April 1, 2010 to July 1, 2013. 2013 Population Estimates. Retrieved from: https://factfinder.census.gov/faces/tableservices/jsf/pages/productview.xhtml?src=bkmk.

[15] National Institute on Drug Abuse. (2015). Nationwide Trends. Retrieved from: https://www.drugabuse.gov/publications/drugfacts/nationwide-trends.

[16] See Valenstein, E. (2002). *Blaming the Brain: The Truth About Drugs and Mental Health*. New York: Free Press, p. 21.

[17] Ibid, p. 37.

[18] For instance, https://psychcentral.com/lib/common-side-effects-of-psychiatric-medications/.

[19] Bigelow, J. & Poremba, A. (2014). Achilles' ear? Inferior human short-term and recognition memory in the auditory modality. *PLOS ONE*. https://doi.org/10.1371/journal.pone.0089914.

[20] See Corrigan, M. (2015, March). Mind-Bottling Malarkey, Medicine, or Malpractice? *Psychology Today*. Retrieved from: https://www.psychologytoday.com/us/blog/kids-being-kids/201503/mind-bottling-malarkey-medicine-or-malpractice.

[21] Insel, T. (2014). Post by Former NIMH Director Thomas Insel: Are Children Overmedicated? Retrieved from: https://www.nimh.nih.gov/about/directors/thomas-insel/blog/2014/are-children-overmedicated.shtml#1.

[22] Forum on Child and Family Statistics. (2017). Retrieved from: https://www.childstats.gov/americaschildren/tables/pop1.asp.

[23] Insel, T. (2014). Post by Former NIMH Director Thomas Insel: Are Children Overmedicated? Retrieved from: https://www.nimh.nih.gov/about/directors/thomas-insel/blog/2014/are-children-overmedicated.shtml#1.

[24] Fuentes, A.; Pineda, M.: & Venkata, K. (2018). Comprehension of top 200 prescribed drugs in the US as a resource for pharmacy teaching, training and practice. *Pharmacy, 6*, 43. https://doi:10.3390/pharmacy6020043.

[25] Drugs.com (20190. Fluoxetine Side Effects. Retrieved from: https://www.drugs.com/sfx/fluoxetine-side-effects.html.

[26] Kukreja, S.; Kalra, G.; Shah, N.; & Shrivastava, A. (2013). Polypharmacy in psychiatry: A review. *Mens Sana Monographs, 11(1)*, 82-99. https:// doi: 10.4103/0973-1229.104497.

[27] Kramer, T. (2001). Mechanisms of action. *Medscape General Medicine, 3(1)*. Retrieved from: https://www.medscape.com/viewarticle/430539.

[28] *Physicians' Desk Reference.* (67th ed.). (2013). Montvale, NJ: PDR Network.

[29] Carpenter, S. (2012, September). That gut feeling. *Monitor on Psychology, 43(8)*, 50. Retrieved from: https://www.apa.org/monitor/2012/09/gut-feeling.

[30] Kirsch, I. (2014). Antidepressants and the Placebo Effect. *Z Psychol, 222(3)*, 128-134; Kirsch, I. (2019). Placebo effect in the treatment of depression and anxiety. *Frontiers in Psychiatry, 10(407)*, 1-9. https://doi:10.3389/fpsyt.2019.00407.

Chapter 10: How Psychiatric Drugs Affect the Brain

[1] Neurons don't actually send meaningful signals to each other like how we can send texts to each other. They merely stimulate their neighboring neurons through changes in their electrochemical properties in a chain reaction.

[2] Jackson, G. (2005). *Rethinking Psychiatric Drugs: A Guide for Informed Consent.* Bloomington, IN: Author-House; Jackson, G. (2009). *Drug-Induced Dementia: A Perfect Crime.* Bloomington, IN: Author-House; Moncrieff, J. (2008). *The Myth of the Chemical Cure: A Critique of Psychiatric Drug Treatment.* Basingstoke, U.K.: Palgrave MacMillan.

[3] Hu, X. (2011). Benzodiazepine withdrawal seizures and management. *Journal of the Oklahoma State Medical Association*, 104(2), 62-65. Retrieved from: https://www.ncbi.nlm.nih.gov/pubmed/21815323.

[4] Adler, J. (2013, April). 10 dangerous drugs once marketing as medicine. *Best Medical Degrees.* Retrieved from: https://www.bestmedicaldegrees.com/10-dangerous-drugs-once-marketed-as-medicine/.

[5] Kemsley, J. (2016). Psychedelic compounds like ecstasy may be good for more than just a high: Scientists are testing whether drugs that alter consciousness can treat intractable mental health conditions. *Chemical & Engineering News, 94(13)*, 28-32. Retrieved from: https://cen.acs.org/articles/94/i13/Psychedelic-compounds-like-ecstasy-just.html.

[6] Murrough, J.; Iosifescu, D.; Chang, L.; Al Jurdi, R.; Green. C.; Perez, A…. & Mathew, S. (2013). Antidepressant effectiveness of ketamine in treatment-resistant major depression: A two-site randomized controlled trial. *American Journal of Psychiatry, 170(10)*, 1134-1142. https://doi:10.1176/appi.ajp.2013.13030392.

[7] Grob, C.; Danforth, A.; Chopra, G.; Hagerty, M.; McKay, C.; Halberstadt, A.; & Greer, G. (2011). Pilot study of psilocybin treatment for anxiety in patients with advanced-stage cancer. *Archives of General Psychiatry, 68(1)*, 71-78. https://doi:10.1001/archgenpsychiatry.2010.116.

[8] Goldschmidt, D. (2019, March). FDA approves ketamine-like nasal spray for depression. *CNN*. Retrieved from: https://www.cnn.com/2019/03/05/health/esketamine-depression-nasal-spray-fda-bn/index.html.

[9] Akagi, H. & Kumar, T. (2002). Akathisia: Overlooked at a cost. *British Medical Journal*. 324:7352, 1506–1507. https://doi.org/10.1136/bmj.324.7352.1506.; Fakhoury, W., Wright, D., & Wallace, M. (2001). Prevalence and extent of distress of adverse effects of antipsychotics among callers to a United Kingdom National Mental Health Helpline. *International Clinical Psychopharmacology*. 16(3): 153-162. https://doi:10.1097/00004850-200105000-00004.; Forcen, F. (2015). Akathisia: Is restlessness a primary condition or an adverse drug effect? *Current Psychiatry. 14:1*, 14-18. Retrieved from: https://www.mdedge.com/psychiatry/article/89620/somatic-disorders/akathisia-restlessness-primary-condition-or-adverse-drug.; Kumar, R., Sachdev, P. (2009). Akathisia and second-generation antipsychotic drugs. *Current Opinion in Psychiatry*. 22:3, 293-299. https://doi:10.1097/YCO.0b013e32832a16da.; Moncrieff, J., Cohen, D., & Mason, J.P. (2009). The subjective experience of taking antipsychotic medication: a content analysis of Internet data. *Acta Psychiatrica Scandinavica*. 120(2): 102-111. https://doi:10.1111/j.1600-0447.2009.01356.; Price, J., Cole, V., & Goodwin, G. (2009). Emotional side effects of selective serotonin reuptake inhibitors: Qualitative study. *The British Journal of Psychiatry*. 195: 211-217. https://doi:10.1192/bjp.bp.108.051110.; Read, J., Cartwright, C., & Gibson, K. (2014). Adverse emotional and interpersonal effects reported by 1829 New Zealanders while taking antidepressants. *Psychiatry Research*. 216: 67-73. https://doi:10.1016/j.psychres.2014.01.042.; & Stubbs, J., Hutchins, D., & Mounty, C. (2000). Relationship of akathisia to aggressive and self-injurious behaviour: A prevalence study in a UK tertiary referral centre. *International Journal of Psychiatry in Clinical Practice*. 4:4, 319-325. https://doi:10.1080/13651500050517894.

[10] Bielefeldt, A.; Danborg, P.; & Gøtzsche, P. (2016). Precursors to suicidality and violence on antidepressants: systematic review of trials in adult healthy volunteers. *Journal of the Royal Society of Medicine, 109(10)*. 381-392. https:// doi:10.1177/0141076816666805; Sharma, T.; Guski, L.; Freund, N. & Gøtzsche, P. (2016). Suicidality and aggression during antidepressant treatment: systematic review and meta-analyses based on clinical study reports. *British Medical Journal, 352*. https:// doi: https://doi.org/10.1136/bmj.i65; Sparks, J. & Duncan, B. (2013). Outside the black Box: Re-assessing pediatric antidepressant prescription. *Journal of the Canadian Academy of Child and Adolescent Psychiatry, 22(3)*. 240-246.

[11] Ruby, C. (2016). White Paper: Psychiatric Drugs and Violence. *Ethical Human Psychology and Psychiatry: An International Journal of Critical Inquiry. 18(1)*. p. 29-35. https://doi:10.1891/1559-4343.18.1.29; Stolzer, J. (2013). The systemic correlation between psychiatric medications and unprovoked mass murder in America. *New Male Studies: An International Journal, 2(2)*, 9-23. Retrieved from: https://leoniefennell.files.wordpress.com/2013/05/the-systemic-correlation-between-psychiatric-medications-and-unprovoked-mass-murder-in-america2.pdf.

[12] Moore, T.; Glenmullen, J.; & Furberg, C. (2010). Prescription drugs associated with reports of violence towards others. *PLoS ONE*, 5(12):e15337. https://doi.org/10.1371/journal.pone.0015337.

[13] Grover, N. (2016, December). FDA drops black box warning on Pfizer's anti-smoking drug. *Reuters*. Retrieved from: https://www.reuters.com/article/us-pfizer-fda/fda-drops-black-box-warning-on-pfizers-anti-smoking-drug-idUSKBN1452JJ.

[14] Melton, G., Petrila, J., Poythress, N., & Slobogin, C. (2017). *Psychological Evaluations for the Courts: A Handbook for Mental Health Professionals and Lawyers (4th Edition)*. New York, NY: Guilford Press. pp. 306-307. In this handbook's section on predicting and managing violent behavior, the authors review the research literature with a keen focus on presenting the most robust and forensically defensible evidence of violence risk factors.

[15] Quinsey, V.; Harris, G.; Rice, M.; & Cormier, C. (2015). *Violent Offenders: Appraising and Managing Risk (3rd Edition)*. Washington, DC: American Psychological Association.

[16] See the analysis and problem of false alarm rates (i.e., false positives) in Chapter 3 on psychological testing and screening.

[17] Hjelmeland, H.; Jaworski, K.; Knizek, B.; & Marsh, I. (2018). Problematic advice from suicide prevention experts. *Ethical Human Psychology and Psychiatry, 20(2)*, 79-85. https://dx.doi.org/10.1891/1559-4343.20.2.79.

[18] Hess, J. (2019). Why have suicides increased after enormous efforts to reduce them? Eternal Core. Retrieved from: https://eternalcore.org/featured/why-have-suicides-increased-after-enormous-efforts-to-reduce-them/.

[19] Nutt, A. (2018). Suicide rates rise sharply across the United States, new report shows. *Washington Post*. Retrieved from: https://www.washingtonpost.com/news/to-your-health/wp/2018/06/07/u-s-suicide-rates-rise-sharply-across-the-country-new-report-shows/.

[20] Levine, B. (2020). "Shit-Life Syndrome," Trump voters, and clueless Dems. *Counterpunch*. Retrieved from: https://www.counterpunch.org/2020/01/03/shit-life-syndrome-trump-voters-and-clueless-dems/.

Chapter 11: Psychotherapy

[1] For instance, see Bader, M. (2009, April). The difference between coaching and therapy is greatly overstated. *Psychology Today*. Retrieved from: https://www.psychologytoday.com/us/blog/what-is-he-thinking/200904/the-difference-between-coaching-and-therapy-is-greatly-overstated; Henschel, T. (2017, February). The difference between coaching and therapy. *Forbes*. Retrieved from: https://www.forbes.com/sites/forbescoachescouncil/2017/02/07/the-difference-between-coaching-and-therapy/#47d5dfe23417.

[2] American Psychological Association. (n.d.). Different Approaches To Psychotherapy. Retrieved from: http://www.apa.org/topics/therapy/psychotherapy-approaches.aspx.

[3] GoodTherapy. (n.d.). Types of Therapy. Retrieved from: https://www.goodtherapy.org/learn-about-therapy/types.

[4] I've searched but cannot find the citation for this study. I believe it was reported in the American Psychological Association (APA) Division 12 journal, *Clinical Psychology*, in the late 1980s or early 1990s.

[5] Attributed to Carl Jung, a younger contemporary and initially a protege of Sigmund Freud. He said, "Until you make the unconscious conscious, it will direct your life and you will call it fate." However, the concept of turning the unconscious into consciousness was Freud's primary focus as well. He believed human distress and troublesome behaviors were because of unconscious conflicts that, when made conscious, eliminated or reduced the problems.

[6] Wampold, B. (2015). How important are the common factors in psychotherapy? An update. *World Psychiatry, 14(3),* 270-277. https://doi:10.1002/wps.20238.

[7] American Psychological Association. (2006, May-June). Evidence-based practice in psychology. *American Psychologist, 61(4)*, 271-285. https://doi:10.1037/0003-066X.61.4.271.

[8] Cleare-Hoffman, H.; Hoffman, L.; & Wilson, S. (2013, July/August). *Existential therapy, culture, and therapist factors in evidence-based practice.* Paper presented at the 121st Annual Convention of the American Psychological Association, Honolulu, HI; Hoffman, L.; Dias, J.; & Soholm, H. (2012, August). *Existential-Humanistic therapy as a model for evidence-based practice.* Paper presented at the 120th Annual Convention of the American Psychological Association, Orlando, FL.

[9]American Psychological Association. (2006, May-June). Evidence-based practice in psychology. *American Psychologist, 61(4)*, 271-285. https://doi:10.1037/0003-066X.61.4.271., p. 273.

[10] Society of Clinical Psychology. (n.d.). Psychological Treatments. Retrieved from: https://www.div12.org/psychological-treatments/.

[11] See Coe, R. (2002). It's the effect size stupid: What effect size is and why it is important. Paper presented at the British Educational Research Association annual conference, Exeter, U.K., September 12-14, 2002. Retrieved from: http://www.cem.org/attachments/ebe/ESguide.pdf.

[12] Image by Kristoffer Magnusson - http://rpsychologist.com/d3/cohend/. Free to use: https://creativecommons.org/licenses/by/4.0/

[13] Cohen, J. (1988). *Statistical Power Analysis for the Behavioral Sciences (2nd Edition).* New York, NY: Lawrence Erlbaum Associates.

[14] Coe, R. (2002). It's the effect size stupid: What effect size is and why it is important. Paper presented at the British Educational Research Association annual conference, Exeter, U.K., September 12-14, 2002. Retrieved from: https://www.cem.org/attachments/ebe/ESguide.pdf; Also using the online calculator at https://www.polyu.edu.hk/mm/effectsizefaqs/calculator/calculator.html.

[15] Hengartner, M. (2018). Raising Awareness for the Replication Crisis in Clinical Psychology by Focusing on Inconsistencies in Psychotherapy Research: How Much Can We Rely on Published Findings from Efficacy Trials? *Frontiers in Psychology, 9(256).* https://doi: 10.3389/fpsyg.2018.00256.

[16] Kamenov, K.; Twomey, C.: Cabello, M.; Prina, A.; & Ayuso-Mateos, J. (2017). The efficacy of psychotherapy, pharmacotherapy and their combination on functioning and quality of life in depression: a meta-analysis. *Psychological Medicine, 47(3)*, 414-425. https://doi:10.1017/S0033291716002774.

[17] Cuijpers, P.; van Straten, A.; Bohlmeijer, E.; Hollon, S.; & Andersson, G. (2010). The effects of psychotherapy for adult depression are overestimated: a meta-analysis of study quality and effect size. *Psychological Medicine, 40(2)*, 211-223. https://doi:10.1017/S0033291709006114.

[18] Leucht, S.; Hierl, S.; Kissling, W.; Dold, M.; & Davis, J. (2012). Putting the efficacy of psychiatric and general medicine medication into perspective: review of meta-analyses. *The British Journal of Psychiatry, 200(2)*, 97-106. https://doi.org/10.1192/bjp.bp.111.096594.

[19] In fact, the RCT has even been criticized as a method for assessing the efficacy of psychiatric drugs. See Cohen, D. & Jacobs, D. (2007). Randomized controlled trials of antidepressants: clinically and scientifically irrelevant. *Debates in Neuroscience, 1*, 44-54. https://doi.org/10.1007/s11559-007-9002-x.

[20] See Shean, G. (2014). Review article: Limitations of randomized control designs in psychotherapy research. *Advances in Psychiatry*, http://dx.doi.org/10.1155/2014/561452; Shedler, J. (2018). Where is the evidence for "evidence-based" therapy? *Psychiatric Clinics of North America, 41(2)*, 319-329. https://doi.org/10.1016/j.psc.2018.02.001.

[21] See Bugental, J. (1987). *The Art of the Psychotherapist: How to Develop the Skills that Take Psychotherapy Beyond Science.* New York, NY: W. W. Norton & Co.; Bugental, J. (1999). *Psychotherapy Isn't What You Think: Bringing the Psychotherapeutic Engagement Into the Living Moment.* Phoenix, AZ: Zeig, Tucker, & Co.

[22] Smedslund, J. (2009). The mismatch between current research methods and the nature of psychological phenomena: What researchers must learn from practitioners. *Theory & Psychology, 19*, 778–794. https://doi.org/10.1177/0959354309345648. I want to recognize and honor the person who referred me to Dr. Smedslund's work. This was Matt Stevenson. Matt was a survivor of the Industry and he was harmed greatly by it. Yet, he continued to fight against it, and he worked brilliantly to expose the inhumanity of labeling people with "mental illness" diagnoses and then subjecting them to coercive actions. Naturally, he and I were allies in this fight. Sadly, Matt's emotional angst about the orthodox system's resistance to changing, and how that resistance was continuing to harm people on a daily basis, overwhelmed him to the point of taking his own life in 2017 in order to ease his pain.

[23] Smedslund, J. (2016). Practicing psychology without an empirical evidence-base: The bricoleur model. *New Ideas in Psychology, 43*, 50-56.
https://doi.org/10.1016/j.newideapsych.2016.06.001., p. 50.

[24] Ibid, p. 51.

[25] Smedslund, J. (2009). The mismatch between current research methods and the nature of
psychological phenomena: What researchers must learn from practitioners. *Theory & Psychology, 19*, 778–794. https://doi.org/10.1177/0959354309345648., p. 785.

[26] Smedslund, J. (2012). The *bricoleur* model of psychological practice. Theory and Psychology, 22(5), 643-657. https://DOI:10.1177/0959354312441277.
[27] See Mahoney, M. (1991). *The Human Change Processes: The Scientific Foundations of Psychotherapy*. New York, NY: Basic Books.

Part II: The Unveiling

[1] Chomsky, N.; Junkerman, J.; & Masakazu, T. (2011). *Power and Terror: Conflict, Hegemony and the Rule of Force*. Boulder, CO: Paradigm Publishers, p. 5.
[2] An interesting example of this kind of ad hominem attack was a 1985 reaction to psychiatrist Lee Coleman, M.D., who became dissatisfied with the Industry for the very reasons outlined in this book. He had been speaking up about its abuses in a series of television interviews. Dr. Coleman received a letter one day from another psychiatrist which stated:

> Dear Dr. Coleman,
>
> I have viewed a number of your television appearances. The vehement denunciations of the mental health system were perplexing until I became aware of your fear of incarceration in a mental institution. This fear is, of course, justified. The impassioned attacks are projected defensive measures to assuage the fear of insanity which is threatening to engulf you and destroy your freedom. Honest and direct relatedness to your destructive feelings will alleviate the compulsive need to act them out in the public forum.
>
> Sincerely yours, [name withheld for privacy]

Luckily, Dr. Coleman is still with us and continues to speak out about the Industry's abuses. See his website at http://coleman.nyghtfalcon.com and his YouTube channel at https://www.youtube.com/channel/UCjf-JH24_C4jhfekn6a2vug.
[3] Scientology has always pursued a strong and well-funded campaign against mainstream psychiatry. It was founded by L. Ron Hubbard in the 1950s and its original tenets are contained in Hubbard's book, *Dianetics: The Modern Science of Mental Health*. Scientology proposes an alternative to the Industry, as reflected in the book's title. CCHR was co-founded in 1969 by Scientology and Thomas Szasz, author of *The Myth of Mental Illness*, which eight years earlier sparked popular professional interest in challenging the orthodox psychiatric system, as explain in the Introduction. Thus, it is not surprising that people would suspect Scientology's clandestine influence in the overall critical psychiatry movement. However, Szasz was very clear that he was not a supporter of Scientology, he merely shared their views about the Industry. In a 2009 interview with the Australian Broadcasting Corporation, he said, "I no more believe in their religion or their beliefs than I believe in the beliefs of any other religion. I am an atheist, I don't believe in Christianity, in Judaism, in Islam, in Buddhism and I don't believe in Scientology. I have nothing to do with Scientology." He explained that the only reason he associated

with them was because of their substantial financial resources that could be crucial in challenging an equally financed Industry. (See https://www.abc.net.au/radionational/programs/allinthemind/thomas-szasz-speaks-part-2-of-2/3138880#transcript). Despite this, many still point to Szasz's partnership with CCHR in an attempt to slander him and the overall critical psychiatry movement. As did Szasz, I also took advantage of CCHR's well-organized public platform in the 2012-2013 timeframe when I was working to raise awareness of how veterans and military members who suffer from war trauma are negatively treated by the VA and military psychiatric systems. Naively, and in hindsight regrettably, I did an interview with one of their journalists, spoke at one of their public functions, accompanied one of their members to congressional meetings, and was interviewed in one of their documentaries. I was also offered a free membership in CCHR, which I declined. My purpose in those instances was to get maximum publicity for a very important cause. It was not to support them or Scientology but to support the victims of the Industry. Since that time, I have decided that any potential benefit gained from their public forum and huge financial resources is not worth damaging the reputation of our message.

[4] Wright, L. (2013). *Going Clear: Scientology, Hollywood, and the Prison of Belief.* New York, NY: Vintage Books.

Chapter 12: The Difference Between Brain and Mind

[1] Rush, B. (1812). *Medical Inquiries and Observations Upon the Diseases of the Mind.* Philadelphia: Kimber & Richardson. Retrieved from: https://archive.org/details/2569037R.nlm.nih.gov.

[2] Ibid, p. 30.

[3] The title of a 1966 Rolling Stones song.

[4] Descartes, R. (1596-1650) (1993). *Meditations on First Philosophy.* Indianapolis, IN: Hackett Publishing Co.

[5] It is now known that the pineal gland produces melatonin and regulates sleep.

[6] Chalmers, D. (1995). Facing up to the problem of consciousness. *Journal of Consciousness Studies*, 2 (3): 200–219. https://doi:10.1098/rstb.2017.0342.

[7] James, W. (1904). A world of pure experience. *Journal of Philosophy, Psychology, and Scientific Methods, 1(20)*, 533-543.

[8] James, W. (1904). Does "consciousness" exist? *Journal of Philosophy Psychology and Scientific Methods, 1(18)*, p. 477-478.

[9] See https://plato.stanford.edu/entries/idealism/ for a summary of this philosophical concept.

[10] As in the psychophysical parallelism explained in Baruch Spinoza's (1632-1677) *Ethics.*

[11] See more about this idea of "structural determinism" in Maturana, H. & Varela, F. (1992). *The Tree of Knowledge: The Biological Roots of Human Understanding.* Boston, MA: Shambhala.

Chapter 13: Emotions and Meaning

[1] Rice, D. (2018, October). Mega Millions jumps to $868 million, second-largest jackpot in US history. *USA Today*. Retrieved from: https://www.usatoday.com/story/news/nation/2018/10/16/mega-millions-powerball-odds-winning-jackpot/1656732002/.

[2] According to the online information-sharing site, Quora. Retrieved from: https://www.quora.com/How-many-people-in-the-US-buy-lottery-tickets-every-year.

[3] Centers for Disease Control and Prevention. (2017). At a Glance 2016 Tobacco Use: Extinguishing the Epidemic. Retrieved from: https://www.cdc.gov/chronicdisease/resources/publications/aag/pdf/2016/tobacco-aag.pdf.

[4] Tomkins, S. (1962). *Affect Imagery Consciousness Volume I: The Positive Affects*. New York, NY: Springer Publishing.; Tomkins, S. (1963). *Affect Imagery Consciousness Volume II: The Negative Affects*. New York, NY: Springer Publishing.; Tomkins, S. (1991). *Affect Imagery Consciousness Volume III: The Negative Affects: Anger and Fear*. New York, NY: Springer Publishing. There is also a very useful website detailing Tomkins's theory at http://www.tomkins.org.

[5] Efran, J. & Greene, M. (2012, May/June). Why we cry: A clinician's guide. Psychotherapy Networker. Retrieved from: https://www.psychotherapynetworker.org/magazine/article/254/why-we-cry.

[6] See Acharya, S. & Shukla, S. (2012). Mirror neurons: Enigma of the metaphysical modular brain. *Journal of Natural Science, Biology, and Medicine, 3(2)*, 118-124. https://doi:10.4103/0976-9668.101878.

[7] Yalom, I (1980). *Existential Psychotherapy*. New York: Basic Books.

[8] Ibid, p. 220.

[9] I am borrowing and somewhat tweaking this analogy, which was presented by Maturana, H. & Varela, F. (1992). *The Tree of Knowledge: The Biological Roots of Human Understanding*. Boston, MA: Shambhala, p. 136.

Chapter 14: Strategies of Escaping Emotional Pain

[1] Cowan, N. (2010). The magical mystery four: How is working memory capacity limited, and why? *Current Directions in Psychological Science, 19(1)*, 51-57.

[2] Watts, A. (1951). *The Wisdom of Insecurity: A Message for An Age of Anxiety*. New York, NY: Vintage Books.

[3] Laing, R. (1967). *The Politics of Experience and the Bird of Paradise*. United Kingdom: Penguin Books, p. 95.

[4] Asch, S. (1951). Effects of group pressure on the modification and distortion of judgments, In H. Guetzkow (Ed.), *Groups, Leadership and Men*. pp. 177-190. Pittsburgh, PA: Carnegie Press; Asch, S. (1955). Opinions and social pressure. *Scientific American. 193 (5):* 31–35; Asch, S. (1956). Studies of independence and conformity: A minority of one against a unanimous majority. *Psychological Monographs, 70(9).* 1-70.

[5] Ty Colbert, Ph.D., personal communication. Dr. Colbert has worked as a clinical psychologist in California for many years. He has dedicated his life to educating both the professionals and the public about the fallacies behind the chemical imbalance model of

"mental illness." He is the author of: Colbert, T. (1996). *Broken Brains or Wounded Hearts: What Causes Mental Illness.* Orange, CA: Kevco Publishing; and Colbert, T. (2017). *The Four False Pillars of Biopsychiatry.* Orange, CA: Kevco Publishing.

Chapter 15: The Willingness to Act

[1] See https://www.zen-buddhism.net/buddhist-principles/four-noble-truths.html.
[2] For those of you suspicious of Eastern religions and perspectives, and for that reason might not respect my views, rest assured I am not a Buddhist. I merely think the Buddhist ideas about emotional pain and personal choice are relevant here.
[3] Perry, P. (2017, June). The Buddhist parable can ease your suffering during a crisis. *Big Think Edge.* Retrieved from: http://bigthink.com/philip-perry/this-buddhist-parable-can-ease-your-pain-during-a-crisis.
[4] Ibid, para 12.
[5] Yerkes, R. & Dodson, J. (1908). The relationship of strength of stimulus to rapidity of habit formation. *Journal of Comparative Neurology and Psychology, 18*, 459-482. Retrieved from: http://www.viriya.net/jabref/the_relation_of_strength_of_stimulus_to_rapidity_of_habit-formation.pdf.
[6] Anastasiou, D. & Kauffman, J. (2013). The social model of disability: Dichotomy between impairment and disability. *The Journal of Medicine and Philosophy. 38*. 441-59. https://doi:10.1093/jmp/jht026.
[7] Pardy, B. (2016). Head starts and extra time: Academic accommodation on post-secondary exams and assignments for cognitive and mental disabilities. *Education and Law Journal, 25*, 191-208. Retrieved from: https://papers.ssrn.com/sol3/papers.cfm?abstract_id=2828420; Pardy, B. (2020). For students, not being disabled is the new disability. *The Epoch Times.* Retrieved from: https://www.theepochtimes.com/for-students-not-being-disabled-is-the-new-disability_3210194.html.
[8] For instance, in Maryland, the Maryland Criminal Procedure Code § 3-109 refers to this as the "test for criminal responsibility," not insanity. The two-prong test is that a defendant is not criminally responsible if at the time of the crime that defendant, because of mental disorder or mental retardation, lacks substantial capacity to: (1) appreciate the criminality of that conduct; or (2) conform that conduct to the requirements of law. Retrieved from: https://advance.lexis.com/container?config=00JAA1NTM5MzBmZC02MTg2LTQzNmEtYmI5Yy0yZWEwYzA1OGEwNTYKAFBvZENhdGFsb2fdgr2eooaZj7MpSZGOIwWq&crid=98090a1b-b2f8-4888-a4c5-eab68b389130&prid=833f7ddb-5f13-4aa2-a7e0-34b061a432fc.
[9] Bond, C. & DePaulo, B. (2006). Accuracy of Deceptive Judgments. *Personality and Social Psychology Review, 10(3)*, 214-234. https://doi:10.1207/s15327957pspr1003_2.
[10] Brock, R. & Lettini, G. (2013). *Soul Repair: Recovering from Moral Injury After War.* Boston, MA: Beacon Press; Meagher, R. & Pryer, D. (Eds.). (2018). *War and Moral Injury: A Reader.* Eugene, OR: Cascade Books.
[11] Efran, J.; Lukens, M.; & Lukens, R. (1980). *Language, Structure, and Change: Frameworks of Meaning in Psychotherapy.* New York, NY: W. W. Norton & Co.

Chapter 16: Final Thoughts

[1] Fromm, E. (1956). *The Sane Society*. London, UK: Routledge & Kegan Paul. pp.163-164.
[2] See the Introduction. Kennedy, J. (1962). Commencement Address at Yale University, June 11, 1962. Online by Gerhard Peters and John T. Woolley, *The American Presidency Project*. Retrieved from: http://www.presidency.ucsb.edu/ws/?pid=29661.
[3] See the Introduction. Szasz, T. (1961). *The Myth of Mental Illness: Foundations of a Theory of Personal Conduct*. New York: Harper & Row.

Index

CPSIA information can be obtained
at www.ICGtesting.com
Printed in the USA
JSHW020859140920
7844JS00001B/1

9 780578 639260